# FINITE MATHEMATICS

## FRANCIS H. HILDEBRAND

*Western Washington State College*

## CHERYL G. JOHNSON

*Kent School District, Washington*

*Prindle, Weber & Schmidt, Incorporated*

*Boston, Massachusetts*

To 1-2-3!

# Preface

This book has been designed to fill the need for a readable, nonrigorous, yet mathematically sound introduction to finite mathematics, the branch of mathematics which does not involve infinite sets, limits, and continuity. It is meant to provide students, who have a working knowledge of elementary algebra, with computational facility in logic, vectors and matrices, probability, statistics, linear programming, and game theory. Throughout the text appear simple examples from business and the social sciences which illustrate how the mathematical concepts can be applied. After studying this text, the student will be well prepared to take more rigorous courses in the topics discussed. In addition, he will be ready to attack more complicated applications of the material in fields such as sociology and business management.

This book may be used in courses intended as one, two, or three quarters of work. The selection of topics for a course less than three quarters will depend, of course, on the needs of the class. As a guide, you may consider Chapters 3 through 6 as the core of the book. Some of the better prepared students may find most of the basic concepts in Chapter 1 a review. The rest of the chapters are relatively independent except that a knowledge of the material in Chapter 3, Vectors and Matrices, is necessary for some of the later sections on probability in Chapter 4 and for some of the game theory techniques in Chapter 7.

This text was first suggested to the authors by Prindle, Weber and Schmidt, Inc. We owe them our primary debt of gratitude for their recommendations and encouragement. We thank W. Frederick Cutlip for his thorough, and often candid, review of the entire manuscript. We also thank Charles M. Gregory and Christopher T. Gregory for their assistance in preparing parts of the answer manuscript for this printing.

F.H.H.<br>C.G.J.

# Contents

——7    Introduction to the Theory of Games

# Some Basic Concepts

# 1

## ——1-1  A Brief Review of Sets

A *set* is a collection of objects called *elements*. For instance, the United States of America is a set of fifty states and the alphabet is a set of twenty-six letters.

Traditionally, sets are denoted by upper case letters such as $A$, $B$, and $C$. The elements that make up sets are listed within braces and separated by commas. Some examples are:

$$A = \{1, 2, 3, 4\},$$
$$B = \{2, 4, 6, 8\},$$
$$C = \{1, 2\}.$$

The elements of $A$ are 1, 2, 3, and 4; the elements of $B$ are 2, 4, 6, and 8; the elements of $C$ are 1 and 2. Sometimes it is inconvenient or impossible to list all the elements of a set. In that case three dots, . . ., are used to indicate "and so on." For instance, if $S$ is the fifty-element set of the states in the United States we could write, for convenience,

$$S = \{\text{Alabama, Alaska, Arizona, Arkansas}, \ldots\}.$$

Similarly, we could write the set of whole numbers as

$$W = \{0, 1, 2, 3, 4, \ldots\},$$

since $W$ has an infinite number of elements.

1

We use the symbol " $\in$ " to abbreviate the phrase "is an element of" or "is a member of." We write, for instance,

$$4 \in W$$

to say that 4 is a member of the set $W$. In turn,

$$\frac{1}{2} \notin W$$

means $\frac{1}{2}$ is not an element of set $W$.

A set may be given by description rather than by listing its elements. For instance,

$$A = \{x: x \text{ is an even number between 1 and 9}\}$$

is read "$A$ is the set of all $x$ such that $x$ is an even number between 1 and 9." Thus,

$$A = \{2, 4, 6, 8\}.$$

Similarly, if $W$ is the set of whole numbers,

$$\{t: t < 5 \text{ and } t \in W\} = \{0, 1, 2, 3, 4\}.$$

All the elements of

$$C = \{1, 2\}$$

are elements of

$$A = \{1, 2, 3, 4\}.$$

When this is true we say $C$ is a *subset* of $A$, and write

$$C \subset A.$$

In this instance set $A$ has at least one element not in $C$. (In fact it has two.) Under this condition set $C$ is known as a *proper subset* of $A$.

Now let $D = \{a, b, c\}$. The subsets of $D$ are

$$\{a\}, \{b\}, \{c\}, \{a, b\}, \{a, c\}, \{b, c\}, \{a, b, c\}, \varnothing.$$

Here $\varnothing$ is the *empty set*, the set with no elements. Of all the subsets of a set such as $D$ only two sets, the set $D$ itself and $\varnothing$, are *not* proper subsets. They are called *improper* subsets.

It is important to note the difference between the empty set $\varnothing$ and the set $\{\varnothing\}$. They are not equivalent. The empty set $\varnothing$ has no elements; but the set $\{\varnothing\}$ has one element, namely $\varnothing$.

It can be shown that if $n$ is the number of elements in a set, then $2^n$ is the number of subsets of the set. In the case of $D$, $n = 3$. Therefore, $2^n = 2^3 = 8$

and there are 8 subsets of *D* as listed above. Notice that $\varnothing$ is a subset of *every* set.

If $\qquad\qquad\qquad\qquad A = \{2, 4, 6, 8\}$

and $\qquad\qquad\qquad\qquad B = \{1, 2, 3, 4\},$

then the *union* of *A* and *B* is

$$A \cup B = \{1, 2, 3, 4, 6, 8\}.$$

The union of two sets is the collection of all the elements which are in at least one of the sets with no elements repeated. Geometrically we could view union as the shaded area in Figure 1-1. A diagram such as Figure 1-1 is called a *Venn diagram.*

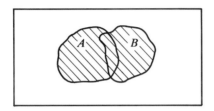

FIGURE 1-1.

It is important to realize the connection between the words "or" and "union." For instance,

$$\{x: x < 5 \text{ and } x \in W\} \cup \{x: x = 8\} = \{0, 1, 2, 3, 4, 8\}$$

is the same as

$$\{x: x < 5 \text{ and } x \in W \text{ or } x = 8\}.$$

Similarly, if $A = \{2, 3\}$ and $B = \{4, 5\}$, then

$$A \cup B = \{2, 3, 4, 5\}$$

is the same as

$$\{x: x \in A \text{ or } x \in B\}.$$

If $\qquad\qquad\qquad\qquad A = \{2, 4, 6, 8\}$

and $\qquad\qquad\qquad\qquad B = \{1, 2, 3, 4\},$

the *intersection* of *A* and *B* is written

$$A \cap B = \{2, 4\}.$$

Only those elements which occur in *both* sets are included in the set known as the intersection. The intersection of two sets *A* and *B* is shown in the Venn diagram in Figure 1-2.

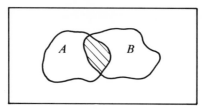

FIGURE 1-2.

If there are no elements that occur in both sets $A$ and $B$, the sets are said to be *disjoint*. That is, $A \cap B = \emptyset$. Suppose, for instance, that $A = \{1, 2, 3\}$ and $B = \{4, 5, 6\}$. Then $A \cap B = \emptyset$.

Just as the union of sets is closely related to the word "or," the intersection of sets is linked with the word "and." For example, if $A = \{2, 3, 5\}$ and $B = \{2, 8, 9\}$, then

$$A \cap B = \{2\}$$

is the same as the set

$$\{x : x \in A \text{ and } x \in B\}.$$

Also,        $\{x : x < 4, x \in W\} \cap \{x : x < 2, x \in W\} = \{0, 1\}$

is the same as

$$\{x : x < 4 \text{ and } x < 2, x \in W\}.$$

The set of all permissible elements of a set $A$ in a given discussion is called the *universe* or *universal set* $U$ for that discussion. The *complement* of $A$, denoted $A'$, is that set such that

$$A \cup A' = U \quad \text{and} \quad A \cap A' = \emptyset.$$

Thus, if

$$U = \{1, 2, 3, 4, 5\}$$

and

$$A = \{1, 2, 3\},$$

then

$$A' = \{4, 5\}$$

since

$$\{1, 2, 3\} \cup \{4, 5\} = \{1, 2, 3, 4, 5\} \quad \text{and} \quad \{1, 2, 3\} \cap \{4, 5\} = \emptyset.$$

As another example, suppose

$$U = \{1, 2, 3, 4, \ldots\}$$

and

$$A = \{2, 4, 6, 8, \ldots\}.$$

Then

$$A' = \{1, 3, 5, 7, \ldots\},$$

since        $\{2, 4, 6, 8, \ldots\} \cup \{1, 3, 5, 7, \ldots\} = \{1, 2, 3, 4, 5, \ldots\}$

and        $\{2, 4, 6, 8, \ldots\} \cap \{1, 3, 5, 7, \ldots\} = \emptyset.$

We may view the complement of a set $A$ geometrically in Figure 1-3. The universal set $U$ in this illustration is the entire rectangle.

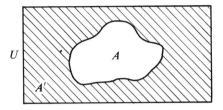

FIGURE 1-3.

*EXERCISES* ————————————————————

*Using set notation write a description of each of the sets in Exercises* 1 *through* 8.

1.  The set $S$ consisting of 8, 10, 12.   $S = \{8, 10, 12\}$
2.  The set $T$ of whole numbers less than 7.   $T = \{1, 2, 3, 4, 5, 6, 7\}$
3.  The set $V$ of the vowels of the alphabet.   $V = \{a, e, i, o, u\}$
4.  The set $S$ of states having a border on the Pacific Ocean.   $S = \{Oreg, Wash, Calif\}$
5.  The set $A$ of whole numbers not less than 13.   $A = \{x : x \leq 13, x \in W\}$
6.  The set of consonants in the word "Mississippi."   $\{M, i, s, s, i, p, p, i\}$
7.  The set $O$ of odd numbers.   $O = \{1, 3, 5, 7, \dots\}$
8.  The set $F$ of numbers between 3 and 21 divisible by 4.

*Use set notation to write each of the statements in Exercises* 9 *through* 16 *in a short way.*

9.  5 is an element of set $W$.   $5 \in W$
10. $x$ is an element of set $X$.   $x \in X$
11. $-1$ is not a member of set $W$.   $-1 \notin W$
12. 14 is an element of the union of $A$ and $B$.   $14 \in (A \cup B)$
13. 17 is not an element of the union of $C$ and $D$.   $17 \notin (C \cup D)$
14. 17 is an element of the complement of $A$.   $17 \in A'$
15. Set $A$ is included in set $B$.   $A \subset B$
16. The empty set is included in set $B$.   $B = \{\emptyset\}$

*Suppose*

$$R = \{0, 1, 2, 5, 6\},$$
$$S = \{2, 4, 6, 8\},$$
$$T = \{1, 3, 5, 7, 11\},$$
$$V = \{9, 10, 11, 12\}.$$

*Exhibit each of the sets in Exercises* 17 *through* 32 *by listing its elements in braces.*

17. $R \cup S$.

18. $\{x: x \in R \text{ or } x \in V\}$.

19. $V \cup R$.

20. $V \cup S$.

21. $(R \cup S) \cup T$.

22. $R \cap S$.

23. $\{x: x \in S \text{ and } x \in T\}$.

24. $T \cup V$.

25. $R \cup (S \cap T)$.

26. $(R \cup S) \cap (R \cup T)$.

27. $S \cap (T \cup V)$.

28. $(S \cap T) \cup (S \cap V)$.

29. $R \cap \varnothing$.

30. $R \cup \varnothing$.

31. $\{x: x \in R \cup S\}$.

32. $\{y: y \in (R \cap S) \cup T\}$.

*Suppose the universe is* $U = \{0, 2, 3, 4, 5, 6, 7, 8, 9, 11\}$ *and* $A = \{2, 4, 6, 8\}$. *Exhibit each of the sets in Exercises* 33 *through* 42.

33. $A'$.

34. $A \cup A'$.

35. $A \cap A'$.

36. $A' \cup A'$.

37. $A \cap A$.

38. $\{a: a < 6, a \in U\}$.

39. $\{x: x \in A'\}$.

40. $\{x: 0 < x < 10, x \in A'\}$.

41. $\{x: x \in A \cap U\}$.

42. $\{x: x \in A \text{ and } x \in A'\}$.

## ——1-2   A Development of the Rational Number System

In many societies today a child learns to count almost as early as he learns to talk. The numbers he is taught are frequently referred to as the *counting numbers* or *natural numbers*

$$N = \{1, 2, 3, \ldots, n, \ldots\},$$

and the *whole numbers*

$$W = \{0, 1, 2, 3, \ldots\}.$$

While the young child would hardly be conscious of the matter, $N$ has two fundamental properties.

First, there is a least or first element in the set. Second, there is no largest or last element in the set. This second aspect is frequently described in the following way. If $n$ is in the set, then $n + 1$ must be in the set. The term $n + 1$ is sometimes referred to as the *successor* of $n$. In $N$ every element except 1 is the successor of some number in the set.

A set may have two properties:

1. The number 1 is a member of the set.
2. If $n$ is in the set, then $n + 1$ is in the set.

Such a set is called an *inductive set*. Therefore, $N$ is an inductive set. In fact it is the smallest inductive set, since every inductive set contains all elements of $N$ and perhaps other elements as well.

Once a youngster learns to count, thereby developing an acquaintance with the set of natural numbers, it is usually many years before he is introduced to $I$, the set of *integers*:

$$I = \{\ldots, \ ^-n, \ldots, \ ^-3, \ ^-2, \ ^-1, 0, 1, 2, 3, \ldots, n, \ldots\}.$$

We can establish a fundamental relationship between $I$ and $N$. First, note that $I$ has no first element as does $N$ but $I$ does satisfy the property that if $n$ is in the set then $n + 1$ is in the set. Note an additional property of $I$ which is not shared by $N$. If $n \in I$ then $n - 1 \in I$. Thus *every element* in $I$ is a successor of some element.

To establish further relationships between $I$ and $N$ we first examine the question of *how many* objects are in a set. If we were asked to make a *count* of a set of objects, say a barrel of apples, we might proceed in the following way. We could remove the first apple and pair it with the number 1; then we could remove the second apple and pair it with the number 2, continuing up to the last apple. If we paired the last apple with the number $n$ we could then state that the *count* of the apples is $n$. We have paired with each apple exactly one number, starting with 1 and proceeding in order up to $n$.

If instead of apples we were asked to count $I$, the set of integers, we could proceed as follows: pair the first counting number, 1, with $0 \in I$; pair $2 \in N$ with $1 \in I$, $3 \in N$ with $^-1$ in $I$, $4 \in N$ with $2 \in I$, .... This procedure pairs the *even* counting numbers with the *positive* integers, thus:

$$\{\ldots \ ^-n, \ldots, \ ^-3, \ ^-2, \ ^-1, 0, 1, 2, 3, 4, \ldots, n, \ldots\}$$
$$\uparrow \ \uparrow \ \uparrow \ \uparrow \qquad \uparrow$$
$$\{2, 4, 6, 8, \ldots, 2n, \ldots\};$$

it also pairs the counting number 1 with the integer 0, and the odd counting numbers with the negative integers, as follows:

$$\{\ldots, \ ^-n, \ldots, \ ^-4, \ ^-3, \ ^-2, \ ^-1, 0, 1, 2, 3, \ldots, n, \ldots\}$$
$$\uparrow \qquad \uparrow \ \uparrow \ \uparrow \ \ \uparrow \ \uparrow$$
$$\{\ldots, (2n + 1), \ldots, \ 9, \ \ 7, \ \ 5, \ \ 3, 1\}.$$

We have just shown that there is a *one-to-one correspondence* between $I$ and $N$. That is, we have paired with each element of $I$ one and only one element of $N$, starting with $1 \in N$ and proceeding in order. Thus a startling relationship exists between $I$ and $N$: they possess the same number of elements. When a set is paired one-to-one with $N$ the set is said to be *denumerable*. Hence, the set $I$ is denumerable.

As the integers are in a sense the next logical system of numbers beyond the whole numbers, so are the rationals the next system beyond the integers.

The positive rational numbers, denoted by $R^+$, are of the form

$$\frac{1}{1}, \frac{1}{2}, \frac{1}{3}, \frac{1}{4}, \cdots, \frac{1}{n}, \cdots,$$

$$\frac{2}{1}, \frac{2}{2}, \frac{2}{3}, \frac{2}{4}, \cdots, \frac{2}{n}, \cdots,$$

$$\frac{3}{1}, \frac{3}{2}, \frac{3}{3}, \frac{3}{4}, \cdots, \frac{3}{n}, \cdots,$$

$$\vdots$$

We can define the rational numbers in several equivalent ways. Two ways are given below.

DEFINITION 1.   A rational number is any number that can be expressed in the form $p/q$, where $p, q \in I$ and $q \neq 0$.

DEFINITION 2.   A rational number is any *repeating* or *terminating decimal*.

By Definition 1, $\frac{1}{2}$, $\frac{3}{1}$, $\frac{2}{3}$, and $\frac{25}{99}$ are rational numbers but $\frac{2}{0}$ is not. By Definition 2 these rational numbers are written respectively, 0.5, 3.0, .66 ... or .$\bar{6}$ and .2525... or .$\overline{25}$. Notice that three dots, or a bar called a *vinculum*, are used to indicate the digits that repeat indefinitely. Thus .$\bar{6}$ and .$\overline{25}$ are repeating decimals, while .5 and 3.0 are terminating decimals, that is decimals that repeat the digit 0 after some point. Here .5 = .$5\bar{0}$ and 3.0 = 3.$\bar{0}$.

Before we can continue our examination of the rational numbers $R$, let us examine the following:

Given any two distinct numbers on a number line as in Figure 1-4,

FIGURE 1-4.

we can locate a number midway between them, namely

$$\frac{a+b}{2}.$$

That is,

$$a < \frac{a + b}{2} < b.$$

See Figure 1-5.

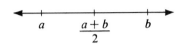

$$\begin{array}{ccc} a & \dfrac{a+b}{2} & b \end{array}$$

FIGURE 1-5.

Consider now two *rational* numbers on the number line in Figure 1-6.

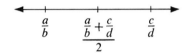

$$\begin{array}{ccc} \dfrac{a}{b} & \dfrac{\dfrac{a}{b}+\dfrac{c}{d}}{2} & \dfrac{c}{d} \end{array}$$

FIGURE 1-6.

We have

$$\frac{a}{b} < \frac{c}{d}.$$

Thus,

$$\frac{a}{b} < \frac{\dfrac{a}{b} + \dfrac{c}{d}}{2} < \frac{c}{d}.$$

Furthermore,

$$\frac{\dfrac{a}{b} + \dfrac{c}{d}}{2}$$

is a rational number, since

$$\frac{\dfrac{a}{b} + \dfrac{c}{d}}{2} = \frac{1}{2}\left(\frac{a}{b} + \frac{c}{d}\right) = \frac{1}{2}\left(\frac{ad + bc}{bd}\right) = \frac{ad + bc}{2bd}.$$

In this way we can always find a rational number between *any* two rational numbers.

Consider the question of "how many" rational numbers there are. Is $R$ denumerable? That is, can $R$ and $N$ be put into a one-to-one correspondence?

We can pair the positive rationals and the odd counting numbers greater than 1 as shown in Figure 1-7.

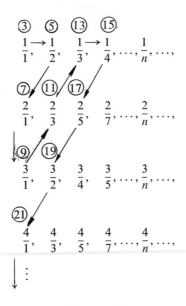

FIGURE 1-7.

In each row of the rectangular pattern of rationals we list only those rational numbers which do not appear in an earlier row. Thus, $\frac{2}{2}$, $\frac{2}{4}$ and $\frac{2}{6}$ are omitted from the second row, since $\frac{1}{1}$, $\frac{1}{2}$ and $\frac{1}{3}$ appear in the first row. This pattern pairs an odd counting number *greater than* 1 with each positive rational number. We can pair the counting number 1 with the rational number $\frac{0}{1}$ and the even counting numbers with the negative rational numbers in a similar way. Thus $R$ is denumerable.

So far we have developed the systems of the counting numbers $N$, the integers $I$, and the rational numbers $R$. One reason that we seek to extend each of these systems is to enable us to solve various classes of equations. For instance, with the counting numbers $N$ we can solve the equation

$$x + a = b$$

if and only if $b > a$. For example, we know that if $x + 2 = 3$, $x = 1$. But we could not solve an equation of the form

$$x + a = b$$

where $a > b$, if we restrict ourselves to counting numbers, For instance,

$$x + 3 = 2$$

has no solution if we require $x \in N$. However, if we allow $x \in I$ then we know that $x = {}^-1$ if $x + 3 = 2$. Next, suppose we have the equation

$$ax = b,$$

where $a$ and $b$ are integers and $a \neq 0$. The solution $x$ to this equation may not happen to be a member of $I$. Suppose, for example, we have

$$2x = 5.$$

Solving this equation requires an $x \in R$. In this case, $x = \frac{5}{2}$. However, even $R$ does not include enough numbers to solve all equations of the form

$$x^2 = a,$$

where $a \in R$. (Consider, for example, $x^2 = 5$.) We need a still more varied number system!

## EXERCISES

*In Exercises 1 through 9 state whether the statement is true or false.*

1.  $W \subset I.$     2.  $W \subset R.$     3.  $I \subset R.$

4.  The set of whole numbers $W$ is denumerable.

5.  The set of even counting numbers is denumerable.

6.  If $a \in I$ and $b \in I$, $\dfrac{a+b}{2} \in I.$     7.  If $a \in R$ and $b \in R$, $\dfrac{a+b}{2} \in R.$

8.  If $a \in N$ and $b \in N$, $a - b \in N.$     9.  If $a \in I$ and $b \in I$, $a - b \in I.$

10.  Construct a pairing between the even counting numbers and the negative rational numbers.

11.  If $a$, $b \in I$ and if $b$ is the successor of $a$, is $\dfrac{a+b}{2}$ an integer?

12.  If $a$ and $b$ are both prime numbers in $N$, is $\dfrac{a+b}{2} \in N$?

13.  Determine which of the following sets are denumerable where $n \in N$:
     a.  $\{4, 16, \ldots, 2^{2n}, \ldots\};$
     b.  $\{3, 9, 27, \ldots, 3^n, \ldots\};$
     c.  $\left\{\dfrac{1}{2}, \dfrac{1}{4}, \dfrac{1}{6}, \ldots, \dfrac{1}{2n}, \ldots\right\}.$

## ——1-3   The Real Number System

Continuing our orderly development of number systems now leads us to the system of *real numbers*, which we shall denote by R. We define these numbers as follows.

DEFINITION.   A *real number* is a number that can be written as either a repeating or nonrepeating infinite decimal.

Note carefully that this definition includes terminating decimals such as 0.54 since $0.54 = 0.54\bar{0}$, a repeating decimal in which the digit 0 repeats. Thus, the real numbers R include all rational numbers. The numbers in R that are not rational numbers are called *irrational numbers*. Examples of irrational numbers are $\sqrt{5}$, $\sqrt{3}$, and $\sqrt{2}$.

The solution of an equation of the form

$$x^2 = a,$$

where $a > 0$, comes from the set of real numbers. For instance, if we have the equation

$$x^2 = 2,$$

then its solutions are

$$x = \sqrt{2}$$

and

$$x = {}^-\sqrt{2},$$

since

$$(\sqrt{2})^2 = 2$$

and

$$({}^-\sqrt{2})^2 = 2.$$

We ordinarily show such a pair of solutions by writing

$$x = {}^{\pm}\sqrt{2}.$$

A real number such as $\sqrt{2}$, which is a nonrepeating infinite decimal, cannot be written out exactly using decimal notation. We know that $\sqrt{2}$ is a number whose square is 2. We can use this fact to aid us in writing a decimal *approximation* to $\sqrt{2}$.

First, we know that $1 < \sqrt{2}$ since $1 \cdot 1 = 1 < \sqrt{2} \cdot \sqrt{2} = 2$. Also, we know that $\sqrt{2} < 2$ since $\sqrt{2} \cdot \sqrt{2} = 2 < 2 \cdot 2 = 4$. (See Problems 15 and 16, Section 1-4.) Hence we know that $\sqrt{2}$ lies somewhere between 1 and 2. That is, $1 < \sqrt{2} < 2$. (See Figure 1-8.)

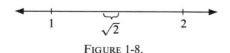

FIGURE 1-8.

To gain a better estimate of just where $\sqrt{2}$ lies between 1 and 2, we divide the interval between 1 and 2 into ten parts of equal length: 1.0, 1.1, 1.2, ..., 1.9, 2.0. Squaring each we find:

$$(1.0)^2 = 1, \qquad (1.6)^2 = 2.56,$$
$$(1.1)^2 = 1.21, \qquad (1.7)^2 = 2.89,$$
$$(1.2)^2 = 1.44, \qquad (1.8)^2 = 3.24,$$
$$(1.3)^2 = 1.69, \qquad (1.9)^2 = 3.61,$$
$$(1.4)^2 = 1.96, \qquad (2.0)^2 = 4.$$
$$(1.5)^2 = 2.25,$$

In particular we see that

$(1.4)^2 = 1.96$, which implies $1.4 < \sqrt{2}$, since $(1.4)^2 = 1.96 < (\sqrt{2})^2 = 2$;

$(1.5)^2 = 2.25$, which implies $\sqrt{2} < 1.5$, since $(1.5)^2 = 2.25 > (\sqrt{2})^2 = 2$.

Thus $\sqrt{2}$ lies between 1.4 and 1.5. More briefly,

$$1.4 < \sqrt{2} < 1.5.$$

Which of the numbers 1.4 and 1.5 is the better approximation to $\sqrt{2}$? In order to find out, we may proceed in either of two ways. We may again cut the interval into ten equal portions: 1.40, 1.41, 1.42, ..., 1.49, 1.50. But this is laborious and there is a simpler way. Since $1.4 < \sqrt{2} < 1.5$, examine $(1.4 + 1.5)/2 = 1.45$. We find $(1.45)^2 = 2.1025$. Therefore, $\sqrt{2} < 1.45$ since $(\sqrt{2})^2 = 2 < (1.45)^2 = 2.1025$. Thus,

$$1.4 < \sqrt{2} < 1.45,$$

which reveals that $\sqrt{2}$ lies nearer to 1.4 than to 1.5; hence 1.4 is the better approximation to $\sqrt{2}$.

Next look at the following array.

| Member of N | Corresponding member of R *between* 0 *and* 1 |
|---|---|
| 1 | $a_1 = .a_{11}\,a_{12}\,a_{13}\,a_{14}\cdots a_{1j}\cdots a_{1n}\cdots$ |
| 2 | $a_2 = .a_{21}\,a_{22}\,a_{23}\,a_{24}\cdots a_{2j}\cdots a_{2n}\cdots$ |
| 3 | $a_3 = .a_{31}\,a_{32}\,a_{33}\,a_{34}\cdots a_{3j}\cdots a_{3n}\cdots$ |
| $\vdots$ | $\vdots$ |
| $i$ | $a_i = .a_{i1}\,a_{i2}\,a_{i3}\,a_{i4}\cdots a_{ij}\cdots a_{in}\cdots$ |
| $\vdots$ | $\vdots$ |
| $m$ | $a_m = .a_{m1}\,a_{m2}\,a_{m3}\,a_{m4}\cdots a_{mj}\cdots a_{mn}\cdots(m<n)$ |
| $\vdots$ | $\vdots$ |

This array suggests that all infinite decimals between 0 and 1 are paired with the counting numbers. The $a_{ij}$ may be interpreted as follows. Each $a_{ij}$ is a digit from the set $\{0, 1, \ldots, 9\}$. The subscripts tell us that $a_{ij}$ is the $j$th digit in the $i$th real number in the above list. For example,

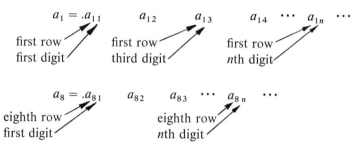

We now construct a number $u$ between 0 and 1 as follows: looking at the real numbers $a_1, a_2, \ldots$, in the above list, let

$$u_1 = \begin{cases} 1 \text{ if } a_{11} = 0 \\ 0 \text{ if } a_{11} \neq 0 \end{cases},$$

$$u_2 = \begin{cases} 1 \text{ if } a_{22} = 0 \\ 0 \text{ if } a_{22} \neq 0 \end{cases},$$

and, in general,

$$u_k = \begin{cases} 1 \text{ if } a_{kk} = 0 \\ 0 \text{ if } a_{kk} \neq 0 \end{cases},$$

for any counting number $k$.

Now consider the infinite decimal $u = .u_1 u_2 u_3 \cdots u_k \cdots$. Is $u$ in the above list? Clearly, $u \neq a_1$, since $u_1 \neq a_{11}$; $u \neq a_2$, since $u_2 \neq a_{22}$; and, in general, $u = a_k$, since $u_k = a_{kk}$. Therefore, $u$ *is a real number between 0 and 1 that does not appear in the above list.* That is, any list of real numbers between 0 and 1 in correspondence with the counting numbers is incomplete, so the real numbers are not denumerable. The counting numbers are insufficient to count even the small portion of $\mathbb{R}$ between 0 and 1.

Thus there are in a sense "more" real numbers than counting numbers. The rational numbers in $\mathbb{R}$ are denumerable; but it turns out that "almost all" real numbers are not rational.

Using simple construction and the Pythagorean Theorem we can construct line segments that have irrational numbers for their measures. For instance, in Figure 1-9 the line segment marked $\sqrt{2}$ has a measure of $\sqrt{2}$, since by the Pythagorean Theorem $\sqrt{1^2 + 1^2} = \sqrt{2}$; and the line segment marked $\sqrt{3}$ has a measure of $\sqrt{3}$, since by the Pythagorean Theorem $\sqrt{1^2 + (\sqrt{2})^2} = \sqrt{1 + 2} = \sqrt{3}$.

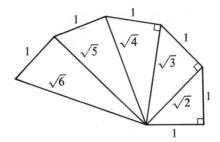

FIGURE 1-9.

*EXERCISES* ───────────────────────────────────────────

*Using rational numbers, approximate the real numbers in Exercises 1 through 6 to one decimal place.*

1.  $\sqrt{3}$.                    2.  $\sqrt{17}$.                    3.  $\sqrt{9}$.

4.  $\sqrt{5}$.                    5.  $\sqrt{13}$.                    6.  $\sqrt{6}$.

7.  Find the measure of the internal diagonal (the one not lying on any of the faces) of the unit cube, that is, the cube with sides of measure 1.

8.  Construct a cube that has an internal diagonal with measure

    a.  $\sqrt{7}$.                b.  $\sqrt{13}$.                c.  $\sqrt{a}$.

9.  Are the irrational numbers denumerable? Justify your answer.

*If a and b are integers and b ≠ 0, then a/b is a rational number, and its decimal equivalent can be found by dividing b into a. For instance,*

$$\frac{3}{4} = 0.75 \quad \text{since } 3 \div 4 = 0.75,$$

$$\frac{1}{7} = 0.\overline{142857} \quad \text{since } 1 \div 7 = .\overline{142857},$$

$$\frac{1}{9} = .\overline{1} \quad \text{since } 1 \div 9 = .\overline{1}.$$

*In Exercises 10–17 find the decimal equivalent of each of the given rational numbers.*

10.  $\frac{2}{9}$                    11.  $\frac{1}{4}$.                    12.  $\frac{1}{6}$.

13.  $\frac{1}{3} = \frac{2}{6}$.              14.  $\frac{5}{8}$.                    15.  $\frac{1}{11}$.

16.  $\frac{1}{16}$.                    17.  $\frac{5}{12}$.

*If a rational number is given in its decimal form and it is terminating, then it is a simple matter to change it into its fractional form a/b. For example,*

$$0.75 \; = \frac{75}{100} = \frac{3}{4},$$

$$0.103 = \frac{103}{1000},$$

$$0.125 = \frac{125}{1000} = \frac{5}{40} = \frac{1}{8},$$

$$0.2 \quad = \frac{2}{10} = \frac{1}{5}.$$

*In Exercises 18–26 find the fractional equivalents of the given terminating decimals.*

| | | |
|---|---|---|
| 18.   0.1 | 19.   0.25. | 20.   0.175. |
| 21.   0.625. | 22.   0.202. | 23.   0.11. |
| 24.   0.2275. | 25.   0.375. | 26.   0.835. |

*If a rational number is given in its decimal form and it is repeating, the following procedure may be used to find an equivalent fraction:*

a.      $N = .121212\ldots$

$100N = 12.\overline{12}$
$\underline{- \; N = -.\overline{12}}$
$99N = 12$

$N = \dfrac{12}{99}$  or  $\dfrac{4}{33};$

b.       $N = .4321321\ldots$

$10000N = 4321.\overline{321}$
$\underline{- \; 10N = - \; 4.\overline{321}}$
$9990N = 4317$

$N = \dfrac{4317}{9990} = \dfrac{1439}{3330}.$

*In Exercises 27–34 find the fractional equivalents of the given repeating decimals.*

| | | |
|---|---|---|
| 27.   0.999... | 28.   0.4$\overline{1}$ | 29.   0.102102... |
| 30.   0.4141... | 31.   0.12341234... | 32.   0.333... |
| 33.   0.65151... | 34.   0.176$\overline{21}$ | |

## ——1-4  Properties of Inequalities

In developing the real number system we used *several elementary* properties of the relations "less than" ($<$) and "greater than" ($>$). In this section we shall explore and apply some fundamental properties of these inequality relations. Students not already acquainted with these properties should carefully note the arguments and suggestions included.

Consider the following properties:

**PROPERTY 1.** If $a$, $b \in \mathbb{R}$, then exactly one of the following conditions holds:

1. $a = b$,
2. $a < b$,
3. $a > b$.

Note that $a < b$ implies that there exists a number $c > 0$ such that $a + c = b$. We also say that $a < b$ means $0 < b - a$; that is, $b - a$ is positive.

**PROPERTY 2.** If $a, b, c \in \mathbb{R}$, then

1. if $a = b$, $a + c = b + c$,
2. if $a < b$, $a + c < b + c$,
3. if $a > b$, $a + c > b + c$.

In other words, we may add the same real number to *both* sides of an equation or inequality without altering the equation or inequality. That is, the equation will remain an equation and the inequality will remain an inequality of the same kind. For $c = 5$ we have the following examples of Property 2:

1. since $3 = 2 + 1$, $3 + 5 = (2 + 1) + 5$ or $8 = 8$,
2. since $7 < 12$, $7 + 5 < 12 + 5$ or $12 < 17$,
3. since $8 > 5$, $8 + 5 > 5 + 5$ or $13 > 10$.

**PROPERTY 3.** If $a, b, c \in \mathbb{R}$, then

1. if $a = b$, $a - c = b - c$,
2. if $a < b$, $a - c < b - c$,
3. if $a > b$, $a - c > b - c$.

Technically, this property is redundant, but it serves to emphasize that $c$ in Property 2 may be negative.

**PROPERTY 4.** If $a, b, c \in \mathbb{R}$ and $c > 0$, then

1. if $a = b$, $ac = bc$,
2. if $a < b$, $ac < bc$,
3. if $a > b$, $ac > bc$.

For $c = 2$ we have the following examples of Property 4:

1.  since $5 = 4 + 1$, $5 \cdot 2 = (4 + 1) \cdot 2$ or $10 = 10$,
2.  since $5 < 7$, $5 \cdot 2 < 7 \cdot 2$ or $10 < 14$,
3.  since $4 > 3$, $4 \cdot 2 > 3 \cdot 2$ or $8 > 6$.

It is extremely important to note that $c$ must be greater than 0 for this property to hold for inequalities. Suppose, for instance, that $c < 0$—say, $c = {}^-2$. Then we would have the following results:

1.  $5 = 4 + 1$, $5 \cdot {}^-2 = (4 + 1) \cdot {}^-2$ or ${}^-10 = {}^-10$;
2.  $5 < 7$, but $5 \cdot {}^-2 \not< 7 \cdot {}^-2$ (read the symbol $\not<$ as "is not less than") since ${}^-10 > {}^-14$;
3.  $4 > 3$, but $4 \cdot {}^-2 \not> 3 \cdot {}^-2$ (read the symbol $\not>$ as "is not greater than") since ${}^-8 < {}^-6$.

These examples illustrate why the following property, Property 5, holds.

PROPERTY 5.   If $a, b, c \in \mathbb{R}$ and $c < 0$, then

1.  if $a = b$, $ac = bc$,
2.  if $a < b$, $ac > bc$,
3.  if $a > b$, $ac < bc$.

PROPERTY 6.   If $a, b, c \in \mathbb{R}$, then

1.  if $a < b$ and $b < c$, then $a < c$ and we may write in order $a < b < c$.
2.  if $a > b$ and $b > c$, then $a > c$ and we may write in order $a > b > c$.

By this property, for instance, $3 < 5$ and $5 < 6$, so $3 < 6$. Also, $6 > 4$ and $4 > 2$, so $6 > 2$; $\frac{1}{2} > \frac{1}{4}$ and $\frac{1}{4} > \frac{1}{8}$, so $\frac{1}{2} > \frac{1}{8}$.

PROPERTY 7.   If $a, b, c, d \in \mathbb{R}$ and $b \neq 0$ and $d \neq 0$, then

1.  if $\dfrac{a}{b} = \dfrac{c}{d}$, $ad = cb$,

2.  if $\dfrac{a}{b} < \dfrac{c}{d}$, $ad < cb$ when $bd > 0$,

3.  if $\dfrac{a}{b} > \dfrac{c}{d}$, $ad > cb$ when $bd > 0$.

We can easily show why this property is true. For instance, if

$$\frac{a}{b} > \frac{c}{d}$$

then
$$\frac{a}{b} \cdot \frac{d}{d} > \frac{c}{d} \cdot \frac{b}{b}$$

by Property 4 since $d/d = b/b = 1$. So

$$\frac{ad}{bd} > \frac{cb}{bd}.$$

Thus,
$$ad > cb.$$

We may apply Properties 6 and 7 to arrange the array of rational numbers

$$\frac{1}{3}, \frac{2}{5}, \frac{6}{7}, \frac{5}{6}$$

in order. To solve such a problem, first consider any two of the numbers, say $\frac{1}{3}$ and $\frac{2}{5}$. We find that

$$\frac{1}{3} < \frac{2}{5} \qquad \text{since } 1 \cdot 5 < 2 \cdot 3$$

by Property 7. Using Property 7 we also find that

$$\frac{2}{5} < \frac{5}{6}, \quad \text{since } 2 \cdot 6 < 5 \cdot 5,$$

and
$$\frac{5}{6} < \frac{6}{7}, \quad \text{since } 5 \cdot 7 < 6 \cdot 6.$$

Since
$$\frac{2}{5} < \frac{5}{6} \qquad \text{and} \qquad \frac{5}{6} < \frac{6}{7}$$

we have by Property 6

$$\frac{2}{5} < \frac{5}{6} < \frac{6}{7}.$$

We can now combine the inequalities

$$\frac{1}{3} < \frac{2}{5} \qquad \text{and} \qquad \frac{2}{5} < \frac{5}{6} < \frac{6}{7}$$

to obtain the final ordering of our four rational numbers using Property 6. We have

$$\frac{1}{3} < \frac{2}{5} < \frac{5}{6} < \frac{6}{7}.$$

Consider now the inequality

$$x + 1 < 2.$$

For what values of $x$ will this inequality be valid? By Property 3

$$x + 1 - 1 < 2 - 1, \quad \text{or} \quad x < 1.$$

We have simplified the original statement so that it is clear that

$$x + 1 < 2 \quad \text{when} \quad x < 1.$$

We say that $x < 1$ is the *solution* of the original inequality

$$x + 1 < 2.$$

This solution consists of *all* numbers and *only* those numbers $x$ for which $x < 1$ will satisfy (make valid) the inequality
$$x + 1 < 2.$$

Now examine the inequality

$$2x + 1 < 2.$$

What values of $x$ satisfy this inequality? By Property 3 we have

$$2x + 1 - 1 < 2 - 1, \quad \text{or} \quad 2x < 1.$$

Multiplying both sides by the same positive number, $\frac{1}{2}$, we have by Property 4

$$\left(\frac{1}{2}\right) \cdot 2x < \left(\frac{1}{2}\right) \cdot 1, \quad \text{or} \quad x < \frac{1}{2}.$$

The solution of $2x + 1 < 2$ is $x < \frac{1}{2}$.

Next we shall solve the *compound inequality*

$$2 < x - 1 < 4.$$

That is, we shall find the values of $x$ that satisfy *both* conditions, namely

$$1. \quad 2 < x - 1 \quad \text{and} \quad 2. \quad x - 1 < 4.$$

To solve $2 < x - 1 < 4$ we find the values of $x$ that will fulfill each condition and then combine the results by Property 6.

Condition 1:

$$2 < x - 1,$$

or, by Property 2, $\qquad 2 + 1 < x - 1 + 1;$

so $\qquad\qquad\qquad\qquad 3 < x.$

Condition 2: Again by Property 2,

$$x - 1 < 4,$$

or $\qquad\qquad\qquad x - 1 + 1 < 4 + 1;$

so $\qquad\qquad\qquad\qquad x < 5.$

Combining the conditions that $3 < x$ and $x < 5$ for the final solution, we get $3 < x < 5$ by Property 6. We can test this solution by substituting any value between 3 and 5 into the original inequality. For instance, take 4. We have $2 < 4 - 1 < 4$ or $2 < 3 < 4$, a true statement.

Now let us solve a variation on the above problem

$$1 < \frac{2x - 1}{3} < 8.$$

We have to satisfy simultaneously these two conditions:

$$1. \quad 1 < \frac{2x - 1}{3} \qquad \text{and} \qquad 2. \quad \frac{2x - 1}{3} < 8.$$

Condition 1 yields:

$$1 \cdot 3 < 2x - 1, \qquad \text{by Property 4}$$
$$3 < 2x - 1,$$
$$3 + 1 < 2x - 1 + 1, \qquad \text{by Property 2}$$
$$4 < 2x,$$
$$2 < x \qquad \text{by Property 4.}$$

Similarly, condition 2 yields:

$$2x - 1 < 3 \cdot 8,$$
$$2x - 1 + 1 < 24 + 1,$$
$$2x < 25,$$
$$x < \frac{25}{2}.$$

Combining the two required conditions, $2 < x$ and $x < \frac{25}{2}$, by Property 6 we find the solution for the original inequality is

$$2 < x < \frac{25}{2}.$$

As a final illustration let us solve the inequality

$$1 < \frac{2}{x - 1} < 4.$$

To solve this inequality we must satisfy both of the following conditions:

$$1. \quad 1 < \frac{2}{x - 1} \qquad \text{and} \qquad 2. \quad \frac{2}{x - 1} < 4.$$

Condition 1: We must have $x - 1 > 0$, since otherwise we would have either $x - 1 = 0$, making the denominator 0, or we would have $x - 1 < 0$, making the quotient $2/(x - 1)$ negative, so that $2/(x - 1)$ could not be greater than 1. If

$$x - 1 > 0 \qquad \text{and} \qquad 1 < \frac{2}{x - 1},$$

then $$\qquad\qquad x > 1 \qquad \text{and} \qquad x - 1 < 2$$

by Properties 2 and 4 respectively. Simplifying, we have

$$x > 1 \qquad \text{and} \qquad x < 3$$

or, equivalently,

$$1 < x \qquad \text{and} \qquad x < 3.$$

Therefore, condition 1 requires that

$$1 < x < 3.$$

Condition 2: Again, we must have $x - 1 > 0$. If

$$x - 1 > 0 \qquad \text{and} \qquad \frac{2}{x - 1} < 4,$$

then

$$x > 1 \qquad \text{and} \qquad 2 < 4(x - 1),$$
$$x > 1 \qquad \text{and} \qquad 2 < 4x - 4,$$
$$x > 1 \qquad \text{and} \qquad 6 < 4x,$$
$$x > 1 \qquad \text{and} \qquad \frac{3}{2} < x,$$

or, equivalently,

$$1 < x \qquad \text{and} \qquad \frac{3}{2} < x.$$

Both of these requirements are met by $\frac{3}{2} < x$. Thus condition 2 requires that $\frac{3}{2} < x$.

To obtain the final solution of

$$1 < \frac{2}{x - 1} < 4,$$

we must combine conditions 1 and 2, which require that $1 < x < 3$ *and* $\frac{3}{2} < x$. By Section 1-1 we know then that we must find

$$\{x : 1 < x < 3\} \cap \left\{ x : \frac{3}{2} < x \right\} = \left\{ x : \frac{3}{2} < x < 3 \right\}.$$

Therefore, we know that the desired solution is

$$\frac{3}{2} < x < 3.$$

To test this solution we can pick a point such as $x = 2$ from the solution interval and substitute it into the original inequality,

$$1 < \frac{2}{x-1} < 4.$$

We obtain

$$1 < \frac{2}{2-1} < 4 \qquad \text{or} \qquad 1 < 2 < 4,$$

a true statement. We may also select a point such as $x = 0$ from outside the solution interval and substitute it into the original inequality. We get

$$1 < \frac{2}{^-1} < 4 \qquad \text{or} \qquad 1 < {}^-2 < 4,$$

a false statement—just as it should be if our solution, $\frac{3}{2} < x < 3$, is correct.

### EXERCISES ────────────────────────────────

1. Order from least to greatest each of the following arrays of real numbers:

   a. $\frac{1}{2}, \frac{2}{3}, \frac{1}{4}, \frac{2}{5}, \frac{5}{8}, \frac{1}{3}.$

   b. $\frac{8}{9}, \frac{7}{6}, 2\frac{1}{3}, \frac{64}{71}, \frac{7}{8}, \frac{6}{7}.$

   c. 2.011, 1.25, 23.7, 21.72, 21.721.

   d. 3.1416, 3.0416, 2.734, 2.737, 3.14165.

*Solve each of the following inequalities. Show your work step by step as in the examples in this section and name the property that makes each of your steps "legal."*

2. $x + 1 < 3.$

3. $2x < 4.$

4. $2x + 1 < 4.$

5. $2x - 1 < 4.$

6. $3x - 2 < 5.$

7. $\frac{1}{2}x - \frac{2}{3} > 4.$

8. $0 < x - 1 < 4.$

9. ${}^-1 < 2x - 1 < 3.$

10. $0 < \dfrac{x+1}{2} < 4.$

11. $0 < \dfrac{2}{x-1} < 3.$

12. $0 < \dfrac{x-1}{x+1}.$

13. ${}^-2 < \dfrac{x-1}{2x+1} < 2.$

14. ${}^-1 < \dfrac{x}{\frac{1}{2}x - \frac{3}{2}} < 3.$

★15. If $0 < a < b$, show that $a^2 < b^2$. (Hint. Use Properties 4-2 and 6-1.)

★16. If $a < b < 0$, show that $b^2 < a^2$.

★17. If $0 < a < b$ and $0 < c < d$, show why $ac < bd$.

★18. If $a < 0$, show why $^-a > 0$.

★19. If $a < b$, show why $^-a > {}^-b$.

★20. If $0 < ab$, show why $a < 0$ and $b < 0$ or $a > 0$ and $b > 0$.

★21. If $a > 0$, show why $\dfrac{1}{a} > 0$.

★22. If $0 < b < a$, show why $\dfrac{1}{a} < \dfrac{1}{b}$.

★23. If $0 < a < x < b$ and $0 < c < y < g$, show why $\dfrac{a}{g} < \dfrac{x}{y} < \dfrac{b}{c}$.

---

## ——1-5   Intervals and Neighborhoods of Real Numbers

Examine the following inequalities and their corresponding graphs:

a.   $1 < x < 2$.

b.   $1 \leqslant x \leqslant 2$.

c.   $1 < x \leqslant 2$.

d.   $1 \leqslant x < 2$.

Each of the preceding inequalities defines an *interval*. Inequality a describes an *open interval*. It may also be denoted $(a, b)$. The parentheses indicate that the endpoints, the point corresponding to 1 and the point corresponding to 2, are not included in the interval. Inequality b describes a *closed interval* since the endpoints are included in the interval. It may also be denoted by [1, 2] where the brackets indicate that the endpoints 1 and 2 are included in the interval. Finally, inequalities c and d describe *half-open intervals* since only one of the endpoints is included in each interval. Inequality c might be denoted by (1, 2] and inequality d might be denoted by [1, 2).

Consider an arbitrary interval $a < x \leqslant b$, as shown in Figure 1-10, where $a$ and $b$ are real numbers.

FIGURE 1-10.

This interval separates the real number line into three nonoverlapping intervals: $(a, b]$; $(-\infty, a]$, which is to the left of $(a, b]$; and $(b, +\infty)$, which is to the right of $(a, b]$. Here the symbols $-\infty$ and $+\infty$ (read "negative infinity" and "positive infinity") are not considered real numbers. That is, they are not points of the set R. They are, however, defined to satisfy the properties:

1.  $-\infty < +\infty$;
2.  if $a \in$ R, then $-\infty < a < +\infty$.

Notice that

$$(-\infty, a] \cup (a, b] \cup (b, -\infty) = (-\infty, +\infty),$$

the set R.

If $c$ is a real number and $a < c < b$, then $c \in (a, b)$, that is, $c$ is in the open interval $(a, b)$. In connection with this idea we have the following definition.

DEFINITION.   An open interval $(a, b)$ that contains $c$ is a *neighborhood of c*.

It is important to note that a neighborhood of a real number $c$ must be an open interval and that the open interval must contain $c$. Also notice that a real number $c$ has an infinite number of neighborhoods.

For instance, if $c = 5$, the following open intervals are only a few of the possible neighborhoods of 5:

$$(4, 6), (^-7, 7), (-\infty, +\infty), (4.98, 5.02), (0, 5.1).$$

Besides being neighborhoods of 5, each of these intervals is a neighborhood of every number between its endpoints. For instance, $(4, 6)$ is a neighborhood of every number between 4 and 6. $(-\infty, +\infty)$ is a neighborhood of every number.

If $c = 5$, the following intervals are *not* neighborhoods of 5:

$$[4, 6], (0, 2), [^-7, 7).$$

Though $[4, 6]$ and $[^-7, 7)$ contain 5, they are not open intervals. On the other hand, $(0, 2)$ is an open interval, but it does not contain 5.

*EXERCISES* ─────────────────────────────────────────

*Use parentheses and/or brackets to write the following intervals in Exercises 1 through 8 in another way.*

1.  $3 \leqslant x \leqslant 5.$

2.  $^-1 < x < 2.$

3.  $7 < x \leqslant 9.$

4.  $^-3 \leqslant x < {^-}1.$

5.  $a \leqslant x < b.$

6.  $a < x \leqslant b.$

7.  $a \leqslant x \leqslant a + 1.$

8.  $a - 1 < x \leqslant a.$

*Write the correct inequality for each of the following intervals.*

9.  $(^-1, 0).$

10.  $[^-2, 3).$

11.  $[^-5, 2].$

12.  $(^-2, 4].$

13.  $(a, c].$

14.  $(b - 1, b + 1).$

15.  $[b, b + 2).$

16.  $[b, b + 2].$

*State whether or not each of the following intervals is a neighborhood of the given number c. If it is not, state why.*

17.  $(3, 4), \quad c = 2\frac{1}{2}.$

18.  $(3, 5), \quad c = 4.$

19.  $[3, 5), \quad c = 4.$

20.  $(2.99, 3{,}01), \quad c = 3.$

21.  $(3, 4), \quad c = 3.$

22.  $(3 - \varepsilon, 3 + \varepsilon), \quad c = 3, \varepsilon > 0.$

23.  $\left(3 - \dfrac{1}{n}, 3 + \dfrac{1}{n}\right), \quad c = 3, n$ a positive integer.

## ──1-6  Bounded Sets

Consider the prime factors of 30 and 105:

The set of *factors* of 30 is $\{1, 2, 3, 5, 6, 10, 15, 30\}$, while the set of factors of 105 is $\{1, 3, 5, 7, 15, 21, 35, 105\}$. $\{1, 3, 5, 15\}$ is called the set of *common factors* of 30 and 105, since each member of the set is a factor of both 30 and 105. The largest element of the set of common factors of 30 and 105 is 15. Thus 15 is called the GCF, *greatest common factor*, of 30 and 105.

When we have a set of numbers and there is a largest value or number for the set, we say that the set is *bounded above* or that it has an *upper bound* (UB). For example, 15 is an upper bound of $\{1, 3, 5, 15\}$. Likewise, the smallest factor shared by 30 and 105 is 1. We say that the set is *bounded below* and has a *lower bound* (LB). Notice that $\{1, 3, 5, 15\}$ has many other upper bounds such as 16, 28, 101, 5,000 and that $\{1, 3, 5, 15\}$ has numerous other lower bounds such as 0, $^-1$, and $^-103$.

Now consider the prime factors of 210 and 180:

The set of factors of 210 is {1, 2, 3, 5, 6, 7, 10, 14, 15, 21, 30, 35, 42, 105, 210}. The set of factors of 180 is {1, 2, 3, 4, 5, 6, 9, 10, 12, 15, 18, 20, 30, 36, 45, 60, 90, 180}. Thus the set of common factors is

$$\{1, 2, 3, 5, 6, 10, 15, 30\},$$

and the GCF of 180 and 210 is 30, an UB of the set. Again, we do not say that 30 is *the* upper bound of the set; it is only one of many upper bounds.

A *common multiple* of two numbers is a number that has the two given numbers as factors. Let us find the common multiples of 6 and 9. The multiples of 6 are the elements of $\{6 \times 1, 6 \times 2, 6 \times 3, 6 \times 4, 6 \times 5, 6 \times 6, \ldots\}$, or $\{6, 12, 18, 24, 30, 36 \ldots\}$. The multiples of 9 are the elements of $\{9 \times 1, 9 \times 2, 9 \times 3, 9 \times 4, 9 \times 5, 9 \times 6, \ldots\}$, or $\{9, 18, 27, 36, 45, 54, \ldots\}$. The common multiples of 6 and 9 are the elements in both $\{6, 12, 18, 24, 30, 36, \ldots\}$ and $\{9, 18, 27, 36, 45, 54, \ldots\}$. Thus the common multiples of 6 and 9 are the elements of

$$L = \{18, 36, 54, \ldots\}.$$

Here 18 is the smallest member of the set of common multiples. It is called the *least common multiple*, LCM, of 6 and 9. 18 is a lower bound of the set $L$. In fact, it is the greatest of the lower bounds of $L$.

Here is another way to find the LCM of two numbers. First find the prime factors of each number. For our example we have

6
/ \
2  3

9
|
3²

Then find the set whose elements are the highest powers of the numbers that are prime factors of either number. In our case, this set would be

$$\{2, 3^2\}.$$

The LCM of 6 and 9 is the product of the elements in this set. Thus the LCM of 6 and 9 is $2 \cdot 3^2 = 18$, just as we found above.

With these examples in mind we make the following definitions.

DEFINITION.   A set $S$ of numbers is *bounded below* if there exists a number $a$, called a *lower bound* (LB), such that for every $x \in S$, $a \leqslant x$.

DEFINITION.   A number $b$ is the *greatest lower bound* (GLB) of a set $S$ of numbers provided that

1.   $b$ is a lower bound of $S$;
2.   if $a$ is any lower bound of $S$, $b \geqslant a$.

It is important to note that a set may have many lower bounds, but only one greatest lower bound. For instance, the set $\{x: 5 \leqslant x \leqslant 7, x \in \mathbb{R}\}$ has many lower bounds, some of which are 4, 0, and $^-10$. However, it has only one greatest lower bound, namely 5.

Similarly, the set $\{x: 5 \leqslant x \leqslant 7, x \in \mathbb{R}\}$ has many upper bounds such as $7\frac{1}{2}$, 10, and 95. However, it has only one least upper bound, 7. With this simple example in mind, along with the examples at the beginning of the section involving common factors and greatest common factors, we make the following definitions.

DEFINITION.   A set $S$ of numbers is *bounded above* if there exists a number $a$, called an *upper bound* (UB), such that for every $x \in S$, $a \geqslant x$.

DEFINITION.   A number $b$ is the *least upper bound* (LUB) of a set $S$ of numbers provided that

1.   $b$ is an upper bound of $S$;
2.   if $a$ is an upper bound of $S$, $b \leqslant a$.

A GLB or a LUB of a set need not be an element of a set as the next examples show. These examples apply the concepts just presented to a topic that was discussed in Exercises 27–34, Section 1–3. What is the LUB of

$$S = \{.27, .2727, .272727, \ldots\}?$$

We already know how to find the fraction that corresponds to the repeating decimal $.\overline{27}$. This fraction is the LUB of $S$! If we let $a = .\overline{27}$, $100a = 27.\overline{27}$ and

$$100a = 27.\overline{27}$$
$$- \ a = -.\overline{27}$$
$$99a = 27$$
$$a = \frac{27}{99} = \frac{3}{11}.$$

Therefore $\frac{3}{11}$ is the LUB of $S$.

Similarly, the LUB of

$$T = \{.9, .99, .999, \ldots\}$$

is the fractional equivalent of $.\bar{9}$. If we let $a = .\bar{9}$, $10a = 9.\bar{9}$. We have

$$10a = 9.\bar{9}$$
$$-a = \phantom{9}.\bar{9}$$
$$\overline{9a = 9\phantom{..}}$$
$$a = 1$$

Therefore 1 is the LUB of $T$.

## EXERCISES

*Find the greatest common factor of the following pairs of numbers.*

1. 28, 14.          2. 12, 35.
3. 75, 21.          4. 120, 84.

*Find the least common multiple of the following pairs of numbers.*

5. 39, 15.          6. 27, 95.
7. 42, 150.          8. 88, 75.

*Find the LUB of each of the following sets.*

9. $\{.67, .6767, \ldots\}$.          10. $\{1.3, 1.33, 1.333, \ldots\}$.
11. $\{.754, .754754, \ldots\}$.          12. $\{.3456, .345656, \ldots\}$.

*Name the GLB and LUB, if they exist, of each of the following sets.*

13. $\{t : 2 \leqslant t \leqslant 3, t \in \mathrm{R}\}$.          14. $\{t : t \geqslant 5, t \in \mathrm{R}\}$.
15. $\{x : x > 5, x \in \mathrm{R}\}$.          16. $\{r : {}^{-}3 \leqslant r < \frac{1}{2}, r \in \mathrm{R}\}$.
17. $\{x : x \leqslant 0, x \in \mathrm{R}\}$.          18. $\{y : y > 3 \text{ or } y \leqslant 2, y \in \mathrm{R}\}$.
19. Must an upper bound of a set be a member of the set? A lower bound?

## ——1-7  Mappings, Relations, and Functions

A map is a picture or a group of symbols that bears some relationship to reality. For instance, a road map lists routes, signs, and cities, roughly corresponding to reality. A treasure map—less complete in a geographical sense—gives a trail to a specific objective. It is evident that maps are useful in our everyday activities.

In mathematics we have need for very specialized maps. In the most general sense a mathematical *relation*, denoted by $h$, gives a correspondence from some set $A$ to some set $B$, as shown by the *mapping* in Figure 1-11.

Figure 1-11 suggests that for each element $x$ in set $A$ there corresponds some element $y$ in set $B$. The basic idea behind a mathematical relation is as simple as that. It may be thought of as a correspondence between sets of elements given by a *rule*. This rule assigns to each element $x$ from some given set $A$

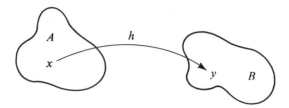

FIGURE 1-11.

an element or elements $y$ of another set $B$. If the rule is denoted by $h$ we may denote such a relation symbolically by

$$h: \quad A \rightarrow B.$$

This notation says that rule $h$ assigns to each element from set $A$ some element or elements from set $B$. For instance our rule might be "divide by 2"; so if $A = \{0, 2, 4, 6\}$ and $B = \{0, 1, 2, 3\}$, we would have by rule $h$ the situation shown by the mapping in Figure 1-12.

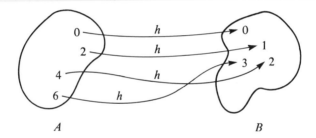

FIGURE 1-12.

The initial set of the relation given by rule $h$, here $A$, is called the *domain*; the second set, here $B$, is called the *range*. In this example, the domain is $\{0, 2, 4, 6\}$ and the range is $\{0, 1, 2, 3\}$.

Now let $h: A \rightarrow B$ describe the relation shown by the mapping in Figure 1-13.

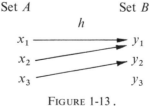

FIGURE 1-13.

Here the domain of $h$ is $\{x_1, x_2, x_3\}$, and the range of $h$ is $\{y_1, y_2\}$.

Next let $h': A \rightarrow B$ describe the relation shown by the mapping in Figure 1-14.

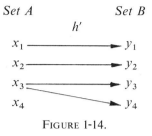

FIGURE 1-14.

From Figure 1-14 we see that the domain of $h'$ is $\{x_1, x_2, x_3\}$, and the range of $h'$ is $\{y_1, y_2, y_3, y_4\}$.

Now suppose $f: \quad A \rightarrow B$ describes the relation shown in Figure 1-15.

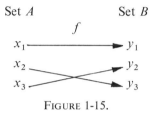

FIGURE 1-15.

The domain of $f$ is $\{x_1, x_2, x_3\}$ and the range of $f$ is $\{y_1, y_2, y_3\}$.

The relation $f$ differs from either $h$ or $h'$. We saw that $h$ maps more than one element from the domain to the same element in the range; that is, $h: \quad x_1 \rightarrow y_1$, and $h: \quad x_2 \rightarrow y_1$. There is said to be a *collapsing* of elements from set $A$. On the other hand, $h'$ maps an element from set $A$ to more than one element in $B$, specifically $h': \quad x_3 \rightarrow y_3$ and $h': \quad x_3 \rightarrow y_4$. This is called a *splitting* of elements from set $A$. However, $f$ maps exactly one element of set $A$ to exactly one element of set $B$. There is no collapsing or splitting of elements from set $A$. We call $f$ a *one-to-one correspondence*.

The relations $h$, $h'$, and $f$ each define a set of *ordered pairs* $(x, y)$ where the first value $x$ in the pair is an element in the domain, set $A$, and the second value $y$ is an element to which $x$ is mapped in the range $B$. Hence, we have the following sets of ordered pairs for the relations discussed above:

$$h = \{(x_1, y_1), (x_2, y_1), (x_3, y_2)\},$$
$$h' = \{(x_1, y_1), (x_2, y_2), (x_3, y_3), (x_3, y_4)\},$$
$$f = \{(x_1, y_1), (x_2, y_3), (x_3, y_2)\}.$$

Each of the mathematical relations $h$, $h'$, and $f$ describes a set of ordered pairs. However, the relations $f$ and $h$ are special relations. They are called *functions* because they are relations that pair each element in the domain to only one element in the range. Notice that $h'$ does not satisfy the requirements for a function because it pairs $x_3$ with more than one element in the range, namely $y_3$ and $y_4$.

The following definition of a function is equivalent to the definition above.

DEFINITION.    $f$ is a function if $f$ is a relation such that if $(x, y)$ and $(x, z) \in f$, then $y = z$.

We can see that $h'$ is not a function by this definition as well, since $(x_3, y_3)$ and $(x_3, y_4) \in h'$, but $y_3 \neq y_4$.

Let us consider some other relations and determine whether they are functions. First we shall examine $f\colon\ x \to 2x$, where $x \in I = \{\ldots, ^-2, ^-1, 0, 1, 2, \ldots\}$. A portion of the set of ordered pairs determined by $f$ is

$$\{(1, 2), (0, 0), (^-1, ^-2), (^-2, ^-4), (^-4, ^-8), \ldots\}.$$

We can say further that $f$ is a function, because it pairs every element $x$ in its domain with only one element in its range, namely $2x$. Because $f$ is a function, we may describe it using the notation

$$f(x) = 2x.$$

If we let $E = \{2n\colon n \in I\} = \{\ldots, ^-4, ^-2, 0, 2, 4, \ldots\}$ we might also write $f(I) = E$, since $E$ is the set of all values of $f(x)$ where $x \in I$. This $f(x)$ notation is usually reserved for relations that are functions.

We might also describe $f$ by writing

$$y = 2x.$$

When this notation is used $x$ is said to be the *independent variable* and $y$ is said to be the *dependent* variable, since the values of $y$ depend on the values that $x$ assumes.

Another relation to consider is

$$s\colon\ x \to y = x^2,$$

where $x \in I = \{\ldots, ^-2, ^-1, 0, 1, 2, \ldots\}$. It defines a set of ordered pairs of the form $(x, x^2)$, where $x \in I$. A portion of this set is

$$s = \{(1, 1), (^-1, 1), (0, 0), (4, 16), (^-4, 16), \ldots\}.$$

Again, it is important to notice that only a part of the set of ordered pairs defined by $s$ is listed above. At any rate, because $s$ does define a set of ordered pairs, we can say that it is a relation. Is $s$ a function as well? Yes! $s$ pairs every element $x$ in $I$, its domain, with only one element in its range, specifically

$x^2$. Therefore, $s$ is a function and we may describe $s$ by $s(x) = x^2$. In addition, if we let $A = \{0, 1, 4, 9, \ldots\}$, where $a \in A$ only if $a = x^2$ for some $x \in I$, we may write $s(I) = A$.

Let us examine another relation,

$$r: \quad 4 \rightarrow x,$$

where $x = \{\ldots, ^-2, ^-1, 0, 1, 2, \ldots\}$. This relation defines a set of ordered pairs, a portion of which is listed below:

$$r = \{(4, ^-2), (4, ^-1), (4, 0), (4, 1), \ldots\}.$$

From this partial list we can see that the ordered pairs in the relation $r$ all have the same first elements, but different second elements. For this reason the relation $r$ does not meet the requirements of a function.

So far we have described functions as relations that have certain properties. It should be clear that functions can be described by mappings, rules, or ordered pairs. Which method is used depends most of all upon the situation.

Many examples of functions can be found in everyday life. A function (rule) is used to figure the postage $y$ cents on a first-class letter weighing $x$ ounces. The telephone company uses a predetermined function to find the toll charge of $y$ dollars on a long distance call from Seattle to San Diego lasting $x$ minutes. The time it takes to fly from one city to another is a function of both the distance between the two cities and the rate at which the airplane flies. These are only a few typical examples of functions encountered in everyday life. Because functions play an all-important role in mathematics, we will be dealing with them constantly in the chapters ahead.

## EXERCISES

1. For each of the following relations describe the correspondence using ordered pairs.

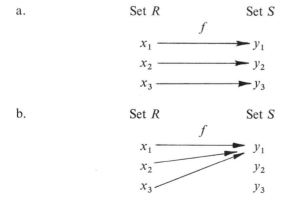

c.

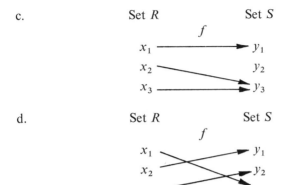

d.            Set R                Set S
                        f
          $x_1$                      $y_1$
          $x_2$                      $y_2$
          $x_3$                      $y_3$

2.   Draw diagrams to picture each of the relations from the set $X = \{x_1, x_2,$ $x_3, x_4\}$ to the set $Y = \{y_1, y_2, y_3, y_4\}$ as described below by the sets of ordered pairs.

a.   $g = \{(x_1, y_1), (x_2, y_2), (x_3, y_3)\}$.
b.   $g = \{(x_1, y_1)\ (x_2, y_2), (x_3, y_3), (x_4, y_4)\}$.
c.   $r = \{(x_1, y_2), (x_2, y_3), (x_3, y_4), (x_4, y_1)\}$.
d.   $q = \{(x_2, y_4)\ (x_3, y_2), (x_4, y_1), (x_4, y_3)\}$.

3.   a–d.   Give the domain and range of each of the relations in Exercise 2.
4.   a.   Which of the relations in Exercise 1 are functions?
     b.   Which of the relations in Exercise 2 are functions?
5.   Classify each of the following as one-to-one, collapsing, or splitting relations.

a.   $y = x$, $x \in R$.               b.   $y = x^2$, $x \in R$.
c.   $y = \sqrt{x}$, $x \in R$, $x \geqslant 0$.     d.   $y = {}^-x^2$, $x \in R$.
e.   $y = x^3$, $x \in R$.              f.   $y = 7$.

6.   a–f.   State whether or not each of the relations given in Exercise 5 is a function.

## _____1-8   Absolute Value

Sometimes the concept of *absolute value* is used to describe certain intervals and neighborhoods. How this description is accomplished will become clear as this section progresses.

DEFINITION.   The *absolute value* of a real number $a$, denoted $|a|$, is

$$|a| = \begin{cases} a \text{ if } a \geqslant 0 \\ {}^-a \text{ if } a < 0 \end{cases}.$$

Some examples of absolute value are

$$|^-7| = {}^-(^-7) = 7, \qquad |3| = 3, \qquad\qquad\qquad |7| = 7,$$
$$|^-3| = {}^-(^-3) = 3, \qquad |0| = 0, \qquad |3 - 3| = |0| = 0.$$

Notice that the absolute value of every real number is nonnegative.

Geometrically, we may think of the absolute value of a number as the distance of that number from 0 on the number line. For instance,

$$|4| = 4 \qquad \text{and} \qquad |^-4| = 4.$$

Both 4 and $^-4$ are 4 units from 0 on the number line. (See Figure 1-16.)

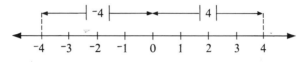

Figure 1-16.

Furthermore, we may use absolute value to represent the distance between two real numbers $a$ and $b$. This distance is either

$$|a - b| \qquad \text{or} \qquad |b - a|.$$

For example, the distance between 2 and $^-3$ on the number line is

$$|2 - (^-3)| = |2 + 3| = |5| = 5,$$

or, equivalently,

$$|^-3 - 2| = |^-5| = 5.$$

From the diagram in Figure 1-17 it is apparent that the distance between 2 and $^-3$ is 5 units, just as expected.

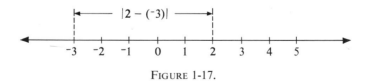

Figure 1-17.

Now, examine the inequalities and their corresponding graphs in Figure 1-18. In all cases $x$ may lie anywhere in the darkened interval on the number line.

Some properties of absolute values and inequalities are shown in the following graphs. Let us discuss methods for solving the inequalities whose graphs appear in Figure 1-18. It will then be more evident how the graphs are obtained.

$|x| \leq 2$

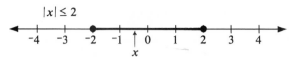

The distance from $x$ to 0 is
less than or equal to 2.

(a)

$|x| \leq 5$

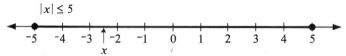

The distance from $x$ to 0 is
less than or equal to 5.

(b)

$|x - 1| \leq 2$

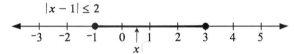

The distance from $x$ to 1 is
less than or equal to 2.

(c)

$|x - 2| \leq 5$

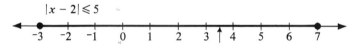

The distance from $x$ to 2 is
less than or equal to 5.

(d)

$|2x - 3| \leq 2$

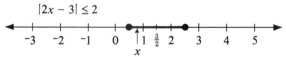

The distance from $x$ to $\frac{3}{2}$ is
less than or equal to 1.

(e)

$|5x - 10| < 15$

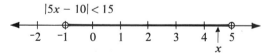

The distance from $x$ to 2 is
less than 3.

(f)

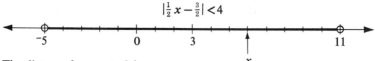

$$\left|\tfrac{1}{2}x - \tfrac{3}{2}\right| < 4$$

The distance from $x$ to 3 is
less than 8.

(g)

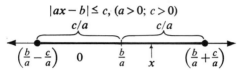

$$|ax - b| \le c, \ (a > 0; \ c > 0)$$

The distance from $x$ to $b/a$ is
less than or equal to $c/a$.

(h)

FIGURE 1-18.

Consider, for instance, the inequality $|x| \le 2$ in Figure 1-18(a). Recall that the absolute value of a number is the distance of that number from 0 on the number line. Thus, an equivalent statement to "$|x| \le 2$" is "the distance of $x$ from 0 is less than or equal to 2." Every such number $x$ lies between $^-2$ and 2 inclusive on the number line. That is, $^-2 \le x \le 2$.

In general, the statement "$|w| < c$," where $w$ is any expression and $c$ is a positive real number, may be taken to mean "$^-c < w < c$." A similar statement can be made concerning "$|w| \le c$."

Now let us examine the inequality $|x - 1| \le 2$ graphed in Figure 1-18(c). By the preceding discussion an equivalent statement is

$$^-2 \le x - 1 \le 2.$$

Applying methods of Section 1-4, we solve this compound inequality as follows:

$$^-2 + 1 \le x - 1 + 1 \le 2 + 1,$$
$$^-1 \le x \le 3.$$

That is, $x$ satisfies

$$|x - 1| \le 2$$

if and only if $x$ satisfies

$$^-1 \le x \le 3.$$

This is in agreement with Figure 1-18(c).

As a final example, consider the inequality of Figure 1-18(h),

$$|ax - b| \le c \quad (a > 0; \ c > 0).$$

We shall first write the equivalent compound inequality, then solve by the methods of Section 1-4:

$$^-c \leqslant ax - b \leqslant c,$$

$$^-c + b \leqslant ax - b + b \leqslant c + b,$$

$$b - c \leqslant ax \leqslant b + c,$$

$$\frac{1}{a}(b - c) \leqslant \frac{1}{a} \cdot ax \leqslant \frac{1}{a}(b + c),$$

$$\frac{b}{a} - \frac{c}{a} \leqslant x \leqslant \frac{b}{a} + \frac{c}{a}.$$

Hence the solution of $|ax - b| \leqslant c$  $(a > 0; c > 0)$ is

$$\frac{b}{a} - \frac{c}{a} \leqslant x \leqslant \frac{b}{a} + \frac{c}{a},$$

in agreement with Figure 1-18(h).

Now consider the inequalities and corresponding graphs in Figure 1-19. In all cases $x$ may lie anywhere on the darkened portion of the number line.

We will solve some of the inequalities graphed in Figure 1-19; then it will be more clear how to obtain the graphs.

Let us consider the inequality of Figure 1-19(a),

$$|x| > 2.$$

Recalling that $|x|$ is just the distance of $x$ from 0 on the number line, we see that the above inequality is equivalent to saying "the distance of $x$ from 0 is greater than 2." Such numbers $x$ fall to the right of 2 or to the left of $^-2$ on the number line. That is,

$$x > 2 \quad \text{or} \quad x < {}^-2.$$

This is in agreement with Figure 1-19(a).

In general, then, the inequality

$$|x| > c \quad (c > 0)$$

is equivalent to the statement

$$x > c \quad \text{or} \quad x < {}^-c.$$

With these observations in mind, let us solve

$$|ax - b| > c \quad (a > 0; c > 0)$$

by first writing an equivalent statement without absolute values, then solving by methods of Section 1-4:

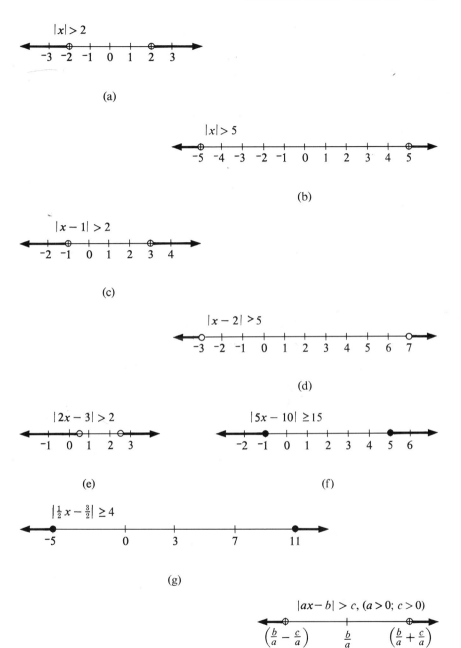

FIGURE 1-19.

$$ax - b > c \quad \text{or} \quad ax - b < {}^-c,$$

$$ax - b + b > c + b \quad \text{or} \quad ax - b + b < {}^-c + b,$$

$$ax > b + c \quad \text{or} \quad ax < b - c,$$

$$\frac{1}{a} \cdot ax > \frac{1}{a}(b + c) \quad \text{or} \quad \frac{1}{a} \cdot ax < \frac{1}{a}(b - c),$$

$$x > \frac{b}{a} + \frac{c}{a} \quad \text{or} \quad x < \frac{b}{a} - \frac{c}{a}.$$

This agrees with Figure 1-19(h).

It is important to notice the relationship between inequalities such as

$$|x| < 3 \quad \text{and} \quad |x| \geqslant 3.$$

We now know that

$$|x| < 3 \text{ is equivalent to } {}^-3 < x < 3$$

and that

$$|x| \geqslant 3 \text{ is equivalent to } x \geqslant 3 \text{ or } x \leqslant {}^-3.$$

Figure 1-20 shows that the union of these two sets of numbers is the entire number line.

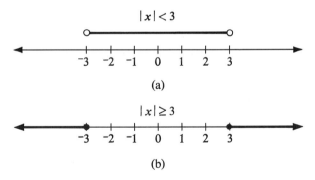

FIGURE 1-20.

If we let

$$A = \{x: \quad |x| < 3\} \text{ and } B = \{x: \quad |x| \geqslant 3\},$$

we could write

$$A \cup B = (-\infty, +\infty).$$

Note that

$$A' = B \quad \text{and} \quad B' = A,$$

where $A'$ is the complement of the set $A$ in the universe $\mathbb{R}$. With these remarks in mind, compare the absolute values and graphs in Figure 1-18 with the corresponding absolute values and graphs in Figure 1-19.

So far in this section we have discussed absolute value and its use in describing certain intervals. Now we will discuss how inequalities involving absolute value can be used to describe certain neighborhoods of a real number $c$. For instance,

$$|x - 3| < 2$$

is a way to write the open interval

$$^-2 < x - 3 < 2,$$

or $\qquad\qquad 1 < x < 5,$

or $\qquad\qquad (1, 5),$

which is a neighborhood of $c = 3$.

Caution! Not all inequalities involving absolute values describe neighborhoods. For instance,

$$|x - 3| > 2,$$

which may be rewritten

$$^-2 > x - 3 \qquad \text{or} \qquad x - 3 > 2,$$

or as

$$1 > x \qquad \text{or} \qquad x > 5,$$

does not describe a neighborhood of $c = 3$. From Figure 1-21 it is clear that the set of numbers $x$ such that $1 > x$ or $x > 5$ is not an open interval which contains $c = 3$.

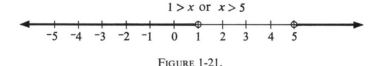

$$1 > x \text{ or } x > 5$$

FIGURE 1-21.

Further, inequalities such as

$$|x - 3| \leqslant 2$$

do not describe a neighborhood of $c = 3$, since the interval determined by $|x - 3| \leqslant 2$, which is

$$^-2 \leqslant x - 3 \leqslant 2,$$

or $\qquad\qquad 1 \leqslant x \leqslant 5,$

or $\qquad\qquad [1, 5],$

is not open.

*EXERCISES* ─────────────────────────────

*Find the absolute value of each of the following real numbers.*

1.  $|2|$.
2.  $|7|$.
3.  $|^-2|$.
4.  $|^-7|$.
5.  $|0|$.
6.  $|^-(^-7)|$.
7.  $|2\frac{1}{2}|$.
8.  $|3\frac{2}{3}|$.
9.  $|^-2\frac{1}{2}|$.
10. $|^-3\frac{2}{3}|$.
11. $|5.1|$.
12. $|7.14|$.
13. $|^-5.1|$.
14. $|^-7.14|$.
15. $|4-3|$.
16. $|10-3|$.
17. $|3-4|$.
18. $|3-10|$.
19. $|^-3-4|$.
20. $|^-3-10|$.

*Plot the graph of each absolute value equation or inequality in Exercises 21 through 32.*

21. $|x|=4$.
22. $|x|=7$.
23. $|x|\leqslant 4$.
24. $|x|<7$.
25. $|x-2|\leqslant 4$.
26. $|x-4|<7$.
27. $|2x-1|\leqslant 4$.
28. $|2x-1|<7$.
29. $\left|\frac{1}{2}x-\frac{1}{4}\right|\leqslant 4$.
30. $\left|\frac{2}{3}x-\frac{1}{3}\right|<7$.
31. $|x-a|<b$.
32. $|x-a|\geqslant b$.

★33. If $|ax-b|\leqslant c$, prove $b/a$ is the midpoint of the graph of the solution set, no matter whether $a>0$ or $a<0$, (Consider each case separately.)

*Plot the graph of each equation or inequality in Exercises 34 through 45.*

34. $|x|\geqslant 3$.
35. $|x|=1$.
36. $|x-2|\geqslant 3$.
37. $|x-1|>4$.
38. $|2x-1|\geqslant 4$.
39. $|3x-2|>6$.
40. $|\frac{1}{3}x-\frac{2}{3}|\geqslant 6$.
41. $|\frac{1}{2}x-1|\geqslant 4$.
42. $|4-x|\geqslant 5$.
43. $|6-x|>4$.
44. $|4-3x|>5$.
45. $|5-10x|\geqslant 25$.
46. Prove $|a+b|\leqslant |a|+|b|$. (*Hint:* Consider cases $a>0$ and $b>0$, $a<0$ and $b<0$, etc.)
47. Prove $|a-b|\leqslant |a|+|b|$.
48. Solve $4\leqslant |3x-1|<7$. (*Hint:* $3x-1\geqslant 0$ or $3x-1<0$. Pursue each possibility.)

*Tell whether or not each of the following describes a neighborhood of* $c = 4$. *If not, tell why.*

49.  $|x - 4| < 2$.

50.  $|x - 4| \leq \frac{1}{2}$.

51.  $|x - 3| < 2$.

52.  $|x - 4| > 2$.

53.  $|x - 4| \geq 2$.

## ——1-9  A Coordinate System

We have already represented numbers as points on a line called a number line. We can extend this procedure to enable us to locate points on a plane by using pairs of numbers. Figure 1-22 shows a vertical line and a horizontal line that intersect at right angles. We call these lines *coordinate axes* or *axes*. The point at which the axes intersect is called the *origin*. Traditionally, the horizontal axis is called the *abscissa* or *x-axis* and the vertical line is called the *ordinate* or *y-axis*. However, other letters such as *p, q, u, v, s,* and *t* are used, depending on the situation. The arrowheads suggest that the axes continue. The plane on which the axes lie is often called the *coordinate plane*. The four parts into which the axes divide the plane are called *quadrants*. The four quadrants are labeled in Figure 1-22.

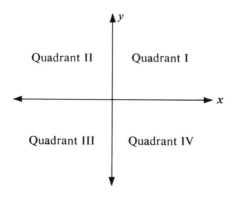

FIGURE 1-22.

Next, we select a unit length, and starting at the origin mark off points along the $x$-axis a unit length apart in both directions. We do the same thing for the vertical axis. Let us agree to let all such points to the right of the origin on the horizontal axis and above the origin on the vertical axis represent positive integers. Also, we will let all such points to the left of the origin on the horizontal axis and below the origin on the vertical axis represent negative integers. (See Figure 1-23.)

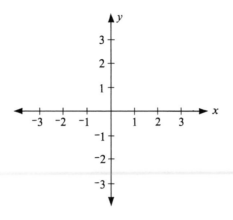

FIGURE 1-23.

Once the integers have been positioned, we can mark in the points representing rational and irrational numbers. As a matter of fact we can conceive of the $x$- and $y$-axes as two distinct number lines, where each point on either one corresponds to some real number.

Let $P$ be any point in the plane of the $x$- and $y$-axes. On the real number line any point can be described by a unique real number. The question arises whether there is some similar way to describe the location of a point on a plane. Let us draw a line $l_y$ parallel to the $y$-axis through $P$. Line $l_y$ must intersect the $x$-axis at one and only one point—say the point corresponding to the number $x_1$. Next let us draw a line $l_x$ parallel to the $x$-axis through $P$. Line $l_x$ must intersect the $y$-axis at some unique point—say the point corresponding to the number $y_1$. (See Figure 1-24.) To distinguish the process by which we obtained $x_1$ from that by which we obtained $y_1$ we write the two numbers as an ordered pair $(x_1, y_1)$. The first member of the ordered pair, $x_1$, is called the $x$-coordinate of $P$, and the second, $y_1$, the $y$-coordinate of $P$. Note that $P$ can have only one $x$-coordinate and only one $y$-coordinate.

Next, let us choose another point $\bar{P}$ with $x$-coordinate $x_2$ and $y$-coordinate $y_2$, as determined by the lines $l_x$ and $l_y$. (See Figure 1-25.) We might well wonder whether it is possible for $(x_1, y_1)$ to be equal to $(x_2, y_2)$ (that is, $x_1 = x_2$ and $y_1 = y_2$, even though $P$ and $\bar{P}$ are different points). The answer

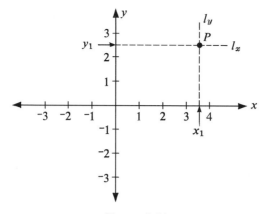

FIGURE 1-24.

is no; for, if $x_1 = x_2$ then the line $l_y$ must be the same as $\bar{l}_y$, and if $y_1 = y_2$ the line $l_x$ must be the same as $\bar{l}_x$. Thus the point $P$ of intersection of $l_x$ and $l_y$ and the point $\bar{P}$ of intersection of $\bar{l}_x$ and $\bar{l}_y$ must be the same. It is possible for $x_1 = x_2$ or $y_1 = y_2$ if $P$ is different from $\bar{P}$; as a matter of fact, $y_1 = y_2$ in Figure1-25. However, both equalities cannot hold if $P$ is different from $\bar{P}$.

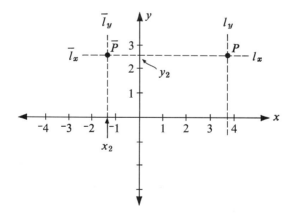

FIGURE 1-25.

Our method of associating an ordered pair with a point is thus one-to-one. That is, for each point $P$ there is only one ordered pair $(x, y)$ of real numbers associated with it, and each ordered pair $(x, y)$ of real numbers corresponds to only one point $P$. Often a point $P$ will be written $P(x, y)$, so that its $x$- and $y$-coordinates may be displayed. Furthermore, we will sometimes refer to the ordered pair $(x, y)$ as a point, although it is really the coordinate representation of a point.

The following are properties of a point $P(x, y)$ with which you should become familiar.

1. $x = 0$ implies $P$ lies on the $y$-axis.
2. $y = 0$ implies $P$ lies on the $x$-axis.
3. $x = y = 0$ implies $P$ is the origin.
4. $x > 0$, $y > 0$ imply $P$ lies in quadrant I.
5. $x < 0$, $y > 0$ imply $P$ lies in quadrant II.
6. $x < 0$, $y < 0$ imply $P$ lies in quadrant III.
7. $x > 0$, $y < 0$ imply $P$ lies in quadrant IV.

Points on a coordinate plane are often used to picture data in the sciences and social sciences. When data is organized in this way it is easy to detect trends if they exist. For example, consider Table 1-1, which gives $p$, the yearly average N.Y. wholesale price of sugar, and $q$, the yearly U.S.A. consumption of sugar, for the period from 1900 to 1914.

Figure 1-26 shows this data plotted on a coordinate plane with the hori-

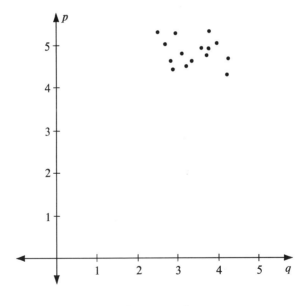

FIGURE 1-26.

zontal axis chosen for $q$ values and the vertical axis chosen for $p$ values. For each year a point is plotted. For instance, for the year 1905 we plot the point (2.95, 5.26). Such a figure is called a *scatter diagram*.

Are there any trends apparent from the scatter diagram in Figure1-26? For instance, is there any evidence that a rise in consumption $q$ is accompanied by a fall in price $p$?

| Year | $q$ (Mn. short tons) | $p$ (cents per pound) | Year | $q$ (Mn. short tons) | $p$ (cents per pound) |
|------|---------------------|----------------------|------|---------------------|----------------------|
| 1900 | 2.49 | 5.32 | 1908 | 3.57 | 4.96 |
| 1901 | 2.66 | 5.05 | 1909 | 3.65 | 4.77 |
| 1902 | 2.87 | 4.46 | 1910 | 3.75 | 4.97 |
| 1903 | 2.86 | 4.64 | 1911 | 3.75 | 5.34 |
| 1904 | 3.10 | 4.77 | 1912 | 3.93 | 5.04 |
| 1905 | 2.95 | 5.26 | 1913 | 4.19 | 4.28 |
| 1906 | 3.21 | 4.51 | 1914 | 4.21 | 4.68 |
| 1907 | 3.35 | 4.65 | | | |

TABLE 1-1.

Now let $P_1(x_1, y_1)$ and $P_2(x_2, y_2)$ be two different points in the $x$, $y$ coordinate plane, and let $\overline{P_1P_2}$ denote the line segment joining them as in Figure1-27. The distance between $P_1$ and $P_2$ is the length or measure of $\overline{P_1P_2}$

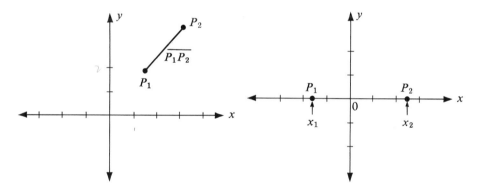

FIGURE 1-27.                    FIGURE 1-28.

and we denote this measure by $m(\overline{P_1P_2})$, a nonnegative number. Since $P_1$ and $P_2$ are uniquely determined by the numbers $x_1$, $y_1$ and $x_2$, $y_2$ respectively, it should be possible to express the number $m(\overline{P_1P_2})$ in terms of $x_1, y_1, x_2, y_2$.

To find such a formula we first ask what $m(\overline{P_1P_2})$ might be if both $P_1$ and $P_2$ lie on the $x$-axis as in Figure1-28. Since $P_1$ and $P_2$ may now be thought of as merely points on a real number line corresponding to the numbers $x_1$ and $x_2$ respectively, we know that the distance between them is $|x_2 - x_1|$, that is $m(\overline{P_1P_2}) = |x_2 - x_1|$.

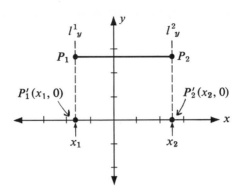

FIGURE 1-29.

Next assume that $P_1$ and $P_2$ do not lie on the $x$-axis, but that $\overline{P_1P_2}$ is parallel to the $x$-axis as shown in Figure 1-29. Construct the lines $l_y^1$ and $l_y^2$ through $P_1$ and $P_2$ parallel to the $y$-axis. Let $P_1'$ and $P_2'$ be the points at which $l_y^1$ and $l_y^2$ intersect the $x$-axis, with coordinates $(x_1, 0)$ and $(x_2, 0)$ respectively. Then from the preceding paragraph $m(\overline{P_1'P_2'}) = |x_2 - x_1|$. Since the points $P_1, P_2, P_1', P_2'$ are the corners of a rectangle, $m(\overline{P_1P_2}) = m(\overline{P_1'P_2'})$. We have then $m(\overline{P_1P_2}) = |x_2 - x_1|$. In an analogous way we can show that if $\overline{P_1P_2}$ lies on a line parallel to the $y$-axis, $m(\overline{P_1P_2}) = |y_2 - y_1|$.

Now let us return to the general problems of finding $m(\overline{P_1P_2})$, when $P_1(x_1, y_1)$ and $P_2(x_2, y_2)$ are any two distinct points of the $x$, $y$ coordinate plane. In Figure 1-30 we show $P_1$ and $P_2$ along with the lines $l_y^2$ and $l_x^1$. Line

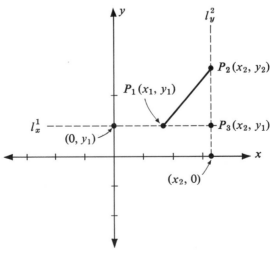

FIGURE 1-30.

$l_y^2$ passes through $P_2$ and is parallel to the y-axis, whereas line $l_x^1$ passes through $P_1$ and is parallel to the x-axis. Lines $l_y^2$ and $l_x^1$ are perpendicular to each other, so they meet at some point, say $P_3$. Points $P_2$ and $P_3$ have the same x-coordinate, since both lie on $l_y^2$. Similarly points $P_1$ and $P_3$ have the same y-coordinate. Thus $(x_2, y_1)$ is the coordinate pair of $P_3$. Now $\overline{P_1 P_3}$ is parallel to the x-axis, hence by the remarks above, $m(\overline{P_1 P_3}) = |x_2 - x_1|$. Similarly, $\overline{P_2 P_3}$ is parallel to the y-axis, hence $m(\overline{P_2 P_3}) = |y_2 - y_1|$. Since $\overline{P_1 P_2}$ is the hypotenuse of the right triangle formed by $P_1, P_2, P_3$, by the Pythagorean Theorem $m(\overline{P_1 P_2}) = \sqrt{[m(\overline{P_1 P_3})]^2 + [m(\overline{P_2 P_3})]^2}$. Consequently,

$$m(\overline{P_1 P_2}) = \sqrt{|x_2 - x_1|^2 + |y_2 - y_1|^2},$$

or

$$\boxed{m(\overline{P_1 P_2}) = \sqrt{(x_2 - x_1)^2 + (y_2 - y_1)^2},}$$

since $|x|^2 = x^2$. We have thus found a formula for the distance between two points in terms of their coordinates. By examining other pairs of points $P_1$ and $P_2$, it may be verified that the above formula holds no matter how $P_1$ and $P_2$ are located in relation to one another.

As an example suppose we want the distance between the points $P_1(3, 2)$ and $P_2(^-3, 1)$, i e. $m(\overline{P_1 P_2})$ as shown in Figure 1-31. Now $x_2 - x_1 = {}^-3 - 3 = {}^-6$ and $y_2 - y_1 = 1 - 2 = {}^-1$. By the distance formula,

$$m(\overline{P_1 P_2}) = \sqrt{(^-6)^2 + (^-1)^2} = \sqrt{37} \approx 6.083.$$

(Here the symbol $\approx$ denotes "is approximately equal to.") Measure $\overline{P_1 P_2}$

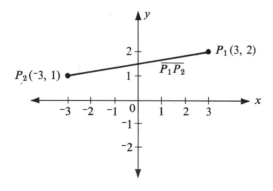

FIGURE 1-31.

to see if this answer is correct! Remember that a unit of length in the coordinate plane in Figure 1-31 is the distance between consecutive integers on
the $x$- and $y$-axes.

*EXERCISES* ——————————————————————————————

1.  a–t.   Give the ordered pairs corresponding to each of the points shown
    on the coordinate plane below.___   $(x_{(0)}, y_{(1)})$

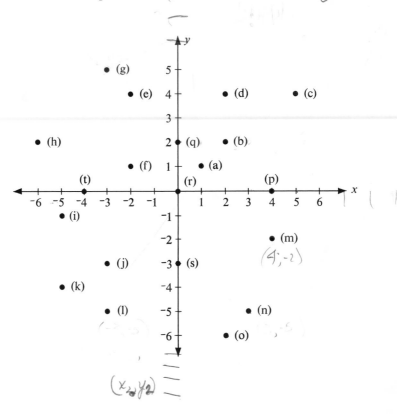

$(x_2, y_2)$

2.  For the points shown in the coordinate plane of Exercise 1 give the
    coordinates of all points in

    a.   Quadrant I.                    b.   Quadrant II.
    c.   Quadrant III.                  d.   Quadrant IV.

3. Draw a coordinate plane and locate the points corresponding to the following ordered pairs.

|     |     |     |
|-----|-----|-----|
| a. $(5, 3)$ | b. $(^-5, 3)$. | c. $(5, ^-3)$. |
| d. $(^-5, ^-3)$. | e. $(^-1, 3)$. | f. $(2, 5)$. |
| g. $(4, 6)$. | h. $(2, ^-2)$. | i. $(^-3, ^-6)$. |
| j. $(0, 2)$. | k. $(\frac{1}{2}, 1)$. | l. $(^-1, \frac{3}{2})$. |

$$x^2 + y^2 = d^2$$

4. Find the distances between the following pairs of points.

a. $(0, 4)$ and $(9, 4)$. ⁹

b. $(2, 8)$ and $(2, 3)$. ⁵

c. $(3, 4)$ and $(^-2, 4)$. ⁵

d. $(12, 3)$ and $(^-2, 3)$. ↤

e. $(1, 2)$ and $(0, 11)$.

f. $(5, 6)$ and $(3, 2)$.   $x_2 - x_1 = 2 = x$

g. $(5, 6)$ and $(^-2, 8)$.

h. $(5, 0)$ and $(^-5, 4)$.   $y_2 - y_1 = 4 = y$

i. $(3, 7)$ and $(^-3, ^-5)$.

j. $(5, 8)$ and $(^-2, ^-10)$.

k. $(3, 2)$ and $(4, ^-5)$.

l. $(8, 3)$ and $(5, ^-1)$.

m. $(^-5, 4)$ and $(^-8, ^-3)$.

n. $(^-8, 4)$ and $(5, ^-5)$.

o. $(^-3, ^-2)$ and $(2, ^-7)$.

p. $(^-10, 2)$ and $(2, ^-10)$.

$$d = \sqrt{(x_2 - x_1)^2 + (y^2 - y')^2}$$
$$\sqrt{(0 - 1)^2} , (11 - 2)^2$$

## —1-10 An Introduction to Graphing

$1 + 81 = 82$

Consider the equation

$$x^2 + y^2 = 4. \tag{1}$$

Let $r$ and $s$ be two real numbers. We say that the ordered pair $(r, s)$ *satisfies* (1) or *is a solution of* (1) if (1) becomes a true statement when $x$ is replaced by $r$ and $y$ is replaced by $s$. For example, $(0, 2)$ is a solution of Equation (1) because

$$0^2 + 2^2 = 4.$$

$(0, ^-2)$, $(2, 0)$, $(^-2, 0)$, $(\sqrt{2}, \sqrt{2})$, $(^-\sqrt{2}, \sqrt{2})$, $(\sqrt{2}, ^-\sqrt{2})$, and $(^-\sqrt{2}, ^-\sqrt{2})$ are also solutions. In fact there are infinitely many solutions of Equation (1). In Section 1-7 we saw that a set of ordered pairs defined a *relation*. There is a very special relation associated with Equation (1), namely, the set $T$ of all solutions of (1). The equation $x^2 + y^2 = 4$ is in a sense an algebraic description of this relation. However, our recent experience with coordinate systems enables us to give a geometric description of $T$. Each ordered pair

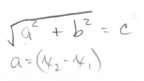

$$\sqrt{a^2 + b^2} = c$$
$$a = (x_2 - x_1)$$

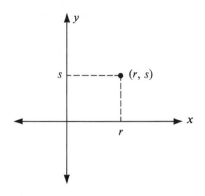

FIGURE 1-32.

$(r, s)$ in $T$ corresponds to a unique point in the $x, y$ coordinate plane. (See Figure 1-32.)

If we plot all the points in $T$ the resulting figure, called the *graph* of $T$, or the graph of Equation (1), will characterize $T$ completely. Of course $T$ is infinite, so that we cannot possibly plot every ordered pair in $T$. We can, however, get an idea of what its graph looks like by plotting several representative points. For example, if we plot the solutions already mentioned we obtain Figure 1-33.

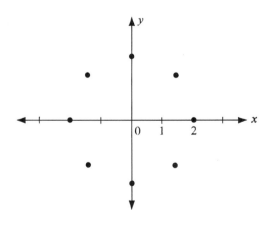

FIGURE 1-33.

It is pretty obvious that the graph is going to be a circle, but let us plot some more points to be sure. A systematic way of plotting points is to make a table like  Table 1-2   in which the first column gives the $x$-coordinate of a solution and the second gives the corresponding $y$-coordinate.

| x | y |
|---|---|
| 1 | $\sqrt{3}$ |
| 1 | $-\sqrt{3}$ |
| $^{-}1$ | $-\sqrt{3}$ |
| $^{-}1$ | $\sqrt{3}$ |
| $\sqrt{3}$ | 1 |
| $-\sqrt{3}$ | 1 |
| $-\sqrt{3}$ | $^{-}1$ |
| $\sqrt{3}$ | $^{-}1$ |

TABLE 1-2.

This begs the question of how one goes about obtaining these solutions. One method is to solve Equation (1) for $y$. Thus

$$y^2 = 4 - x^2,$$

and so

$$y = \pm\sqrt{4 - x^2}. \tag{2}$$

Now if we select a value for $x$, Equation (2) yields two values for $y$ such that $(x, y)$ is a solution of Equation (1). Note, however, that if we try an $x$ greater than 2 or less than $^{-}2$ the expression inside the radical is negative and we do not get any value for $y$. Equation (2) is trying to tell us that there are in fact no solutions of Equation (1) for which $|x| > 2$, that is, no point on the graph has an $x$-coordinate to the right of 2 or to the left of $^{-}2$. Indeed, Figure 1-33 seems to bear this out.

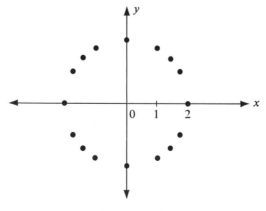

FIGURE 1-34.

Adding the points in our table to those of Figure 1-33 we obtain Figure 1-34. We are now strongly convinced that the graph is a circle of radius 2 about the origin and so we can go ahead and fill in all the remaining points with a compass to obtain Figure 1-35.

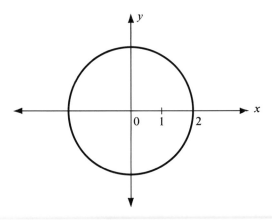

FIGURE 1-35.

Now consider the equation

$$y = |x|.\qquad(3)$$

Table 1-3 gives a set of solutions for Equation (3).

| x | y |
|---|---|
| ⁻3 | 3 |
| ⁻2 | 2 |
| ⁻1 | 1 |
| 0 | 0 |
| 1 | 1 |
| 2 | 2 |
| 3 | 3 |

TABLE 1-3.

These solutions are plotted in Figure 1-36.

Apparently the graph of Equation (3) is going to consist of two half-lines meeting at the origin, which make a 45° angle with the x-axis as shown in Figure 1-37.

The graph of Figure 1-37 differs from that of Figure 1-35 in one important respect. Any vertical line cuts the graph of Figure 1-37 at not more than one point. (See Figure 1-38.) In other words, for each $x$ there is at most, in fact exactly, one $y$ such that the point with coordinates $(x, y)$ belongs to the graph.

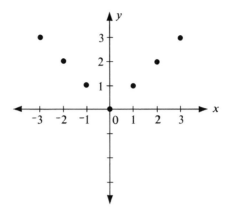

Figure 1-36.

This will be the case for the graph of any equation which can be put in the form

$$y = f(x), \tag{4}$$

where $f$ stands for any mathematical expression involving $x$ which yields at most one number upon substitution of a number for $x$. For example, Equation (3) is such an equation. However, Equation (1) is not, because when we try to put it in the form of Equation (4), we obtain Equation (2), and $\pm\sqrt{4 - x^2}$ yields two numbers for $y$ when a number is substituted in for $x$.

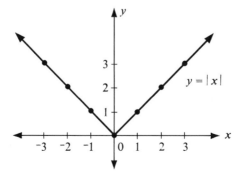

Figure 1-37.

In Section 1-7 we defined a *function* as a relation whose ordered pairs $(x, y)$ satisfied the restriction that for each $x$ there could be only one $y$. Hence the set of all solutions of an equation like (4) is a function. The expression $f(x)$ may be thought of as the *algebraic* definition of this function, and hence we will often speak of $f(x)$ as a function itself.

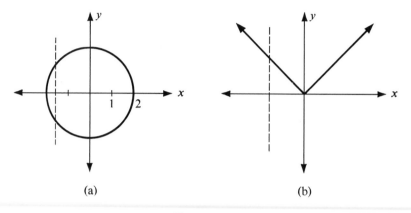

(a)                                    (b)

FIGURE 1-38.

As a third example we investigate the equation

$$x + 2y = 6. \tag{5}$$

It is easy to see that for any $x$ only one $y$ will satisfy Equation (5). Hence this equation defines a function. Solving for $y$ we find

$$y = 3 - \frac{1}{2}x, \tag{6}$$

hence $f(x) = 3 - \frac{1}{2}x$. We know that this graph of Equation (6) will be such that any vertical line can intersect it at not more than one point. Let us check to see that this is indeed so. Using Equation (6) we compute the entries in Table 1-4

| $x$ | $y$ |
|---|---|
| $^-3$ | $4\frac{1}{2}$ |
| $^-2$ | $4$ |
| $^-1$ | $3\frac{1}{2}$ |
| $0$ | $3$ |
| $1$ | $2\frac{1}{2}$ |
| $2$ | $2$ |
| $3$ | $1\frac{1}{2}$ |

TABLE 1-4.

Plotting these ordered pairs on an *x-y* coordinate plane yields Figure 1-39.The graph appears to be a straight line. Hence, any vertical line will intersect it at only one point.

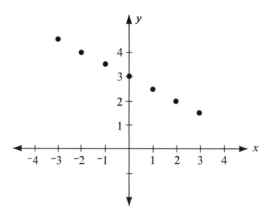

FIGURE 1-39.

Finally consider the equation

$$y = x. \tag{7}$$

We can graph this equation without doing any plotting at all, for the points with equal *x*- and *y*-coordinates must be symmetrically placed with respect to the *x*- and *y*-axis. Thus they all fall on the line making an angle of 45° with the positive parts of the *x*- and *y*-axes. Notice that the graph of $y = {}^{-}x$ is a line bisecting the other two quadrants. (See Figure 1-40.)

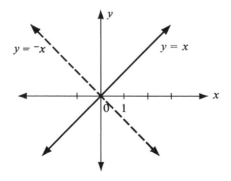

FIGURE 1-40.

*Using the technique described in this section, draw the graphs corresponding to each of the following equations.*

1.  $y = {}^{-}x$.
2.  $y = 2x + 1$.
3.  $2x - 4y = 6$.
4.  $|y| = |x|$.
5.  $x^2 + y^2 = 1$.
6.  $x^2 + y^2 = 9$.
7.  $x^2 - y^2 = 4$.
8.  $y = x^2$.
9.  $y = 2x^2$.
10.  $x = y^2$.
11.  $y = x^2 - 2x + 1$.
12.  $y = x^3 - 1$.
13.  $y = 2|x|$.
14.  $y = |x - 1|$.
15.  $y = |x| + 1$.
16.  $x^2 + y^2 = {}^{-}1$.

## ——1-11 The Line

In the previous section we saw that the graphs of the relations $y = x$ and $x + 2y = 6$ seemed to be straight lines. It is always possible that we did not really plot enough points to make sure that these graphs were straight lines, however, it can be shown that any equation of the type

$$ax + by = c \quad (a, b \text{ not both zero}) \tag{1}$$

does represent a line. Conversely, it can be shown that any straight line is the graph of an equation of the form (1). (Thus an equation of the form (1) is often called a *linear equation*.) We omit the proof (it is not difficult, but rather long) and instead discuss the relationship of the geometry of the lines to the numbers $a$, $b$, and $c$ of Equation (1).

Consider first the case when $b = 0$. Then by hypothesis $a \neq 0$. Thus, if we divide both sides of Equation (1) by $a$, we obtain

$$x = k, \tag{2}$$

where $k = \dfrac{c}{a}$. Equation (2) is the equation of a vertical line $l$ intersecting the x-axis at $k$. The graph of $x = k$ is shown in Figure 1-41. Any point $P(x, y)$ lying on $l$ must have an x-coordinate of $k$, and, conversely, any point $P(x, y)$ with $x = k$ must be on $l$.

If $b \neq 0$ then we may divide Equation (1) through by $b$ and obtain

$$\frac{a}{b}x + y = \frac{c}{b} \qquad y = mx + k, \tag{3}$$

where $k = c/b$ and $m = {}^{-}(a/b)$. Note that Equation (3) expresses $y$ as a *function* of $x$, i.e. for each value of $x$ there is only one $y$ for which $(x, y)$ satisfies (3). Hence any line whose equation is of the form $y = mx + k$ cannot be vertical.

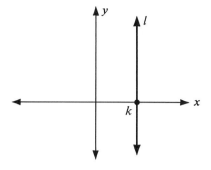

FIGURE 1-41.

Let us see what the graph of Equation (3) looks like for various values of
$m$ and $k$. First set $k = 0$ so that

$$y = mx. \tag{4}$$

A solution of Equation (4) is (0, 0) so all lines of type (4) must pass through
the origin.

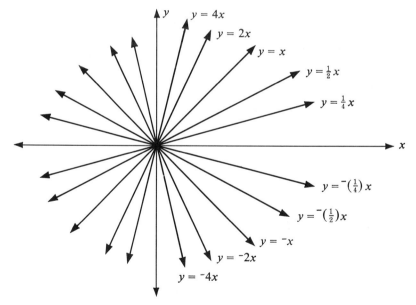

FIGURE 1-42.

Figure 1-42 shows the graphs of Equation (4) for various values of $m$.
The line $y = {}^-4x$ corresponding to $m = {}^-4$ slopes down to the right quite
steeply. However, as $m$ increases the lines become less steep. For example,

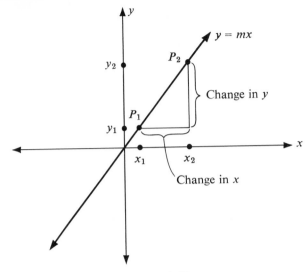

FIGURE 1-43.

the line $y = {}^{-}(\frac{1}{4})x$ is almost level. The line $y = 0$ corresponding to $m = 0$ is not labelled because it is simply the $x$-axis. When $m > 0$ the lines slope up to the right instead of down. The line $y = \frac{1}{4}x$ is not very steep; however, the line $y = x$ makes a 45° angle with the $x$-axis. The line $y = 4x$ is quite steep; if we were to plot lines with very large $m$, it would be difficult to distinguish them from the $y$-axis. Note, however, that regardless of how large $m$ becomes, the $y$-axis cannot be represented in the form $y = mx$.

It appears that the number $m$ is a measure of how steep the line $y = mx$ is, and consequently $m$ is called the *slope* of the line $y = mx$. The actual numerical significance of $m$ can be expressed as follows. Let $P_1(x_1, y_1)$ and $P_2(x_2, y_2)$ be any two distinct points on the line $y = mx$ as shown in Figure 1-43. Since $y_2 = mx_2$ and $y_1 = mx_1$ we have

$$y_2 - y_1 = mx_2 - mx_1$$
$$y_2 - y_1 = m(x_2 - x_1)$$

or

$$\frac{y_2 - y_1}{x_2 - x_1} = m.$$

If we think of $y_2 - y_1$ and $x_2 - x_1$ as the change in the $y$-coordinate and the $x$-coordinate respectively as we pass from $P_1$ to $P_2$, then

$$m = \frac{\text{change in } y}{\text{change in } x}.$$

Note that this ratio is the same regardless of the choice of $P_1$ and $P_2$, since it always turns out to be $m$.

Now let us allow $k$ to be nonzero. The form of the equation

$$y = mx + k$$

tells us that the line $y = mx + k$ is simply the line $y = mx$ shifted in the vertical direction $k$ units. To illustrate this fact we plot the lines $y = x + k$ for various values of $k$ in Figure 1-44.

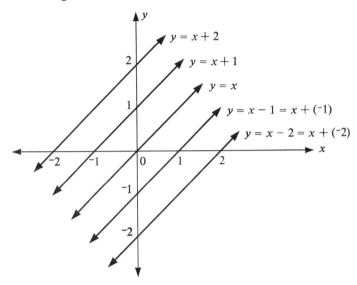

FIGURE 1-44.

Note that the lines in Figure 1-44 are all parallel and merely shifted *up* from $y = x$ for $k > 0$ and *down* from $y = x$ for $k < 0$. Note that each line intersects the $y$-axis at $y = k$. For this reason $k$ is called the *y-intercept* of the line $y = mx + k$. Furthermore, $m$ is still regarded as the *slope* of this more general type of line, because the addition of the constant $k$ has no effect on the steepness of the line.

If we are given the slope and $y$-intercept of some line $l$, we can determine the equation of $l$ immediately from Equation (3). Often, however, we will be given two different points $P_1(x_1, y_1)$ and $P_2(x_2, y_2)$ lying on $l$ and asked to determine the equation of $l$. (Remember that two distinct points determine a unique line.) If $x_2 = x_1$ then $l$ is vertical and its equation is $x = x_1$ or, equivalently, $x = x_2$. Otherwise, $x_1, x_2, y_1, y_2$ must satisfy

$$y_1 = mx_1 + k,$$
$$y_2 = mx_2 + k,$$

(5)

for some values of $m$ and $k$. We may solve (5) as a system of two simultaneous equations for the two unknowns $m$ and $k$. Then the equation of $l$ will be $y = mx + k$.

For instance, suppose we would like the equation of the line $l$ passing through the points $(^-1, 4)$ and $(2, 3)$. By the equations in (5) we have

$$3 = m \cdot 2 + k$$

$$4 = m(^-1) + k$$

or

$$3 = 2 \cdot m + k$$

$$4 = {}^-m + k.$$

Subtracting the second equation from the first gives us

$$^-1 \ = \ 3 \cdot m,$$

or

$$\frac{^-1}{3} = m.$$

If we substitute $m = {}^-\frac{1}{3}$ into either of the original equations, say $4 = {}^-m + k$ we obtain

$$4 = {}^-\left(\frac{^-1}{3}\right) + k$$

$$\frac{11}{3} = k.$$

Thus the equation of the line $l$ passing through $(^-1, 4)$ and $(2, 3)$ is

$$y = \frac{^-1}{3}x + \frac{11}{3}.$$

We have said very little about Equation (1). When given an equation such as (1), it is convenient to transform it immediately into the form (2) if $b = 0$, or the form (3) if $b \neq 0$. This is because these forms allow us to visualize easily the graph of the line represented by Equation (1). Clearly $x = k$ may be graphed quickly. We know immediately that one point on the line $y = mx + k$ is the point $y = k$ on the $y$-axis. If we are familiar with how $m$ corresponds to steepness then our line is simply that line passing through $(0, k)$ with slope $m$. Otherwise, we can plot a second point, say, $(1, m + k)$ and construct a line passing through both points.

Suppose as an example we are given the equation of the line

$$2x + 3y = 6.$$

To transform it to the form $y = mx + k$, we first subtract $2x$ from sides of the equation to obtain

$$3y = 6 - 2x.$$

Then if we divide both sides by 3 and rearrange the terms on the right-hand side of the equation, we have

$$y = {}^{-}\left(\frac{2}{3}\right)x + 2.$$

From this form we can immediately say that the graph of $2x + 3y = 6$ is a line passing through $(0, 2)$ with a slope of ${}^{-}\frac{2}{3}$. (See Figure 1-45.)

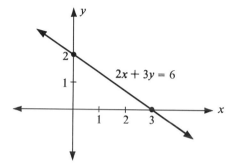

FIGURE 1-45.

Graphs of lines have proved to be very useful in many fields. For instance, in economics *demand curves* have been used to illustrate demand, the definite relationship between the market price of a good such as sugar or cotton and the quantity demanded of that good. Sometimes the demand curve turns out to be a straight line. Figure 1-46 shows a simplified demand curve for " gray

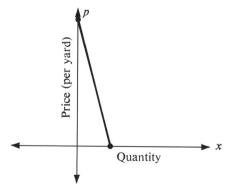

FIGURE 1-46.    Demand curve for cotton.

goods" or cotton. (It is conventional to mark values of $x$, the quantity, on the horizontal axis, and to mark values of $p$, the price, on the vertical axis.) Notice that for a small quantity of "gray goods" available, the price is higher. But as the quantity increases, the price becomes lower. This example illustrates why demand curves slope downward. Also notice that the line is confined to the first quadrant, since we are considering only positive quantities and prices.

Graphs of lines are also used to illustrate *supply curves*, the curves which give the relation between market prices and the amounts producers are willing to supply. Figure 1-47 gives a simplified supply curve for land. Notice from Figure 1-47 that for higher market prices suppliers are willing to put more land on the market. This explains why supply curves usually slope upward.

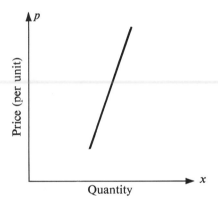

FIGURE 1-47.    Supply curve for land.

Graphs of straight lines are often used to show trends of inequality. For instance, Figure 1-48, which shows 1962 distribution of *income* in the U.S.A., consists of two curves. The straight line is called the curve of *absolute equality* of income since any point on the curve corresponds to a certain per cent, say $n$, of the people and to the same per cent $n$ of income. If 1% of the people had 1% of the income, 2% of the people had 2% of the income and so on, we could say that there exists equality of income. However, this is not the case. The shaded area between the line, the curve of absolute equality, and the curve, the actual distribution of U.S. income in 1962, shows the deviation from absolute equality.

Figure 1-49 also shows how a line is used to show trends of inequality. The straight line shows absolute equality of income, the curves lines show actual distribution of income for army officers, professors, doctors, and lawyers, and the shading shows the deviation of each profession from absolute equality.

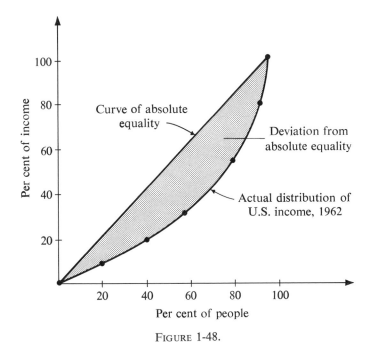

FIGURE 1-48.

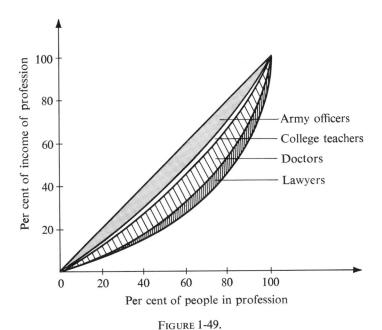

FIGURE 1-49.

*EXERCISES* ─────────────────────────────────

1. Give the slope and $y$-intercept of the graph of each of the following equations.
   a. $y = 3x + 2$.
   b. $y = {}^-3x + 2$.
   c. $y = 3x - 2$.
   d. $y = {}^-3x - 2$.
   e. $y = {}^-\frac{3}{2}x + 2$.

2. Find the equation of a straight line such that
   a. $m = 1$ and $k = 4$.
   b. $m = 2$ and $k = 3$.
   c. $m = \frac{3}{2}$ and $(4, 7)$ is on the line.
   d. $m = 5$ and $(10, 15)$ is on the line.
   e. $(1, 2)$ and $(\frac{1}{2}, \frac{3}{4})$ are on the line.
   f. $(5, 3)$ and $({}^-1, \frac{2}{3})$ are on the line.

3. Convert each of the following linear equations to slope-intercept form and give the slope and $y$-intercept of each.
   a. $3x - 2y = 12$.
   b. $3x = 4y - 12$.
   c. $2y = 4 - 3x$.
   d. $6x - 7y = 42$.

4. Graph each of the following linear equations.
   a. $y = 3x - 2$.
   b. $y = {}^-2x + 3$.
   c. $4x + 2y = 12$.
   d. $6x - 3y = 15$.

5. In Figure 1-49 (page 65), which of the four professions shows the least amount of inequality of income? Which shows the most?

6. In Figures 1-48 and 1-49 what angle do the lines of absolute equality make with the $x$-axis? What is the slope of each line of absolute equality?

7. State whether the graphs of each of the following linear equations would make appropriate supply curves or appropriate demand curves.
   a. $p = 5x + 30$.
   b. $3p - 4x = 28$.
   c. $14p + 15x = 52$.
   d. $x = \dfrac{15 - 2p}{3}$.

8. Examine Figure 1-50. What conclusions may be drawn about the relative positions of

$$y = nx \quad \text{and} \quad y = \frac{{}^-1}{n}x$$

and of

$$y = nx + k \quad \text{and} \quad y = \frac{{}^-1}{n}x + k,$$

where $n \neq 0$?

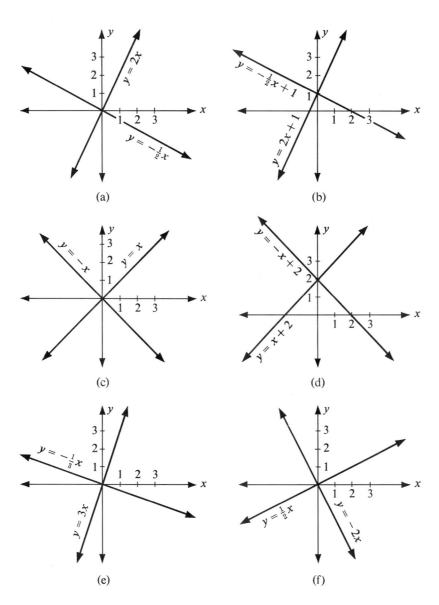

FIGURE 1-50.

# An Introduction to Logic

**2**

—— 2-1  Introduction

The basic problem of logic is to determine whether or not a given statement is true if one already knows the truth or falsity of the statements on which the given statement is based. At an everyday level a knowledge of logic helps to sort out the "straight-thinkers" among politicians, advertisers, and so on from those who jump to invalid conclusions. At a more technical level, logic is the basis of most computer languages, since a computer is continually directed to do one thing if a certain statement is true and another if the statement is false. In this chapter we will be most concerned with the basic structure of logic and its application to mathematical proofs.

A statement is a sentence that can be assigned a *truth value*. That is, a statement is a sentence that can be regarded as either true or false. Not all sentences are statements! For example, the sentences below are not statements because they are neither true nor false.

"What is your name?" (A question)

"Keep to the right!" (A command)

"How beautiful it is!" (An exclamation)

A statement is an assertion. Consider the assertions below:

a. "The Dow-Jones Industrial Average went down yesterday."

b. "Three is less than five."

c. "Boston is not in Massachusetts."

d. "A rhombus is a square."

e. "It is cold."

The assertion in (a) can be regarded as true or false depending upon what change there actually was in the Dow-Jones Industrial Average yesterday. Therefore (a) is a statement.

The assertion in (b) is said to be true, because of the general agreement concerning the meaning of "three-ness," "five-ness," and "is less than." Thus, (b) is a statement.

The assertion in (c) is false, because it does not correspond to reality. That is, it is generally known that Boston is in Massachusetts. Thus, (c) is a statement.

The assertion in (d) is said to be false, because a rhombus need not have all of the properties required in the definition of a square. (Namely, the angles of a rhombus are not necessarily right angles.) Therefore, (d) is a statement.

The assertion in (e) might be either true or false depending on a person's idea of "cold." For instance, a person raised in the tropics might well consider 70° cold, while someone else might think 70° too warm. However, to simplify matters, we will assume in cases such as this that the definitions of words like "cold" have been agreed upon. Making this assumption we can thus assign (e) a truth value. Thus, (e) can be considered a statement.

Since all of the statements in (a)–(e) express only one thought they are called *simple statements*. A combination of two or more simple statements is a *compound statement*. The following sentences are compound statements.

a.   "The President's popularity went up last week and the Vice President's popularity went down."

b.   "We will go to the movie or we will go to the picnic."

c.   "If the stock's price goes below 14, I will buy 100 shares."

Sometimes compound statements are disguised. For instance, the statement      "We will go into business or law after graduation."
is a compound statement, because it is actually a shortened version of the sentence

"We will go into business after graduation
↑
simple statement

or we will go into law after graduation."
↑
simple statement

Similarly, the sentence      "If he comes, we will go together."

is the compound statement      "If he comes, then we will go together."

with the word "then" understood. On the other hand, the sentence

"He and I will go into business together after graduation."

is a simple statement, because it expresses the thought that

"We (namely he and I) will go into business together after graduation."

Finally, there is no doubt that the following sentence is complex!

> "If we both major in business or if we both major in medicine, we plan to open up offices in Texas and Oklahoma after graduation."

It is also a compound statement made up in turn of several different forms of compound statements in the following way:

> "If ... or ..., (then) ... and ...."

In these examples the words "and," "or," and "if ... then" are used to form compound statements from simple statements. Together with "if and only if" and "not," these words are the most common *connectives*. In the next section we will determine how the truth value of these new statements can be determined.

*EXERCISES* ————————————————————————

*For each of the following sentences (a) Tell whether or not it is a statement. (b) If it is a statement, tell whether it is simple or compound.*

1. The cat is black.
2. If the cat is black it is not white.
3. The cat is black and it is playful.
4. The cat was black or the cat was yellow.
5. I will attend the ball game if it doesn't rain.
6. It will rain or it will snow tomorrow.
7. The rain is falling at a rapid rate.
8. If it rains and snows then it will be cold.
9. Shut the door!
10. Did you return his call?
11. How I wish they would decide to join!
12. Let's go together.
13. I'll be in either San Diego or Los Angeles that day.
14. They will not be in San Diego that day.

—— 2-2  Logical Structure

When dealing with statements it will be convenient to use variables such as $P$, $Q$, $R$, $S$, and $T$ to stand for simple statements. We will also use symbols to stand for connectives.

The symbol $\sim$ is used to denote "not." Thus if the variable $P$ stands for the simple statement

> "The Dow-Jones Industrial Average went down yesterday."

then $\sim P$ is the new simple statement

"The Dow-Jones Industrial Average did not go down yesterday."

$\sim P$ is called the *negation* of *P*.

By definition of a simple statement *P* is either true or false. If *P* is true, $\sim P$ is false. If *P* is false, $\sim P$ is true. Table 2-1 summarizes these two possi-

| $P$ | $\sim P$ |
|:---:|:---:|
| T | F |
| F | T |

TABLE 2-1.

bilities. Such a table is called a *truth table*. Note that *P* and $\sim P$ cannot be simultaneously true or false.

We could have chosen the truth table in Table 2-2 to show the relationship between *P* and $\sim P$. The first row says that $\sim P$ is true when *P* is true. The second row says that $\sim P$ is false when *P* is false. However, this does not correspond to the commonly used meaning of "not." For this reason we will use the truth table in Table 2-1 for $\sim$, not the truth table in Table 2-2 or any other truth table for *P* and $\sim P$.

| $P$ | $\sim P$ |
|:---:|:---:|
| T | T |
| F | F |

TABLE 2-2.

The symbol $\wedge$ is used to denote the connective "and." Thus, if *P* is the simple statement

"The Dow-Jones Industrial Average went down yesterday."

and *Q* is the simple statement

"General Motors went up."

then $P \wedge Q$ denotes the compound statement

"The Dow-Jones Industrial Average went down yesterday
and General Motors went up."

$P \wedge Q$ is called the *conjunction* of *P* and *Q*.

We can determine the truth value of a compound statement $P \wedge Q$ by examining the truth value of *P* and *Q* separately. If *P* and *Q* are both true, then it is generally agreed that the compound sentence $P \wedge Q$ is true, because of the meaning of the word "and." Similarly, if either $P$ or $Q$ is false, then $P \wedge Q$ is false. And if $P$ and $Q$ are both false, $P \wedge Q$ is certainly false. These four possible cases are summarized in the truth table in Table 2-3 with simple examples. Note that to describe all possible cases for $P \wedge Q$, we must show all possible combinations of truth values for the separate statements $P$ and $Q$.

| $P$ | $Q$ | $P \wedge Q$ | Example |
|-----|-----|-----|---------|
| T | T | T | Snow is white and rain is wet. |
| T | F | F | Snow is white and rain is dry. |
| F | T | F | Snow is red and rain is wet. |
| F | F | F | Snow is red and rain is dry. |

TABLE 2-3.

The symbol $\vee$ is used to denote the connective "or." If $P$ is the simple statement

"The Dow-Jones Industrial Average went down yesterday."

and $Q$ is the simple statement

"General Motors went up."

then $P \vee Q$ denotes the compound statement

"The Dow-Jones Industrial Average went down yesterday
or General Motors went up."

$P \vee Q$ is called the *disjunction* of $P$ and $Q$.

We sometimes use the word "or" in conversation to mention mutually exclusive alternatives, such as

"We will go to school or we will not."
"Today is the 24th or the 25th of the month."

In such a case, "or" means "at least one, but not both." This is said to be the *exclusive* use of the word "or," since choice of one alternative excludes the other.

Now look at the sentence

"I will have ice cream or cake."

The choices here are not mutually exclusive, although in conversation we usually mean

"I will make a choice between ice cream and cake."

However, to the mathematician, this sentence means

"I will have ice cream or cake *or both*."

This is called the *inclusive* use of "or"; both possibilities are included. We will use the inclusive "or" throughout this text.

To determine the truth value of the compound statement $P \lor Q$ we must again examine the truth values of $P$ and $Q$ separately. In agreement with everyday usage, the compound statement $P \lor Q$ is certainly true if either $P$ or $Q$ is true and certainly false if both $P$ and $Q$ are false. Because we are using the inclusive "or," $P \lor Q$ is also true if both $P$ and $Q$ are true. Table 2-4 summarizes these four cases in the truth table for $\lor$, the inclusive "or." A simple example for each case is also given.

| $P$ | $Q$ | $P \lor Q$ | Example |
|-----|-----|------------|---------|
| T | T | T | Snow is white or rain is wet. |
| T | F | T | Snow is white or rain is dry. |
| F | T | T | Snow is red or rain is wet. |
| F | F | F | Snow is red or rain is dry. |

TABLE 2-4.

The symbol $\rightarrow$ is used to denote the connective "if ... then." For instance, if $P$ is the simple statement

"The Dow-Jones Industrial Average went down yesterday."

and $Q$ is the simple statement

"General Motors went up."

$P \rightarrow Q$ is used to denote the compound statement

"If the Dow-Jones Industrial Average went down yesterday,
then General Motors went up."

The compound statement $P \rightarrow Q$, formed from $P$ and $Q$, is called a *conditional* statement.

The simple statement following "if" is called the *hypothesis*, while the simple statement following "then" is called the *conclusion*. In our example $P$ is the hypothesis and $Q$ is the conclusion.

In a compound statement of the form $P \rightarrow Q$, the word "then" is sometimes omitted. However, the meaning of the statement is not changed. For our example we could write

"If the Dow-Jones Industrial Average went down yesterday,
General Motors went up."

Sometimes the if-clause follows the then-clause. For our example, we could write

"General Motors went up, if the Dow-Jones Industrial
Average went down."

without changing the meaning of the statement.

The truth value of $P \to Q$ can be determined by examining the truth values of $P$ and $Q$. Table 2-5 gives the truth table generally used for $P \to Q$.

| $P$ | $Q$ | $P \to Q$ |
|:---:|:---:|:---:|
| T | T | T |
| T | F | F |
| F | T | T |
| F | F | T |

TABLE 2-5.

The following example illustrates the reasons for the truth values of $P \to Q$ in the table.

Suppose Rex makes the following statement.

"If I get a job, then I will buy a motorcycle."

Here $P$ is the simple statement

"I get a job."

and $Q$ is the simple statement

"I will buy a motorcycle."

Without doubt if $P$ is true and $Q$ is true, then $P \to Q$ is true.

Suppose Rex fails to get a job. Then $P$ is false. Rex has no commitment since he may buy the motorcycle or not. No one would consider him untruthful in either case ($P$ false, $Q$ true; $P$ false, $Q$ false). Consequently the truth values of $P \to Q$ in lines 3 and 4 of Table 2-5 are true.

The only time Rex could be called a liar would be if he got a job (making $P$ true) and did not buy a motorcycle (making $Q$ false). That is why, when $P$ is true and $Q$ is false, the truth value of $P \to Q$ is considered to be false. This is the only case in which a conditional is false.

Related to any conditional $P \to Q$ are its *converse*, *inverse*, and *contrapositive*. In Table 2-6 there is a definition and example of each of these related statements. In the examples $P$ is once again the statement

"I get a job."

and $Q$ is the statement

"I will buy a motorcycle."

Consider the conditional $P \to Q$. Sometimes instead of saying

"If $P$, then $Q$,"

| Relation | | Example |
|---|---|---|
| Conditional | $P \rightarrow Q$ | If I get a job, then I will get a motorcycle. |
| Converse | $Q \rightarrow P$ | If I get a motorcycle, then I will get a job. |
| Inverse | $\sim P \rightarrow \sim Q$ | If I do not get a job, then I will not get a motorcycle. |
| Contrapositive | $\sim Q \rightarrow \sim P$ | If I do not get a motorcycle, then I will not get a job. |

TABLE 2-6.

in mathematics, it is said that

"$P$ is a sufficient condition for $Q$."

or

"$Q$ is a necessary condition for $P$."

So, for example, consider $P \rightarrow Q$ to be

"If two angles are congruent, then they have the same measure."

where $P$ is the statement

"Two angles are congruent."

and $Q$ is the statement

"They have the same measure."

It can then be said that

"The fact that two angles are congruent is a sufficient condition for the two angles to have the same measure."

Also it can be said that

"The fact that two angles have the same measure is a necessary condition for the two angles to be congruent."

The *biconditional,* denoted $P \leftrightarrow Q$, is closely tied to the conditional. ($P \leftrightarrow Q$ is read "$P$ if and only if $Q$.") For example, if $P$ is the simple statement

"I will have a job."

and $Q$ is the simple statement

"I am hired."

The biconditional, $P \leftrightarrow Q$, is

"I will have a job if and only if I am hired."

A biconditional asserts that if $P$ is true, then $Q$ is true and if $P$ is false, then $Q$ is false. The biconditional $P \leftrightarrow Q$ is true in these cases and false in all others. See Table 2-7 for the truth table of $P \leftrightarrow Q$.

| $P$ | $Q$ | $P \leftrightarrow Q$ |
|---|---|---|
| T | T | T |
| T | F | F |
| F | T | F |
| F | F | T |

TABLE 2-7.

In mathematics every logically correct definition when changed to the "if ... then" form is reversible. In other words, a logically correct definition can be put in the "if and only if" form. For instance, consider the following definition of congruent line segments:

"Two line segments are said to be congruent if and only if they have the same length."

Sometimes instead of saying

"$P$ if and only if $Q$"

for

$$P \leftrightarrow Q$$

it is said in mathematics that

"$P$ is necessary and sufficient for $Q$"

or

"$Q$ is necessary and sufficient for $P$."

Thus the statement of the form $P \leftrightarrow Q$

"Two angles are congruent if and only if they have the same measure."

can be reworded as

"The fact that two angles are congruent is necessary and sufficient for them to have the same measure."

*EXERCISES* ─────────────────────────────────────

1.  Suppose $P$ represents "the chief cause of pollution is overpopulation" and $Q$ represents "the world is doomed." Write
    a.   $\sim P$, the negation of $P$.
    b.   $\sim Q$, the negation of $Q$.

    c.   $P \wedge Q$, the conjunction of $P$ and $Q$.

    d.   $P \vee Q$, the disjunction of $P$ and $Q$.

    e.   $\sim P \wedge \sim Q$.

    f.   $\sim P \vee \sim Q$.

2.  Given $P \rightarrow Q$ and that $P$ represents "it is raining" and $Q$ represents "the grass is green." Write

    a.   The converse of $P \rightarrow Q$.

    b.   The inverse of $P \rightarrow Q$.

    c.   The contrapositive of $P \rightarrow Q$.

3.  If $P \rightarrow Q$ is true, is the inverse of the converse true or false?

4.  Write the converse of "If I win, then I will be happy."

5.  Write the contrapositive of "If it has 4 feet, it is a dog."

6.  Given the implication

        "If all wriggles are fraps then some fraps are frips."

  write

    a.   The converse.

    b.   The inverse.

    c.   The contrapositive.

7.  Given the statement

        "If it is cold, then we will not go."

  Write

    a.   The statement in symbol form.

    b.   The converse, inverse, and contrapositive in symbol form.

    c.   The converse of the inverse in symbol form.

    d.   The inverse of the converse of the statement.

    e.   The converse of the contrapositive of the statement.

    f.   The contrapositive of the converse of the statement.

## —— 2-3  Logical Relations

    Let $R$ be a compound statement. $R$ is said to be *logically true*, denoted $R \equiv$ True, if $R$ is always true regardless of the truth values of the simple statements that compose $R$.

    For example, consider the truth table in Table 2-8 for $Q \vee \sim Q$. Note that when $Q$ is true, $\sim Q$ is false and when $Q$ is false, $\sim Q$ is true, since a statement and its negation are never simultaneously true or false. We obtain the entries of the $Q \vee \sim Q$ column from the second and third rows of Table 2-4. Since $Q \vee \sim Q$ is always true regardless of the truth values of $Q$ and $\sim Q$, we can write

$$Q \vee \sim Q \equiv \text{True.}$$

A logically true statement such as this is called a *tautology*.

| $Q$ | $\sim Q$ | $Q \vee \sim Q$ |
|---|---|---|
| T | F | T |
| F | T | T |

$Q \vee \sim Q$ always true

TABLE 2-8.

We can define *logically false* similarly.

Let $R$ be a compound statement. $R$ is said to be *logically false*, denoted $R \equiv$ False, if $R$ is always false regardless of the truth values of the simple statements that compose $R$.

For example, consider the truth table in Table 2-9 for $Q \wedge \sim Q$. Note again that $Q$ and $\sim Q$ are never simultaneously true or false. We obtain the entries for the $Q \wedge \sim Q$ column from the second and third rows of Table 2-3.

| $Q$ | $\sim Q$ | $Q \wedge \sim Q$ |
|---|---|---|
| T | F | F |
| F | T | F |

$Q \wedge \sim Q$ always false

TABLE 2-9.

Since these entries are both false, we can write

$$Q \wedge \sim Q \equiv \text{False}.$$

A logically false statement such as this is called a *contradiction*.

Now let $R$ and $S$ be statements at least one of which is compound. Then we say $R$ *implies* $S$, written $R \Rightarrow S$, if and only if $R \rightarrow S$ is logically true. Let us analyze the rather complicated statement $Q \rightarrow (Q \vee \sim Q)$ to see if we may write $Q \Rightarrow (Q \vee \sim Q)$. (The parentheses are inserted so that there is no doubt what is meant. Always use parentheses or brackets when in doubt. For instance, $P \rightarrow Q \wedge \sim Q$ might mean $(P \rightarrow Q) \wedge \sim Q$ or $P \rightarrow (Q \wedge \sim Q)$.) In order to do so, we need to consider all possible pairs of truth values of $Q$ and $Q \vee \sim Q$. Since $Q \vee \sim Q$ is always true, we need only consider the two possibilities shown in Table 2-10. How can we fill in the third column with the corresponding truth values of $Q \rightarrow (Q \vee \sim Q)$?

| $Q$ | $Q \vee \sim Q$ | $Q \rightarrow (Q \vee \sim Q)$ |
|---|---|---|
| T | T | |
| F | T | |

TABLE 2-10.

To answer this question note that the form of $Q \rightarrow (Q \vee \sim Q)$ is like that of $P \rightarrow Q$, with $P$ replacing the $Q$ in our given statement and $Q$ replacing

$(Q \vee \sim Q)$. Table 2-5 gives the truth values for $P \to Q$ corresponding to all possible pairs of truth values of $P$ and $Q$. Interpreting Table 2-5 by thinking "$Q$" when it says "$P$," and $(Q \vee \sim Q)$ when it says "$Q$," we obtain Table 2-11. We are interested in only the first and third rows of Table 2-5, since they correspond to the rows we seek to complete in Table 2-10.

| $\begin{matrix}Q\\\sout{P}\end{matrix}$ | $\begin{matrix}Q \vee \sim Q\\\sout{Q}\end{matrix}$ | $\begin{matrix}Q \to (Q \vee \sim Q)\\\sout{P \to Q}\end{matrix}$ |
|:---:|:---:|:---:|
| $\to$    T | T | T |
| T | F | F |
| $\to$    F | T | T |
| F | F | T |

TABLE 2-11.

The completed table for $Q \to (Q \vee \sim Q)$ is shown as Table 2-12. We thus see

| $Q$ | $Q \vee \sim Q$ | $Q \to (Q \vee \sim Q)$ |
|:---:|:---:|:---:|
| T | T | T |
| F | T | T |

TABLE 2-12.

that $Q \to (Q \vee \sim Q)$ is a tautology (always true), so we may write $Q \Rightarrow (Q \vee \sim Q)$. This example illustrates how truth tables for the basic logical connectives can be used to build up truth tables for complicated statements.

Next suppose $R$ and $S$ are statements at least one of which is compound. Then we say that $R$ *is equivalent to* $S$, written $R \Leftrightarrow S$ if and only if $R \leftrightarrow S$ is logically true.

Consider the truth table in Table 2-13. We use the truth tables for the basic connectives to build up the truth table for $[(P \wedge \sim Q) \to \sim P] \leftrightarrow (P \to Q)$, in the order indicated by the circled numbers. The arrows indicate the tables in Section 2-2 from which the column entries are obtained. Since the entries in the $[(P \wedge \sim Q) \to \sim P] \leftrightarrow (P \to Q)$ column are all true,

$$[(P \wedge \sim Q) \to \sim P] \leftrightarrow (P \to Q)$$

is logically true. Thus we can write

$$[(P \wedge \sim Q) \to \sim P] \Leftrightarrow (P \to Q).$$

Table 2-14 shows in a similar manner that

$$(\sim Q \to \sim P) \Leftrightarrow (P \to Q).$$

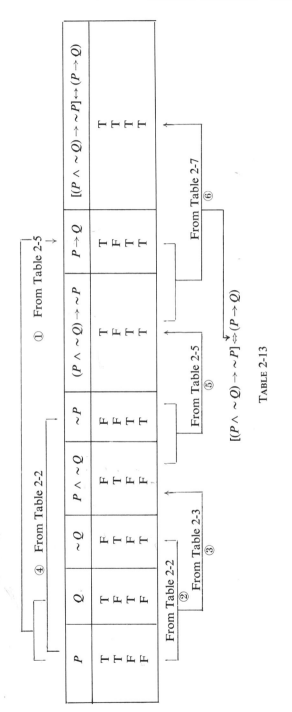

| $P$ | $Q$ | $\sim Q$ | $P \wedge \sim Q$ | $\sim P$ | $(P \wedge \sim Q) \to \sim P$ | $P \to Q$ | $[(P \wedge \sim Q) \to \sim P] \leftrightarrow (P \to Q)$ |
|---|---|---|---|---|---|---|---|
| T | T | F | F | F | T | T | T |
| T | F | T | T | F | F | F | T |
| F | T | F | F | T | T | T | T |
| F | F | T | F | T | T | T | T |

① From Table 2-5

④ From Table 2-2

From Table 2-2    ③ From Table 2-3

② From Table 2-2

⑤ From Table 2-5

From Table 2-7    ⑥

$$[(P \wedge \sim Q) \to \sim P] \Leftrightarrow (P \to Q)$$

Table 2-13

| P | Q | P → Q | ~P | ~Q | ~Q → ~P | (~Q → ~P) ↔ (P → Q) |
|---|---|-------|-----|-----|---------|---------------------|
| T | T | T | F | F | T | T |
| T | F | F | F | T | F | T |
| F | T | T | T | F | T | T |
| F | F | T | T | T | T | T |

$$(\sim Q \rightarrow \sim P) \Leftrightarrow (P \rightarrow Q)$$

TABLE 2-14.

The order in which we completed columns is again shown by the circled numbers. The reader is invited to describe which basic table was used for each step. Remember that $\sim Q \rightarrow \sim P$ is called the *contrapositive* of $P \rightarrow Q$. We have just shown that *P → Q and its contrapositive are logically equivalent.* That is, they are *both true or both false.* Sometimes it is easier to tell whether $P \rightarrow Q$ is true or false by examining its contrapositive.

Similarly, it can be shown that $[(P \wedge \sim Q) \rightarrow Q] \Leftrightarrow (P \rightarrow Q)$ (Table 2-15) and $[(P \wedge \sim Q) \rightarrow (R \wedge \sim R)] \Leftrightarrow (P \rightarrow Q)$ (Table 2-16).

| P | Q | ~Q | P ∧ ~Q | (P ∧ ~Q) → Q | P → Q | [(P ∧ ~Q) → Q] ↔ (P → Q) |
|---|---|-----|--------|--------------|-------|--------------------------|
| T | T | F | F | T | T | T |
| T | F | T | T | F | F | T |
| F | T | F | F | T | T | T |
| F | F | T | F | T | T | T |

$$[(P \wedge \sim Q) \rightarrow Q] \Leftrightarrow (P \rightarrow Q)$$

TABLE 2-15.

*It is important to note that any statement can be substituted for any of its logical equivalents.*

EXERCISES ———————————————————————

*Construct truth tables for each of the following theorems.*

1.  THEOREM 1.   $[P \wedge (Q \vee R)] \Leftrightarrow [(P \wedge Q) \vee (P \wedge R)]$.
2.  THEOREM 2.   $[P \vee (Q \wedge R)] \Leftrightarrow [(P \vee Q) \wedge (P \vee R)]$.
3.  THEOREM 3.   $(P \leftrightarrow Q) \Leftrightarrow [(P \rightarrow Q) \wedge (Q \rightarrow P)]$.

| $P$ | $Q$ | $R$ | $\sim Q$ | $P \land \sim Q$ | $\sim R$ | $R \land \sim R$ | $(P \land \sim Q) \to (R \land \sim R)$ | $P \to Q$ | $[(P \land \sim Q) \to (R \land \sim R)] \leftrightarrow (P \to Q)$ |
|---|---|---|---|---|---|---|---|---|---|
| T | T | T | F | F | F | F | T | T | T |
| T | T | F | F | F | T | F | T | T | T |
| T | F | T | T | T | F | F | F | F | T |
| T | F | F | T | T | T | F | F | F | T |
| F | T | T | F | F | F | F | T | T | T |
| F | T | F | F | F | T | F | T | T | T |
| F | F | T | T | F | F | F | T | T | T |
| F | F | F | T | F | T | F | T | T | T |

$$[(P \land \sim Q) \to (R \land \sim R)] \Leftrightarrow (P \to Q)$$

TABLE 2-16

4.  THEOREM 4.  $[(P \to Q) \wedge (Q \to R)] \Rightarrow (P \to R)$.
5.  •THEOREM 5.  $\sim(\sim P) \Leftrightarrow P$.
6.  THEOREM 6.  $(P \to Q) \Leftrightarrow \sim P \vee Q$.
7.  THEOREM 7.  $(P \wedge \sim P) \Rightarrow Q$.
8.  THEOREM 8.  $(P \wedge Q) \Rightarrow P$.
9.  THEOREM 9.  $(P \wedge Q) \Rightarrow (P \vee Q)$.

*Remove parentheses where no ambiguity will result. Tell what interpretations might wrongly result from removal of necessary parentheses.*

10.  $[P \to (Q \vee R)]$.    11.  $(P \to Q) \wedge R$.    12.  $\sim(P) \to [\sim(Q \vee R)]$.
13.  $(R \to S) \to Q$.    14.  $R \to (S \to Q)$.

*Let P be any compound or simple statement. We will denote by T(P) the truth value of P, setting*

$$T(P) = \begin{cases} 1 \text{ if } P \text{ is true} \\ 0 \text{ if } P \text{ is false} \end{cases}$$

*15.  Verify the following from the truth tables given so far
   a.  $T(\sim P) = 1 - T(P)$.
   b.  $T(P \vee Q) = T(P) + T(Q) - T(P)T(Q)$.
   c.  $T(P \wedge Q) = T(P)T(Q)$.
   d.  $T(P \to Q) = 1 - T(P) + T(P)T(Q)$.
   e.  $T(P \leftrightarrow Q) = 1 - T(P) - T(Q) + 2T(P)T(Q)$.
*16.  Note that for any natural number $N$, $(T(P))^N = T(P)$ regardless of $P$. Using this fact and repeated use of Exercise 15 derive the following:
   a.  $T[(P \to Q) \wedge (Q \to P)] = T(Q \leftrightarrow P)$.
   b.  $T(P \to Q) = T[(P \wedge \sim Q) \to \sim P]$.
   c.  $T(P \to Q) = T(\sim Q \to \sim P)$.
   d.  $T(P \to Q) = T[(P \wedge \sim Q) \to Q]$.
*17.  a.  Let $S$ be the compound statement

$$[\sim(P \wedge \sim Q)] \vee (\sim Q \vee P).$$

Show that $T(S) = 1$. Explain why this means that $S$ is logically true.
   b.  Let $R$ be the compound statement $(\sim P) \wedge (\sim Q)$ and $S$ the compound statement $\sim(P \vee Q)$. Show that $T(S \leftrightarrow R) = 1$. Explain why this means $S$ and $R$ are logically equivalent.
   c.  From Exercise 15e we obtain $T(S \leftrightarrow R) = 1$ if $T(S) = T(R)$. Use this fact, and the equations in 16a–d, to write four new equations of the form $T(S \leftrightarrow R) = 1$; conclude in each case that $S \Leftrightarrow R$.

## —— 2-4   Quantifiers

So far we have dealt with statements that have been either true or false, but not both simultaneously. Now consider the following assertion:

"They are tall."

It is impossible to assign a truth value to this assertion, because we do not know to what the word "they" refers. For instance "they" could have any of the following meanings:

"They are tall."
↓

a.   "Trees are tall."
b.   "Those brothers are tall."
c.   "Giraffes are tall."
d.   "Tales are tall."

The substitution of the words "trees," "those brothers," "giraffes," and "tales" for the word "they" in the assertions in (a)–(d) makes it easier to assign truth values to them. However, some ambiguities still exist. For instance, the assertion in (a) might be considered true or false, depending upon factors such as the kind of tree and the age of the tree. We can, however, use *quantifiers*, words such as *all*, *every*, *any*, *some*, and *no*, to make the assertion

"Trees are tall."

specific enough so that a truth value can be assigned. (This assumes, of course, that some agreement has been reached concerning the meaning of tall.) We have:

e.   "All trees are tall."                          False
f.   "Every tree is tall."                          False
g.   "Any tree is tall."                            False
h.   "Some trees are (at least one tree is) tall."  True
i.   "No trees are tall."                           False

Sentences such as those above, which contain quantifiers, are called *general statements*.

Now consider the mathematical assertion

"The absolute value of a real number is greater than the number."

If we let the variable $x$ stand for the number, we can write this assertion as

$$|x| > x.$$

It is impossible to give this assertion a truth value unless we know exactly to what number $x$ refers. Just as in the example, "Trees are tall.", we can use quantifiers to clarify the meaning intended. Table 2-17 shows how this can be done for our example with the quantifiers all, every, any, some, and no. Also shown are the symbols used to denote these quantifiers, as well as the truth values which can be given for each general statement.

Table 2-18 gives the negations of some of the general statements in (e)–(i) and in Table 2-17.

| Quantifier | Symbol | Read as | General statement | Truth value | Example |
|---|---|---|---|---|---|
| All (every, any) | ∀ | "For all" ("for every," "for any") | $(\forall x)\lvert x\rvert > x$ | False | $\lvert 10\rvert = 10 \not> 10;\ \lvert 2\rvert = 2 \not> 2$ |
| Not all (every) | $\sim\forall$ or $\not\forall$ | "For not all" ("for not every") | $(\sim\forall x)$ or $(\not\forall x)\lvert x\rvert > x$ | True | $\lvert 10\rvert = 10 \not> 10$ |
| Some | ∃ | "There exists (at least one)" or "for some" | $(\exists x)\lvert x\rvert > x$ | True | $\lvert {}^-2\rvert = 2 > {}^-2$ |
| No | $\sim\exists$ or $\not\exists$ | "There does not exist (at least one)" or "for no" | $(\sim\exists x)$ or $(\not\exists x)\lvert x\rvert > x$ | False | $\lvert {}^-2\rvert = 2 > {}^-2$ |

TABLE 2-17.

| General statement | Negation |
|---|---|
| All (every, any) trees are tall. | (There exists) at least one tree (that) is not tall. |
| Some trees are (i.e., at least one tree is) tall. | No trees are tall. |
| No trees are tall. | Some trees are (i.e., at least one tree is) tall. |
| $(\forall x)\ |x| > x$ | $(\exists x)\ |x| \not> x$ |
| $(\not\forall x)\ |x| > x$ | $(\forall x)\ |x| > x$ |
| $(\exists x)\ |x| > x$ | $(\not\exists x)\ |x| > x$ |
| $(\not\exists x)\ |x| > x$ | $(\exists x)\ |x| > x$ |

TABLE 2-18.

*EXERCISES*

*Write the negation of each statement.*

1. All numbers are even.
2. Some wabbles are snappes.
3. Every plane figure has points.
4. All lines intersect.
5. Some rabbits hop.
6. Every frap is a bip.
7. No bunnies are rabbits.
8. $(\exists x)|x| \geq x.$
9. $(\forall x)|x| \geq x.$
10. $(\forall x)x \neq x.$
11. $(\sim \exists x)x \neq x.$

*Write out what each statement says. Let $S_x$: x is a student. Let $R_x$: x is a radical.*

12. $(\forall x)S_x \to R_x.$
13. $(\exists x)S_x \to R_x.$
14. $(\exists x)R_x \to S_x.$
15. $(\sim \exists x)S_x \to \sim R_x.$
16. $(\sim \forall x)R_x \to \sim S_x.$
17. $(\forall x)S_x \to \sim R_x.$
18. $(\sim \exists x)R_x \to \sim S_x.$
19. $(\sim \forall x) \sim R_x \to \sim S_x.$
20. $(\sim \exists x) \sim R_x \to S_x.$

—— 2-5  Venn Diagrams: An Alternate Approach to Proving Theorems of Logic

We can often gain insight into a logical statement or relationship between logical statements by using a Venn diagram. Let us introduce this device by means of an example. Suppose $P$ is the statement

"$x$ is a white rabbit."

This statement has a variable $x$ that may be replaced by any particular rabbit. When such a replacement is made the statement then takes on the value $T$ or the value $F$, depending upon the replacement chosen for $x$. Two things should be apparent:

1. The statement $P$ applies to rabbits, rather than cows, pigs, or aardvarks. That is, the universe $\mathcal{U}$ to which $P$ applies is the set of all rabbits.

2.   There are some replacements for *x* which make *P* true, and others which make *P* false. Those replacements of *x* for which *P* is true make up the *truth set* of *P*.

The situation might be diagramed in the following way:

Let 𝒰 be represented by a rectangle. Let those objects in 𝒰 for which *P* is true be represented by a subset of 𝒰. Occasionally, shading will be used to call attention to certain areas. For our present example, 𝒰 is the set of all rabbits, and *P* is the set of all white rabbits. (See Figure 2-1). Although the

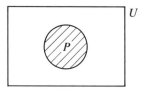

FIGURE 2-1.

shaded subset is labeled *P*, it represents "those objects for which statement *P* is true," the truth set of *P*. Those objects in 𝒰 but *outside P* are objects for which statement *P* is *false*.

With this scheme of representation, we can build more complicated diagrams representing the "truth sets" of compound statements. The shaded regions in Figure 2-2(a)–(c) show the truth sets of ∼*P*, *P* ∨ *Q*, and *P* ∧ *Q* respectively.

Figure 2-2(a) pictures ∼*P* as the set of points outside of the region

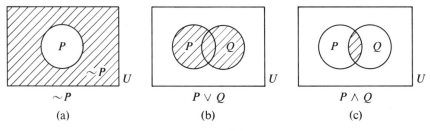

| ∼*P* | *P* ∨ *Q* | *P* ∧ *Q* |
| (a) | (b) | (c) |

FIGURE 2-2.

representing *P*. From Chapter 1 we know that this is the region corresponding to the complement of *P*.

In Figure 2-2(b) the truth set of *P* ∨ *Q* is the set of points in either *P* or *Q* or both. Remember that *P* ∨ *Q* is true when *P* or *Q* or both are true. In other words, the diagram corresponding to the truth set of *P* ∨ *Q* is actually the union of *P* and *Q*, *P* ∪ *Q*.

Figure 2-2(c) shows the diagram corresponding to the truth set of *P* ∧ *Q*, the set of points that lie in both *P* and *Q* simultaneously. Remember that

$P \wedge Q$ is true when $P$ and $Q$ are simultaneously true. In other words, the diagram corresponding to the truth set of $P \wedge Q$ is actually the intersection of $P$ and $Q$, $P \cap Q$.

Venn diagrams can also be used to depict implications. For example, the statement $P \rightarrow Q$ can be interpreted as

"For any object $x$, if $x$ is in the truth set of $P$ then $x$ is in the truth set of $Q$." This relationship between $P$ and $Q$ is shown in Figure 2-3(a),

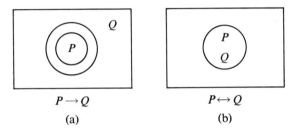

FIGURE 2-3.

where $P$ is a subset of $Q$. Figure 2-3(b) displays the relationship $P \leftrightarrow Q$. There $P = Q$.

We can also use Venn diagrams to show that a compound statement $R$ is logically true. Since $R$ is logically true if and only if it is true in every possible case, the truth set of $R$ in this case must be the universe $\mathcal{U}$. In Section 2-3 we used a truth table to show that

$$Q \vee \sim Q \equiv \text{True.}$$

Figure 2-4 shows that $Q \vee \sim Q \equiv \text{True}$, using Venn diagrams. This is so,

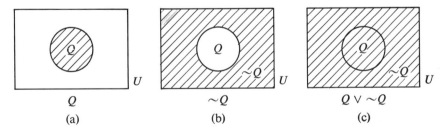

FIGURE 2-4.   $Q \vee \sim Q \equiv \text{True.}$

since $Q \cup \sim Q = \mathcal{U}$.

Similarly, a compound statement $R$ is logically false if and only if $R$ is false in every possible case. Thus the truth set of $R$ in this case must be the empty set. We used a truth table in Section 2-3 to show that

$$Q \wedge \sim Q \equiv \text{False.}$$

Figure 2-5 shows this using a Venn diagram, since $Q \cap \sim Q = \varnothing$. The truth set of each statement is shaded in the corresponding diagram. In particular, the set $\varnothing$ is shaded in Figure 2-5(c).

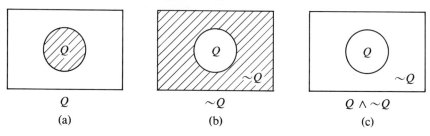

| $Q$ | $\sim Q$ | $Q \wedge \sim Q$ |
|:---:|:---:|:---:|
| (a) | (b) | (c) |

FIGURE 2-5.   $Q \wedge \sim Q \equiv$ False.

In Section 2-3 we saw that if $R$ and $S$ are two statements, at least one of which is compound, then $R$ implies $S$ if and only if $R \rightarrow S$ is logically true. In terms of the truth sets of $R$ and $S$, $R \rightarrow S$ is logically true if and only if the truth set of $R$ is a subset of the truth set of $S$. Figure 2-6 shows that

$Q$ a subset of $Q \vee \sim Q$

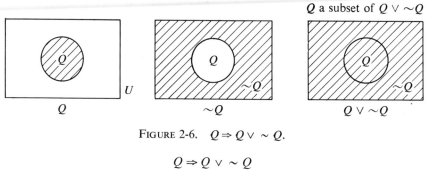

| $Q$ | $\sim Q$ | $Q \vee \sim Q$ |
|:---:|:---:|:---:|

FIGURE 2-6.   $Q \Rightarrow Q \vee \sim Q$.

$$Q \Rightarrow Q \vee \sim Q$$

since the truth set of $Q$ is a subset of the truth set of $Q \vee \sim Q = U$. This was also shown in the truth table in Table 2-12.

In Section 2-3 we also said that two statements $R$ and $S$ (at least one of which is compound) are equivalent if and only if $R \leftrightarrow S$ is logically true. In terms of sets, $R \Leftrightarrow S$ if and only if the truth set of $R$ is the same as the truth set of $S$. The Venn diagram in Figure 2-7 shows that

$$\sim(R \vee S) \Leftrightarrow (\sim R \wedge \sim S).$$

In similar fashion, the Venn diagrams of Figure 2-8 show that

$$\sim(R \wedge S) \Leftrightarrow (\sim R \vee \sim S).$$

In words, for statements $R$ and $S$ the negation of $R$ or $S$ is equivalent to the negation of $R$ and the negation of $S$. And the negation of $R$ and $S$ is equivalent to the negation of $R$ or the negation of $S$.

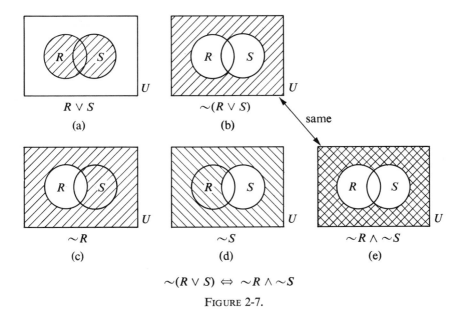

$\sim(R \vee S) \Leftrightarrow \sim R \wedge \sim S$

FIGURE 2-7.

Venn diagrams can also be used to test the validity of an argument. Consider the following reasoning:

All rabbits ($R$) are four legged ($F$).
Charlie ($C$) is a rabbit ($R$).
Therefore Charlie ($C$) is four legged ($F$).

FIGURE 2-8.    $\sim(R \wedge S) \Leftrightarrow (\sim R \vee \sim S)$.

Using notation for connectives we could write this argument as

$$((R \to F) \wedge (C \to R)) \to (C \to F).$$

Is the conclusion $C \to F$ justifiable? To see, we can use Venn diagrams as in Figure 2-9 to see whether

$$(R \to F) \wedge (C \to R)$$

implies

$$(C \to F).$$

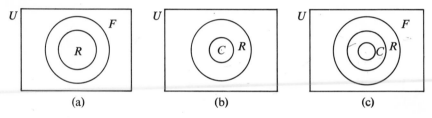

(a)                    (b)                    (c)

FIGURE 2-9.

The universe $\mathscr{U}$ may be any set containing all objects to which the present discussion might apply. For example, let us take the universe to be the set of all animals. We then obtain the diagrams of Figure 2-9, where (a) depicts $R \to F$, (b) shows $C \to R$, and (c) shows the combined effect of (a) and (b). Since in (c) $C$ is a subset of $F$, the relationship $C \to F$ is true. Thus the argument leading to the conclusion that Charlie has four legs is valid.

EXERCISES ————————————————————————————————

Draw a Venn diagram to represent each of the following statements.

1.  $\sim(P \vee Q)$.          2.  $\sim(P \wedge Q)$.          3.  $P \wedge \sim Q$.
4.  $\sim P \vee Q$.          5.  $\sim R \vee \sim Q$.

Use Venn diagrams to determine which of the following statements are valid.

6.  $[P \wedge (Q \vee R)] \leftrightarrow [P \wedge Q) \vee (P \wedge R)]$.
7.  $[P \vee (Q \wedge R)] \leftrightarrow [(P \vee Q) \wedge (P \vee R)]$.
8.  $(P \vee P) \to P$.          9.  $(P \wedge P) \to P$.

Use Venn diagrams to determine whether the following arguments are valid.

10.  a.   If prices continue to rise, then inflation is coming.
          Inflation is coming.
          Therefore prices will continue to rise.

b.  If it is cold today, then it will be cold tomorrow.
    It will not be cold tomorrow.

    Therefore it is cold today.
c.  If you have a square, then you have a rectangle.
    You have a square.

    Therefore you have a rectangle.
d.  If you have a square, then you have a rectangle.
    You do not have a rectangle.

    Therefore you do not have a square.
e.  If $R$ gets a job, then he will marry $S$.
    $R$ married $S$.

    Therefore $R$ got a job.
f.  $R$ says if he gets a job then he will marry $S$.
    $R$ did not marry $S$.

    Therefore $R$ was a liar.
g.  If it rains tomorrow, then $2 + 2 = 7$.
    It rains tomorrow.

    Therefore $2 + 2 = 7$.

## ——— 2-6   Proof

A proof is a convincing argument that a given statement is true. Such an argument usually starts with certain basic facts, definitions, or assumptions that the reader is willing to accept, and proceeds, by means of the logical process illustrated in the "Charlie is a rabbit" example of the preceding section, to persuade the reader that the given statement is indeed true, by proceeding from true statement to true statement.

For example, consider the statement $S$: "If $ABCD$ is a square, then $ABCD$ is a rhombus." What basic assumptions or definitions are likely to be needed in order to establish the truth of $S$? Certainly we shall need the following definitions:

A *square* is a quadrilateral whose sides all have equal measure and whose angles are all right angles.

A *rhombus* is a quadrilateral whose sides all have equal measure.

Having these definitions before us, we can easily see that the given statement $S$ is true. What if its truth were not so obvious? Is there some way to organize and present our thinking so that any reader capable of following a logical argument would be convinced of the truth of $S$? Let us examine one such method of formal presentation.

PROVE:   If $ABCD$ is a square, then $ABCD$ is a rhombus.

$P$                              $Q$

(That is, we seek to prove that $P \to Q$ is true, where $P$ and $Q$ have the interpretations shown above. The proof begins with accepting the *hypothesis P* and showing that the *conclusion Q* must then follow.)

PROOF.

| Statement | Reason (statement is true) |
|---|---|
| 1. *ABCD* is a square. (*P*) | 1. Hypothesis. |
| 2. If *ABCD* is a square, then *ABCD* has four equal sides and *ABCD* has four right angles. | 2. Definition of a square. (Note that statement 2 has form $P \to (S \wedge T)$.) |
| 3. *ABCD* has four equal sides and four right angles. | 3. Follow from 1 and 2 by noting that $[P \wedge (P \to (S \wedge T)] \Rightarrow (S \wedge T)$. |
| 4. *ABCD* has four equal sides. | 4. Follows from 3 by $(S \wedge T) \Rightarrow S$. |
| 5. *ABCD* is a rhombus. (*Q*) | 5. Follows from 4 by definition of rhombus. |

With statement 5, our proof is complete, since we have proceeded from the hypothesis to the desired conclusion by (it is hoped) steps that are beyond question. Such a proof, from *hypothesis* to *conclusion* of the given statement, is called a *direct proof*.

The proof in our example may seem a bit stiff, unnatural, and lengthy, but it does spell out clearly, in statements of very precise logical structure, how each step was achieved. The more confident reader or writer may prefer an abbreviated form, in which precision is sacrificed for brevity; but one should always be able to construct a precise, formal proof if challenged by a doubter. We now show a shortened form of the same proof.

PROVE.    If *ABCD* is a square, then *ABCD* is a rhombus.

PROOF.

| Statement | Reason |
|---|---|
| 1. *ABCD* is a square. | 1. Hypothesis. |
| 2. Every square is a rhombus. | 2. Follows from definitions of square, rhombus. |
| 3. *ABCD* is a rhombus. | 3. Logical consequence of 1 and 2. |

Of course, direct proofs are usually not as short and simple as the example above. They are, instead, an extension of the same general form.

For instance, suppose we wanted to prove the following, where $P$ and $S$ are statements.

PROVE.   If $P$, then $S$.

The proof could take this form:

PROOF.

| Statement | Reason |
|-----------|--------|
| 1. $P$ is true | 1. An assumption. |
| 2. If $P$ is true, then $Q$ is true. | 2. By some definition, property, axiom, or previously proved theorem. |
| 3. $Q$ is true. | 3. Follows from 1 and 2 by $[P \wedge (P \to Q)] \Rightarrow Q$. |
| 4. If $Q$ is true, then $R$ is true. | 4. By some definition, property, axiom, or previously proved theorem. |
| 5. $R$ is true. | 5. From 3 and 4, by $[Q \wedge (Q \to R)] \Rightarrow R$. |
| 6. If $R$ is true, then $S$ is true. | 6. By some definition, property, axiom, or previously proved theorem. |
| 7. $S$ is true. | 7. From 5 and 6 by $[R \wedge (R \to S)] \Rightarrow S$. |

Again, the confident writer or reader could do without steps 3 and 5.
Sometimes it is easier to prove that a statement

$$P \to Q \text{ is true}$$

*indirectly.* In Section 2-3 we showed that

$$(\sim Q \to \sim P) \Leftrightarrow (P \to Q),$$

$$[(P \wedge \sim Q) \to \sim P] \Leftrightarrow (P \to Q),$$

$$[(P \wedge \sim Q) \to Q] \Leftrightarrow (P \to Q),$$

and

$$[(P \wedge \sim Q) \to (R \wedge \sim R)] \Leftrightarrow (P \to Q).$$

Thus if we prove that any one of these four logical equivalences is true, we have proved indirectly that $P \to Q$ is true. Examples for each of these four methods are given below.

1.  *Proof of contrapositive:* $(\sim Q \rightarrow \sim P) \Leftrightarrow (P \rightarrow Q)$.

PROVE.    If $x$ is a prime greater than 2, then $x$ is odd. (Here $P$ is the statement "$x$ is a prime greater than 2." $Q$ is the statement "$x$ is odd." The universe for this statement is the set of positive integers.)

PROOF.

| Statement | Reason |
|---|---|
| 1.  $x$ is even (i.e., $x$ is not odd). | 1.  Assumption ($\sim Q$). |
| 2.  If $x$ is even, then $x = 2b$, where $b$ is a positive integer. | 2.  Definition of even number. |
| 3.  If $x = 2b$, for whole number $b$ greater than 0, then $x$ is divisible by 2. | 3.  Property of divisibility. |
| 4.  If $x$ is divisible by 2, then $x = 2$ or $x$ is not prime. | 4.  Definition of prime number. |
| 5.  $x = 2$ or $x$ is not prime ($\sim P$) | 5.  Logical consequence of 1–4. |

Since we have shown that $\sim Q \rightarrow \sim P$ is true, we know by its logical equivalence that $P \rightarrow Q$ is true. We have proved the given statement *indirectly*, by proving a different (but equivalent) statement instead.

2.  *Proof using* $((P \wedge \sim Q) \rightarrow \sim P) \Leftrightarrow (P \rightarrow Q)$.

PROVE.    If $l \parallel m$ and $n \perp l$, then $n \perp m$. (Remember $\parallel$ is the symbol for "is parallel to" and $\perp$ is the symbol for "is perpendicular to.") Here $P$ is the statement "$l \parallel m$ and $n \perp l$," $Q$ is the statement "$n \perp m$." See Figure 2-10.

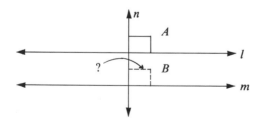

FIGURE 2-10

Assume $\angle A$ and $\angle B$ ($\angle$ stands for the word "angle") are the corresponding angles formed by the transversal $n$ and the lines $l$ and $m$, respectively.)

PROOF.

| Statement | Reason |
| --- | --- |
| 1. $l \parallel m, n \perp l, n \not\perp m$ ($n \not\perp m$ means $n$ not perpendicular to $m$). | 1. Assumption of $P \wedge \sim Q$. |
| 2. If $l \parallel m$, $n \perp l$, $n \not\perp m$, then $m° \angle B \neq m° \angle A = 90°$. ($m° \angle B$ is the symbol for "measure in degrees of angle $B$.") | 2. Definition of $\perp$ lines. |
| 3. If $m° \angle B \neq m° \angle A$, then $l \not\parallel m$ ($l \not\parallel m$ means $l$ is not parallel to $m$). | 3. Contrapositive of theorem stating "If $l \parallel m$, measures of corresponding angles are equal." |
| 4. $l \not\parallel m$ ($\sim P$). | 4. Logical consequence of 2 and 3. |

Since we have shown that $(P \wedge \sim Q) \to \sim P$ is true, we know by its logical equivalence that $P \to Q$ is true. The given statement has been proved indirectly.

3.  $[(P \wedge \sim Q) \to Q)] \Leftrightarrow (P \to Q)$.

**PROVE.** If $n$ and $m$ are odd, $n + m$ is even. (Here $P$ is the statement "$n$ and $m$ are odd." $Q$ is the statement "$n + m$ is even.")

PROOF.

| Statement | Reason |
| --- | --- |
| 1. $n, m$ odd; $n + m$ odd (i.e., $n + m$ is not even). | 1. Assumption of $P \wedge \sim Q$. |
| 2. If $n, m$ odd and $n + m$ odd, then $n = 2a + 1$, $m = 2b + 1$ and $n + m = (2a + 1) + (2b + 1) = 2a + 2b + 2$ for integers $a$ and $b$. | 2. Definition of odd number. |
| 3. If $n + m = 2a + 2b + 2$, then $n + m$ is divisible by 2. | 3. Property of divisibility. |
| 4. If $n + m$ is divisible by 2, then $n + m$ is even. | 4. Definition of even number. |
| 5. $n + m$ is even. ($Q$). | 5. Logical consequence of 3 and 4. |

We have shown that $(P \wedge \sim Q) \to Q$ is true. By its logical equivalence we have thus shown that the given statement $P \to Q$ is true.

4.  *Proof by contradiction:*

$$[(P \wedge \sim Q) \to (R \wedge \sim R)] \Leftrightarrow (P \to Q).$$

**PROVE.** If $n$ is odd, $n^2$ is odd. (Here $P$ is the statement "$n$ is odd." $Q$ is the statement "$n^2$ is odd.")

PROOF.

| Statement | Reason |
|---|---|
| 1. $n$ is odd and $n^2$ is even (i.e., not odd). | 1. Assumption of $P \wedge \sim Q$. |
| 2. If $n$ is odd and $n^2$ is even, then $n = 2a + 1$, $n^2 = (2a + 1)^2$ and $n^2 = 2b$, for integers $a$ and $b$. | 2. Definition of odd and even numbers. |
| 3. If $n^2 = (2a + 1)^2$ and $n^2 = 2b$, then $n^2 = 4a^2 + 4a + 1$ and $n^2 = 2b$. | 3. Property from algebra for squaring expressions. |
| 4. If $n^2 = 4a^2 + 4a + 1$ and $n^2 = 2b$, then $n^2$ is not divisible by 2 and $n^2$ is divisible by 2. | 4. Property of divisibility. |
| 5. If $n^2$ is not divisible by 2 and $n^2$ is divisible by 2, then $n^2$ is odd and $n^2$ is even. | 5. Definition of odd and even numbers. |
| 6. $n^2$ is odd ($R$) and $n^2$ is even ($\sim R$). | 6. Logical consequence of 4 and 5. |

This conclusion $R \wedge \sim R$ is a contradiction, since a single number $n^2$ cannot be simultaneously even and odd! Therefore, we have shown that $(P \wedge \sim Q) \rightarrow (R \wedge \sim R)$ is true, so by its logical equivalence we know that the given statement $P \rightarrow Q$ is true.

When it does not seem possible to prove a statement, it may be that the statement is false! In that case it may be possible to *disprove* the statement using one of the methods below.

    1.   *Disproof by Contradiction.*

Assume the given statement $P$ is true. If it can be shown that

$$P \rightarrow Q \text{ is true,}$$

where $Q$ contradicts a known definition, property, axiom or theorem previously proved (i.e., $Q$ is false), then $P$ is false. This case corresponds to the last line in the truth table for $P \rightarrow Q$ as indicated by the small arrow in Table 2-19. There $P \rightarrow Q$ is true and $Q$ is false. The truth value of $P$ is thus false.

| $P$ | $Q$ | $P \rightarrow Q$ | |
|---|---|---|---|
| T | T | T | |
| T | F | F | |
| F | T | T | |
| F | F | T | $\leftarrow$ |

TABLE 2-19.

Here is an example of disproof by contradiction.

PROVE.   The square of every even number $n$ is odd. (This statement is $P$.)

DISPROOF.

| Statement | Reason |
|---|---|
| 1. The square of every even number $n$ is odd. | 1. Assumption of $P$. |
| 2. If the square of every even number $n$ is odd, then $n = 2a$ and $n^2 = (2a)^2 = 4a^2 = 2b + 1$, where $a$ and $b$ are integers. | 2. Definition of odd and even numbers. |
| 3. If $n^2 = 4a^2 = 2b + 1$, then $n^2$ is both even and odd. ($Q$) | 3. Definition of odd and even number. |

Statement $Q$ is false, since $n^2$ is a *single* number. It cannot be even and odd simultaneously.

We can therefore conclude that the statement, "The square of every even number $n$ is odd," is false, since taking it to be true leads us to a false conclusion.

2. *Disproof by Counterexample.*

From Section 2-4, recall that the negation of any statement $P$ in which the quantifiers *all, any* or *every* appear is a statement in which the quantifier *there exists* (at least one) appears. For instance, consider the statement $P$

"All numbers divisible by 3 are divisible by 9."

A counterexample to this statement is 12, since 12 is divisible by 3, but is not divisible by 9. Since we have exhibited that the negation $\sim P$ of the given statement

"There exists at least one number (namely 12) divisible by 3 which is not divisible to 9."

is true, the given·statement $P$ is false. We have disproved the given statement by counterexample.

A warning! It is possible to disprove statements by counterexample as we have demonstrated above. However, it is not possible to prove a statement by giving examples.

### EXERCISES

1. Prove that if $a|b$ and $a|c$ then $a|(b + c)$ and $a|(b - c)$. ($a$, $b$ and $c$ are integers.)
2. Prove that if $a|b$ and $b|c$ then $a|c$.
3. Prove that the number of prime numbers is infinite. (*Hint*: Assume the statement is false.)
4. Prove that every integer divisible by 10 is divisible by 5.
5. Prove that every prime $P > 2$ is of the form $4n + 1$ or $4n + 3$.
6. Disprove that all prime integers are odd.
7. Prove that the square of every odd integer is of the form $8n + 1$.
8. Prove that every prime number $P > 2$ ends with one of the digits 1, 3, 7, 9.

# Vectors and Matrices  3

## —3-1  Row and Column Vectors

*A row vector* is an ordered collection of numbers written in a row. Some examples are

$$(0 \quad 0 \quad 0), (1 \quad 0 \quad 2 \quad 3) \text{ and } (5 \quad {}^-3 \quad 7).$$

The individual numbers in each of these row vectors are called *components*. The components of our first example are all 0. The components of our second example are 1, 0, 2, and 3. The second component of our third example is $^-3$.

More generally, we may also speak of $n$-component row vectors such as $\mathbf{v} = (v_1 \, v_2 \, v_3 \, \ldots \, v_n)$. $\mathbf{v}$ has $n$ components.

We also speak of *column vectors*, which are ordered collections of numbers written in a column. Some examples are

$$\begin{pmatrix} 0 \\ 2 \end{pmatrix} \quad \begin{pmatrix} 3 \\ 2 \\ 1 \end{pmatrix} \quad \begin{pmatrix} 5 \\ {}^-3 \\ {}^-\frac{1}{2} \\ 4 \end{pmatrix} \quad \begin{pmatrix} {}^-1 \\ 0 \\ 0 \\ 0 \\ 1 \end{pmatrix}.$$

Each number appearing in a column vector is called a component also. For instance, our third example has four components. The vector

$$\mathbf{u} = \begin{pmatrix} u_1 \\ u_2 \\ \vdots \\ u_n \end{pmatrix}$$

is called an $n$-component column vector.

A vector with all components 0 except for one that is 1 is called a *unit vector*. The vectors

$$\begin{pmatrix} 0 \\ 0 \\ 1 \end{pmatrix} \quad \text{and} \quad (0 \ 1 \ 0 \ 0)$$

are unit vectors.

101

Two row vectors are said to be equal if and only if the corresponding components of the vectors are equal; similarly for two column vectors. A column vector cannot equal a row vector. Note that two equal vectors have the same number of components. For example,

$$(1 \quad 2) = (1 \quad 2), \qquad (1 \quad 2) \neq (2 \quad 3), \qquad \begin{pmatrix} 1 \\ 2 \\ 3 \end{pmatrix} = \begin{pmatrix} 1 \\ 2 \\ 3 \end{pmatrix},$$

$$\begin{pmatrix} 1 \\ 3 \\ 5 \end{pmatrix} \neq (1 \quad 3 \quad 5) \qquad \text{and} \qquad \begin{pmatrix} 1 \\ 3 \\ 5 \end{pmatrix} \neq \begin{pmatrix} 1 \\ 3 \\ 7 \end{pmatrix}.$$

We may add (or subtract) two row vectors or two column vectors if, and only if, they have the same number of components. We perform the addition (or subtraction) by adding (or subtracting) corresponding components. For instance,

$$\begin{pmatrix} 1 \\ 5 \\ ^-2 \end{pmatrix} + \begin{pmatrix} 7 \\ ^-3 \\ 0 \end{pmatrix} = \begin{pmatrix} 1 + 7 \\ 5 + ^-3 \\ ^-2 + 0 \end{pmatrix} = \begin{pmatrix} 8 \\ 2 \\ ^-2 \end{pmatrix},$$

and

$$\begin{pmatrix} 1 \\ 5 \\ ^-2 \end{pmatrix} - \begin{pmatrix} 7 \\ ^-3 \\ 0 \end{pmatrix} = \begin{pmatrix} 1 - 7 \\ 5 - ^-3 \\ ^-2 - 0 \end{pmatrix} = \begin{pmatrix} ^-6 \\ 8 \\ ^-2 \end{pmatrix},$$

while

$$(1 \quad 3) + (0 \quad 3) = (1 + 0 \quad 3 + 3) = (1 \quad 6),$$

and

$$(1 \quad 3) - (0 \quad 3) = (1 - 0 \quad 3 - 3) = (1 \quad 0).$$

In general, if $\mathbf{u} = (u_1 \, u_2 \, \dots \, u_n)$ and $\mathbf{v} = (v_1 \, v_2 \, \dots \, v_n)$,

$$\mathbf{u} \pm \mathbf{v} = (u_1 \pm v_1 \quad u_2 \pm v_2 \, \dots \, u_n \pm v_n).$$

And, if

$$\mathbf{u} = \begin{pmatrix} u_1 \\ u_2 \\ \vdots \\ u_n \end{pmatrix} \qquad \text{and} \qquad \mathbf{v} = \begin{pmatrix} v_1 \\ v_2 \\ \vdots \\ v_n \end{pmatrix},$$

$$\mathbf{u} \pm \mathbf{v} = \begin{pmatrix} u_1 \pm v_1 \\ u_2 \pm v_2 \\ \vdots \\ u_n \pm v_n \end{pmatrix}.$$

Is there a row vector $\mathbf{z}$ such that

$$(1 \quad 2 \quad 3) + \mathbf{z} = (1 \quad 2 \quad 3)?$$

For addition or subtraction to be possible, such a vector $\mathbf{z}$ must be a three-component row vector. Let us represent $\mathbf{z}$ temporarily as

$$\mathbf{z} = (z_1 \quad z_2 \quad z_3).$$

Then we would like

$$(1 \quad 2 \quad 3) + (z_1 \quad z_2 \quad z_3) = (1 + z_1 \quad 2 + z_2 \quad 3 + z_3)$$
$$= (1 \qquad 2 \qquad 3).$$

Consequently, by definition of equal vectors we want

$$1 + z_1 = 1$$
$$2 + z_2 = 2$$
$$3 + z_3 = 3.$$

This means we must have

$$\mathbf{z} = (0 \quad 0 \quad 0).$$

Similarly, the vector $\mathbf{z}$ such that

$$\mathbf{z} + \begin{pmatrix} 2 \\ {}^-4 \\ 8 \end{pmatrix} = \begin{pmatrix} 2 \\ {}^-4 \\ 8 \end{pmatrix},$$

is

$$\mathbf{z} = \begin{pmatrix} 0 \\ 0 \\ 0 \end{pmatrix}.$$

In general,

$$(a_1 \quad a_2 \ldots a_n) + \mathbf{z} = (a_1 \quad a_2 \ldots a_n)$$

if and only if $\mathbf{z}$ is the $n$-component row vector

$$\mathbf{z} = (0 \quad 0 \ldots 0).$$

There is a similar generalization for column vectors. We shall use the symbol $\mathbf{0}$ to symbolize such row or column zero vectors.

Besides adding or subtracting two row or column vectors we may also multiply a number $c$ by a vector $\mathbf{v}$ if we multiply each component of $\mathbf{v}$ by $c$. For instance,

$$3 \begin{pmatrix} 1 \\ {}^-3 \\ 0 \end{pmatrix} = \begin{pmatrix} 3 \cdot 1 \\ 3 \cdot {}^-3 \\ 3 \cdot 0 \end{pmatrix} = \begin{pmatrix} 3 \\ {}^-9 \\ 0 \end{pmatrix},$$

and

$$\tfrac{1}{2}(2 \quad 4 \quad 6) = (\tfrac{1}{2} \cdot 2 \quad \tfrac{1}{2} \cdot 4 \quad \tfrac{1}{2} \cdot 6)$$
$$= (1 \qquad 2 \qquad 3).$$

More generally,

$$c(v_1 \quad v_2 \cdots v_n) = (cv_1 \quad cv_2 \cdots cv_n),$$

and

$$c\begin{pmatrix} v_1 \\ v_2 \\ \vdots \\ v_n \end{pmatrix} = \begin{pmatrix} cv_1 \\ cv_2 \\ \vdots \\ cv_n \end{pmatrix}.$$

Vectors are valuable aids in arranging large amounts of information. Suppose the column vector $v_{2068}$ has twelve components, where, for instance, the first component gives the price of zubitrons in January of 2068, the second component gives the price of zubitrons in February, 2068, and the twelfth and last component gives the price of zubitrons in December, 2068. If we have another twelve-component column vector, $v_{2069}$, showing the price of zubitrons for each month of 2069, we could subtract the first vector from the second to find the changes in monthly prices from 2068 to 2069. Suppose

$$v_{2068} = \begin{pmatrix} \$112.00 \\ \$111.00 \\ \$122.50 \\ \$119.00 \\ \$117.25 \\ \$118.00 \\ \$116.30 \\ \$117.25 \\ \$113.25 \\ \$112.00 \\ \$115.20 \\ \$113.25 \end{pmatrix} \quad \text{and} \quad v_{2069} = \begin{pmatrix} \$114.25 \\ \$110.50 \\ \$124.25 \\ \$123.00 \\ \$121.30 \\ \$117.25 \\ \$120.45 \\ \$121.25 \\ \$119.75 \\ \$120.70 \\ \$116.75 \\ \$116.75 \end{pmatrix}.$$

Then

$$v_{2069} - v_{2068} = \begin{pmatrix} +\$2.25 \\ -\ 0.50 \\ +\ 1.75 \\ +\ 4.00 \\ +\ 4.05 \\ -\ 0.75 \\ +\ 4.15 \\ +\ 4.00 \\ +\ 6.50 \\ +\ 8.70 \\ +\ 1.55 \\ +\ 3.50 \end{pmatrix}.$$

This resulting column vector gives the change in price of zubitrons for any month in 2069 as compared to the corresponding month in 2068. From the fourth entry in the new vector we see that the price of zubitrons in April of 2069 was $4.00 above the price of zubitrons in April of 2068; and the second entry in the vector $v_{2069} - v_{2068}$ tells us that in February of 2069 the price of zubitrons was $0.50 below the price of zubitrons in February of 2068.

Now suppose the price of zubitrons for each month in 2000 was exactly one-half the price of zubitrons for the corresponding month in 2068. Then by multiplying vector $v_{2068}$ by $\frac{1}{2}$ we would obtain $v_{2000}$ showing the month-by-month price of zubitrons in 2000. That is,

$$\frac{1}{2} \cdot v_{2068} = \begin{pmatrix} 56.00 \\ 55.50 \\ 61.25 \\ 59.50 \\ 58.63 \\ 59.00 \\ 58.15 \\ 58.63 \\ 56.63 \\ 56.00 \\ 57.60 \\ 56.63 \end{pmatrix} = v_{2000}.$$

We see from the eleventh entry of $v_{2000}$ that the price of zubitrons in November of the year 2000 was $57.60. In fact we can read off from the resulting vector, $v_{2000}$, the price of zubitrons in any month of the year 2000.

*EXERCISES* ——————————————————————————————————

1.  Write the row vector whose first component is 3, whose second component is ⁻8, and whose third component is 0.

2.  Write the column vector whose first component is 2, whose second component is 0, and whose third and fourth components are both ⁻1.

*Compute wherever possible the quantities below for the following vectors. If the computation is not possible, give reasons.*

$$\mathbf{u} = \begin{pmatrix} 2 \\ -1 \end{pmatrix}, \qquad \mathbf{v} = \begin{pmatrix} 5 \\ 4 \end{pmatrix}, \qquad \mathbf{w} = \begin{pmatrix} ^-5 \\ 3 \\ 0 \end{pmatrix},$$

$$\mathbf{r} = \begin{pmatrix} 2 \\ ^-4 \\ 6 \end{pmatrix}, \qquad \mathbf{s} = \begin{pmatrix} 6 \\ 3 \\ 0 \end{pmatrix}, \qquad \mathbf{z} = \begin{pmatrix} 0 \\ 0 \\ 0 \end{pmatrix},$$

$$\mathbf{a} = (^-3 \quad 5 \quad 7), \qquad \mathbf{b} = (10 \quad ^-9 \quad 1), \qquad \mathbf{c} = (^-2 \quad 3 \quad 1).$$

3. $\mathbf{u} + \mathbf{v}$.

4. $\mathbf{v} + \mathbf{u}$

5. $\mathbf{w} + \mathbf{z}$.

6. $\mathbf{z} + \mathbf{w}$.

7. $\mathbf{r} - \mathbf{s}$.

8. $\mathbf{a} + \mathbf{b}$.

9. $\mathbf{b} - \mathbf{a}$.

10. $2\mathbf{u}$.

11. $3\mathbf{a}$.

12. $-5\mathbf{r}$.

13. $\mathbf{v} + \mathbf{w}$.

14. $\mathbf{s} + \mathbf{a}$.

15. $3\mathbf{b} + \mathbf{a} + 2\mathbf{c}$.

16. $2(\mathbf{a} + \mathbf{b} - \mathbf{c})$.

17. $\mathbf{c} - \mathbf{a} + 2\mathbf{b}$.

18. $3(\mathbf{w} + \mathbf{r}) - \mathbf{s}$.

19. $2(\mathbf{b} + \mathbf{c})$.

20. $2\mathbf{b} + 2\mathbf{c}$.

21. Are

$$\begin{pmatrix} 1 \\ 2 \\ 3 \end{pmatrix} \quad \text{and} \quad \begin{pmatrix} 4/4 \\ 2.0 \\ 99/33 \end{pmatrix}$$

equal vectors? Why or why not?

22. Are

$$(3 \quad 2 \quad 1) \quad \text{and} \quad \begin{pmatrix} 3 \\ 2 \\ 1 \end{pmatrix}$$

equal vectors? Why or why not?

23. If $(3 \quad 2 \quad 1 \quad 0) = (v_1 \quad v_2 \quad v_3 \quad v_4)$, find $v_1, v_2, v_3, v_4$.

24. If

$$2\begin{pmatrix} -2 \\ 0 \\ 1 \end{pmatrix} = \begin{pmatrix} x_1 \\ x_2 \\ x_3 \end{pmatrix},$$

find $x_1, x_2, x_3$.

25. If $-2(4 \quad 2 \quad -1) - (1 \quad 0 \quad 4) = (y_1 \quad y_2 \quad y_3)$, find $y_1, y_2, y_3$.

26. If

$$\begin{pmatrix} 0 \\ 0 \\ 0 \end{pmatrix} + 4\begin{pmatrix} r_1 \\ r_2 \\ r_3 \end{pmatrix} = \begin{pmatrix} 0 \\ 0 \\ 0 \end{pmatrix},$$

find, $r_1, r_2, r_3$.

27. Write a column vector to summarize the information on the evolution of human brain volume given in the following table.

| Stage | Average volume of brain in cubic centimeters |
|---|---|
| Chimpanzee | 393.8 |
| Australopithecus | 507.9 |
| Homo Erectus | 973.7 |
| Neanderthal | 1422.3 |

28. Write a row vector to summarize the information on human life expectancy given in the table below.

| Period | Life expectancy in years |
|---|---|
| Neanderthal Europe | 29.4 |
| Cro-Magnon Europe | 32.4 |
| Bronze Age Austria | 38 |
| 14th Century England | 38 |
| Present U.S.A. | 70 |

29. Consider the following table giving price information on four computer stocks listed on the New York Stock Exchange.

| Company | 1971 Price Range to May 6 | |
|---|---|---|
| | High | Low |
| Burroughs Corp. | $138\frac{3}{4}$ | $104\frac{1}{2}$ |
| Control Data Corp. | 85 | 47 |
| IBM | $365\frac{3}{4}$ | 310 |
| National Cash Register | 47 | $37\frac{1}{2}$ |

   a. Write a column vector, $v_{high}$, giving the 1971 highs of the four companies in the table.

   b. Write a column vector, $v_{low}$, giving the 1971 lows of the four companies in the table.

   c. Use vector subtraction to find the column vector, $v_{range}$, giving the difference between the high and low prices of each of the four companies in the table.

30. The following table gives the breakdown by party of the number of seats held in the Italian Chamber of Deputies as a result of the 1968 general elections.

| Political leaning | Number of seats held in Italian Chamber of Deputies |
|---|---|
| Republicans | 9 |
| United Socialists | 91 |
| Proletarian Socialists | 23 |
| Communists | 177 |
| Christian Democrats | 266 |
| Liberals | 31 |
| Monarchists | 6 |
| Social Movement | 24 |
| Other | 3 |

a.  Write a column vector, $\mathbf{v}_{\text{seats}}$, showing the information in the above table concerning the number of seats held by each of the political parties shown.

b.  There are 630 seats in the Chamber of Deputies. Multiply the vector, $\mathbf{v}_{\text{seats}}$ in (a), by the appropriate number to obtain a column vector, $\mathbf{v}_{\text{frac}}$, showing the fraction of seats held by each party in the table.

31.  The following graphs show the consumption in billions of units of cigarettes and cigars from 1960 to 1967. Use the graphs for (a)—(c).

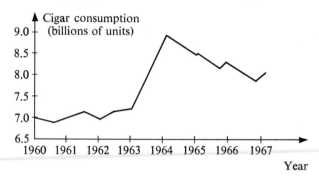

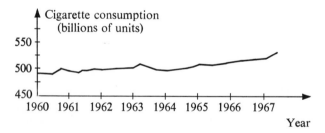

a.  Write an eight-component column vector, $\mathbf{v}_{\text{cigars}}$, showing the number of cigars in billions of units being consumed at the start of each year from 1960 to 1967 inclusive.

b.  Write an eight-component column vector, $\mathbf{v}_{\text{cigarettes}}$, showing the number of cigarettes in billions of units being consumed at the start of each year from 1960 to 1967 inclusive.

c.  Find the column vector, $\mathbf{v}_{\text{difference}}$, showing the difference in the consumption of cigars and cigarettes at the start of each year from 1960 to 1967 inclusive. Use vector subtraction.

## ——3-2  The Multiplication of Two Vectors

So far we have seen how we may add or subtract any two column vectors having the same number of components or any two row vectors having the same number of components. We have also examined the process of multiplying either a column vector or a row vector by a number. In this section we will find a way of combining a *row* vector and a *column* vector. This method will prove very useful for certain kinds of calculations. Consider the following examples.

Suppose Rufus and Helda Jones went into a grocery store to buy some supplies for a party. They purchased:

> 2 bottles red wine @ $3.50 per bottle,
> 3 bottles white wine @ $2.50 per bottle,
> 2 loaves of french bread @ $.40 per loaf,
> 1 pound of blue cheese @ $1.50 per pound,
> 1 pound of cheddar cheese @ $.90 per pound,
> 3 packages potato chips @ $.50 per bag,
> 12 apples @ $.10 apiece.

Let us represent their purchases by means of the following row vector **q**:

$$\mathbf{q} = (2 \quad 3 \quad 2 \quad 1 \quad 1 \quad 3 \quad 12)$$

| ↑ | ↑ | ↑ | ↑ | ↑ | ↑ | ↑ |
|---|---|---|---|---|---|---|
| bottles | bottles | loaves | pounds | pounds | packages | number |
| red | white | french | blue | cheddar | potato | of |
| wine | wine | bread | cheese | cheese | chips | apples |

And let us represent the prices of these items as the column vector **p**.

$$\mathbf{p} = \begin{pmatrix} 350 \\ 250 \\ 40 \\ 150 \\ 90 \\ 50 \\ 10 \end{pmatrix}$$

cents per bottle red wine,
cents per bottle white wine,
cents per loaf french bread,
cents per pound blue cheese,
cents per pound cheddar cheese,
cents per package potato chips,
cents per apple.

How much did the Joneses spend on their party? The natural thing would be to multiply the quantity vector **q** by the price vector **p**. The multiplication the cashier would perform to obtain the correct bill would be:

$$\mathbf{q} \cdot \mathbf{p} = (2 \quad 3 \quad 2 \quad 1 \quad 1 \quad 3 \quad 12) \begin{pmatrix} 350 \\ 250 \\ 40 \\ 150 \\ 90 \\ 50 \\ 10 \end{pmatrix}$$

$$= 2 \cdot 350 + 3 \cdot 250 + 2 \cdot 40 + 1 \cdot 150 + 1 \cdot 90 + 3 \cdot 50 + 12 \cdot 10$$
$$= 700 + 750 + 80 + 150 + 90 + 150 + 120$$
$$= 2040 \text{ cents or } \$20.40.$$

The preceding form for multiplication of a row vector by a column vector looks promising. Let us examine another example.

Two enterprising young college graduates, Webb and Cutlip, have decided to form a mutual fund with a special slant they hope will prove successful. Their plan is to buy stock only in small, unknown companies. They decide, after much study, to invest the following amounts in these companies:

> 150 shares of Newby Nuclear @ $7.50 per share,
> 200 shares of Bixby Drugs @ $16.00 per share,
> 550 shares of Hamburger Haven @ $5.00 per share,
> 100 shares of International Computer @ $37.00 per share,
> 1,000 shares of Oliver Oceanography @ $27.00 per share.

What was the initial investment? Again, let us represent the purchase by a row vector $\mathbf{q}$:

$$\mathbf{q} = (\quad 150 \qquad 200 \qquad 550 \qquad 100 \qquad 1{,}000 \quad )$$

| ↑ | ↑ | ↑ | ↑ | ↑ |
|---|---|---|---|---|
| Newby Nuclear | Bixby Drugs | Hamburger Haven | International Computer | Oliver Oceanography |

And let us represent the prices of these stocks by the column vector $\mathbf{p}$:

$$\mathbf{p} = \begin{pmatrix} 7\frac{1}{2} \\ 16 \\ 5 \\ 37 \\ 27 \end{pmatrix}$$

dollars per share, Newby Nuclear,
dollars per share, Bixby Drugs,
dollars per share, Hamburger Haven,
dollars per share, International Computer,
dollars per share, Oliver Oceanography.

To compute the total amount of the investment we would want the multiplication of the vectors $\mathbf{q}$ and $\mathbf{p}$ to take this form:

$$\mathbf{q} \cdot \mathbf{p} = (150 \quad 200 \quad 550 \quad 100 \quad 1{,}000) \begin{pmatrix} 7\frac{1}{2} \\ 16 \\ 5 \\ 37 \\ 27 \end{pmatrix}$$

$$= 150 \cdot 7\frac{1}{2} + 200 \cdot 16 + 550 \cdot 5 + 100 \cdot 37 + 1{,}000 \cdot 27$$

$$= 1{,}125 + 3{,}200 + 2{,}750 + 3{,}700 + 27{,}000$$

$$= \$37{,}775.$$

Webb and Cutlip spent $37,775 upon their first entry into the stock market.

We shall adopt, in general, the process suggested in the two preceding examples for the multiplication of a row vector by a column vector.

DEFINITION.   Let **u** be a row vector $(u_1\ u_2\ \ldots\ u_n)$ and **v** be a column vector

$$\begin{pmatrix} v_1 \\ v_2 \\ \vdots \\ v_n \end{pmatrix}$$

with the same number of components $n$. Then

$$\mathbf{u} \cdot \mathbf{v} = (u_1\ u_2\ \cdots\ u_n) \begin{pmatrix} v_1 \\ v_2 \\ \vdots \\ v_n \end{pmatrix} = u_1 v_1 + u_2 v_2 + \cdots + u_n v_n.$$

So, for instance,

$$(1\quad 2\quad 3) \begin{pmatrix} 0 \\ 1 \\ {}^-2 \end{pmatrix} = 1 \cdot 0 + 2 \cdot 1 + 3 \cdot {}^-2 = {}^-4.$$

Do not overlook the requirement in this definition that the two vectors being multiplied must have the same number of components. It is most important. We may not multiply the vectors

$$(1\quad 2) \qquad \text{and} \qquad \begin{pmatrix} 1 \\ 2 \\ 3 \end{pmatrix},$$

since they do not have the same number of components. Also note that the result of multiplying a row vector by a column vector is always a *number*.

*EXERCISES* ——————————————————————————

*Given the following vectors, carry out (if possible) the computations called for in Exercises 1 through 10. If the computation is not possible, give reasons.*

$$\mathbf{a} = (1\quad 3), \qquad \mathbf{b} = ({}^-1\quad 0\quad 3), \qquad \mathbf{c} = (5\quad {}^-3\quad 2),$$

$$\mathbf{u} = \begin{pmatrix} 5 \\ -2 \end{pmatrix}, \qquad \mathbf{v} = \begin{pmatrix} 3 \\ 2 \\ -1 \end{pmatrix}, \qquad \mathbf{w} = \begin{pmatrix} 7 \\ 0 \\ 2 \end{pmatrix}.$$

1.  **a** · **u**.
2.  **a** · **v**.
3.  **b** · **w**.
4.  **c** · **v**.
5.  3**a** · **u**.
6.  $^-2\mathbf{c} \cdot \mathbf{w}$.
7.  $\frac{1}{2}\mathbf{b} \cdot 2\mathbf{w}$.
8.  **c** · (**v** + **w**).
9.  (**b** + **c**) · **v**.
10.  **b** · **v** + **c** · **w**.

11. Consider the following shopping list, with unit prices given for each item.

| | |
|---|---|
| 2 half-gallon cartons of sherbet | $.79 each |
| 3 loaves bread | $.39 each |
| 1 head lettuce | $.20 each |
| $\frac{1}{2}$ pound tomatoes | $.44/lb. |

    a. Write the quantity (row) vector for the shopping list above.
    b. Write the price (column) vector for the shopping list above.
    c. Use vector multiplication to find the total amount spent on groceries.

12. A young investor has the following portfolio of stocks.

| Number shares | Company | Last price |
|---|---|---|
| 25 | Johnson-Johnson | 96 1/2 |
| 100 | Safeway | 28 1/4 |
| 50 | Boeing | 67 3/4 |
| 150 | Castle and Cooke | 50 1/2 |
| 10 | RCA | 112 |

    a. Write the quantity (row) vector for the portfolio.
    b. Write the price (column) vector for the portfolio.
    c. Use vector multiplication to find the total value of the portfolio.

13. Last evening Art North had the following dinner:

    1 six-ounce steak
    1 baked potato
    $\frac{1}{2}$ cup peas
    3 rolls
    2 tablespoons strawberry jam
    1 tablespoon butter
    1 piece apple pie
    2 cups skim milk

These foods have the following calorie ratings:

| Food | Calorie rating |
|---|---|
| Steak | 110 /ounce |
| Potato, baked | 100 each |
| Peas | 68 /cup |
| Rolls | 115 each |
| Jam | 55 /tablespoon |
| Butter | 100 /tablespoon |
| Pie | 330 /slice |
| Milk | 80/cup |

a.  Write a quantity (row) vector for the dinner.
b.  Write a calorie (column) vector for the dinner.
c.  Use vector multiplication to find the number of calories in Art North's dinner.

## ——3-3  Matrices

With this discussion of matrices we are turning to the mathematics of very recent times. The English mathematician, Arthur Cayley, introduced the algebra of matrices in 1857.

A *matrix* (plural, *matrices*) is a rectangular array of numbers. Some examples are:

$$\begin{pmatrix} 1 \\ 2 \\ 3 \end{pmatrix}, \quad (1 \ ^{-}1 \ 2), \quad \begin{pmatrix} 1 & ^{-}1 \\ 3 & 2 \end{pmatrix}, \quad \begin{pmatrix} 1 & 2 \\ 3 & 4 \\ 5 & 6 \end{pmatrix},$$

$$\begin{pmatrix} ^{-}1 & 2 & 3 & ^{-}4 \\ ^{-}5 & 10 & ^{-}20 & ^{-}30 \end{pmatrix} \quad \text{and} \quad \begin{pmatrix} 1 & 3 & 5 & ^{-}7 \\ 8 & 1 & 6 & 15 \\ 21 & 1 & 1 & \frac{1}{2} \\ 7 & 0 & 0 & 1 \end{pmatrix}.$$

In particular, column and row vectors are special cases of matrices, but we often distinguish them by name. The numbers that make up a matrix are its *entries* or *elements*.

In the matrix

$$A = \begin{pmatrix} 1 & 12 & 3 \\ 4 & 2 & 0 \end{pmatrix},$$

there are 2 rows and 3 columns. The number 0 is in the second row and third column. The number 12 is in the first row, second column. That is,

$$A = \begin{pmatrix} 1 & 12 & 3 \\ 4 & 2 & 0 \end{pmatrix} \quad \begin{matrix} \leftarrow \text{row 1} \\ \leftarrow \text{row 2.} \end{matrix}$$
$$\begin{matrix} \uparrow & \uparrow & \uparrow \\ \text{col.} & \text{col.} & \text{col.} \\ 1 & 2 & 3 \end{matrix}$$

In general it is convenient to write a matrix $B$ as

$$B = \begin{pmatrix} b_{11} & b_{12} & b_{13} & \cdots & b_{1n} \\ b_{21} & b_{22} & b_{23} & \cdots & b_{2n} \\ b_{31} & b_{32} & b_{33} & \cdots & b_{3n} \\ \vdots & \vdots & \vdots & \vdots & \vdots \\ b_{m1} & b_{m2} & b_{m3} & \cdots & b_{mn} \end{pmatrix}.$$

Here $m$ is the number of rows in matrix $B$ and $n$ is the number of columns in matrix $B$. The symbol $b_{ij}$ is used to stand for a general entry of matrix $B$. In particular, if $i$ is any integer from 1 to $m$ and $j$ is any integer from 1 to $n$, then $b_{ij}$ stands for the entry in row $i$, column $j$ of the matrix $B$.

Hence, in our preceding numerical example, $A$, $a_{23} = 0$ since 0 is the element in the second row, third column. We say $A$ is a $2 \times 3$ matrix (read "two by three"). If the size of $A$ is important in a discussion, we write $A_{m \times n}$ to say that $A$ is an $m \times n$ matrix.

If we have an $m \times n$ matrix where $m = n$ we have a special matrix called a *square* matrix. $C$ is an example of a square $2 \times 2$ matrix where $m = n = 2$.

$$C = \begin{pmatrix} -\frac{1}{2} & 7 \\ 4 & 3 \end{pmatrix}.$$

Two matrices that have the same number of rows and the same number of columns are *equal* if the corresponding entries are equal. Thus

$$\begin{pmatrix} 1 & 2 \\ 3 & 4 \end{pmatrix} = \begin{pmatrix} 1 & 2 \\ 3 & 4 \end{pmatrix};$$

but

$$\begin{pmatrix} 1 & 2 \\ 3 & 4 \end{pmatrix} \neq \begin{pmatrix} 2 & 1 \\ 4 & 3 \end{pmatrix},$$

and

$$\begin{pmatrix} 1 & 3 & 5 \\ 2 & 4 & 6 \end{pmatrix} \neq \begin{pmatrix} 1 & 2 \\ 3 & 4 \\ 5 & 6 \end{pmatrix}.$$

Matrices, like vectors, provide an excellent way to organize data. The following matrix gives the numbers (in millions) of the people belonging to the purple, lavender, and pink "races" on the planets Mars, Venus, Neptune and Saturn in 1984.

|  | Mars | Venus | Neptune | Saturn |  |
|---|---|---|---|---|---|
| Purple | 17 | 13 | 11 | 3 |  |
| Lavender | 28 | 7 | 10 | 8 | $= P.$ |
| Pink | 3 | 12 | 7 | 71 |  |

Note that each column of the matrix $P$ is a three-component column vector showing the distribution of "races" on a particular planet. Also notice that each of the rows of $P$ is a four-component row vector giving the number of people of a certain color on each of the four planets.

Now suppose the matrix $P'$ gives the *change* in population in millions for each group on each planet between the years 1984 and 2000.

|  | Mars | Venus | Neptune | Saturn |  |
|---|---|---|---|---|---|
| Purple | 2 | $^-0.2$ | 2 | 0.15 |  |
| Lavender | $^-1$ | 1.5 | 3 | 0.25 | $= P'.$ |
| Pink | 0.5 | 3 | 1.5 | 11 |  |

Then the matrix formed by adding corresponding elements of the matrices $P$ and $P'$ gives the population for each group on each planet in 2000. We shall call the matrix formed in this way the *sum* of the matrices $P$ and $P'$.

$$P + P' = \begin{pmatrix} 17 & 13 & 11 & 3 \\ 28 & 7 & 10 & 8 \\ 3 & 12 & 7 & 71 \end{pmatrix} + \begin{pmatrix} 2 & ^-0.2 & 2 & 0.15 \\ ^-1 & 1.5 & 3 & 0.25 \\ 0.5 & 3 & 1.5 & 11 \end{pmatrix}$$

$$= \begin{pmatrix} 17 + 2 & 13 + ^-0.2 & 11 + 2 & 3 + 0.15 \\ 28 + ^-1 & 7 + 1.5 & 10 + 3 & 8 + 0.25 \\ 3 + 0.5 & 12 + 3 & 7 + 1.5 & 71 + 11 \end{pmatrix}$$

$$= \begin{pmatrix} 19 & 12.8 & 13 & 3.15 \\ 27 & 8.5 & 13 & 8.25 \\ 3.5 & 15 & 8.5 & 82 \end{pmatrix}.$$

More generally we shall agree that it is possible to add (or subtract) two matrices if and only if they have the same number of rows and the same number of columns. So, for example, we may perform each of the following matrix additions and subtractions:

$$\begin{pmatrix} 2 & 0 \\ 1 & 3 \end{pmatrix} + \begin{pmatrix} ^-1 & ^-1 \\ 0 & ^-1 \end{pmatrix} = \begin{pmatrix} 2 + ^-1 & 0 + ^-1 \\ 1 + 0 & 3 + ^-1 \end{pmatrix}$$

$$= \begin{pmatrix} 1 & ^-1 \\ 1 & 2 \end{pmatrix},$$

$$\begin{pmatrix} ^-8 & ^-7 \\ ^-6 & ^-5 \\ ^-4 & ^-3 \end{pmatrix} + \begin{pmatrix} 1 & 0 \\ 0 & 1 \\ ^-1 & 1 \end{pmatrix} + \begin{pmatrix} 2 & 8 \\ 4 & 10 \\ 6 & 12 \end{pmatrix} = \begin{pmatrix} ^-8 + 1 + 2 & ^-7 + 0 + 8 \\ ^-6 + 0 + 4 & ^-5 + 1 + 10 \\ ^-4 + ^-1 + 6 & ^-3 + 1 + 12 \end{pmatrix}$$

$$= \begin{pmatrix} ^-5 & 1 \\ ^-2 & 6 \\ 1 & 10 \end{pmatrix},$$

and

$$\begin{pmatrix} 1 & 2 \\ 3 & 5 \end{pmatrix} - \begin{pmatrix} ^-1 & 2 \\ ^-3 & 4 \end{pmatrix} = \begin{pmatrix} 1 - ^-1 & 2 - 2 \\ 3 - ^-3 & 5 - 4 \end{pmatrix}$$

$$= \begin{pmatrix} 2 & 0 \\ 6 & 1 \end{pmatrix}.$$

However, we may not perform the matrix additions and subtractions below:

$$\begin{pmatrix} 2 & 0 \\ 1 & 3 \end{pmatrix} + \begin{pmatrix} 2 & 3 \\ 1 & 1 \\ 3 & 2 \end{pmatrix},$$

$$\begin{pmatrix} {}^-2 & {}^-3 & {}^-4 & 0 \\ 1 & 2 & 3 & 0 \end{pmatrix} - \begin{pmatrix} 1 & 2 & 3 \\ 4 & 5 & 6 \end{pmatrix},$$

$$\begin{pmatrix} 2 & 4 \\ 6 & 8 \\ 10 & 12 \end{pmatrix} + \begin{pmatrix} 2 & 6 & 10 \\ 4 & 8 & 12 \end{pmatrix}.$$

In general we say

$$A \pm B = \begin{pmatrix} a_{11} & a_{12} \cdots & a_{1n} \\ a_{21} & a_{22} \cdots & a_{2n} \\ \vdots & \vdots & \vdots \\ a_{m1} & a_{m2} \cdots & a_{mn} \end{pmatrix} \pm \begin{pmatrix} b_{11} & b_{12} \cdots & b_{1n} \\ b_{21} & b_{22} \cdots & b_{2n} \\ \vdots & \vdots & \vdots \\ b_{m1} & b_{m2} \cdots & b_{mn} \end{pmatrix}$$

$$= \begin{pmatrix} a_{11} \pm b_{11} & a_{12} + b_{12} \cdots & a_{1n} \pm b_{1n} \\ a_{21} \pm b_{21} & a_{22} \pm b_{22} \cdots & a_{2n} \pm b_{2n} \\ \vdots & \vdots & \vdots \\ a_{m1} \pm b_{m1} & a_{m2} \pm b_{m2} \cdots & a_{mn} \pm b_{mn} \end{pmatrix}.$$

## EXERCISES

*Consider the matrices below:*

$$A = \begin{pmatrix} 2 \\ 2 \\ {}^-3 \end{pmatrix}, \qquad B = \begin{pmatrix} 3 & 2 \\ 1 & {}^-7 \end{pmatrix}, \qquad C = \begin{pmatrix} 0 & 4 & {}^-1 & 0 \\ 2 & 0 & {}^-4 & 5 \\ 6 & 0 & 1 & 3 \\ 4 & 2 & 1 & 3 \end{pmatrix},$$

$$D = \begin{pmatrix} 2 & 4 \\ 6 & 8 \\ 10 & 12 \end{pmatrix}, \qquad E = \begin{pmatrix} 1 & 0 & 1 \\ 0 & 2 & 5 \\ 0 & 0 & 3 \end{pmatrix}, \qquad F = \begin{pmatrix} 1 & 0 & 0 \\ 0 & 1 & 0 \end{pmatrix},$$

$$G = \begin{pmatrix} 9/3 & 2.00 \\ 10/10 & 49/{}^-7 \end{pmatrix}, \qquad H = (5 \quad 6 \quad 8).$$

*For each of the exercises below give the name of the matrix described. (There may be more than one matrix fitting the given description.)*

1. A $3 \times 2$ matrix.                    2. A square matrix.

3. Two equal matrices.                    4. A $3 \times 1$ matrix.

5. A $1 \times 3$ matrix.                    6. A $2 \times 3$ matrix.

*State whether or not the matrices in each of the following pairs are equal.*

7. $\begin{pmatrix} 5 & 4 \\ 3 & 2 \end{pmatrix}$,    $\begin{pmatrix} 5 & 4 \\ 3 & 2 \end{pmatrix}$.

8. $\begin{pmatrix} 2 & 3 \\ 4 & 5 \\ 6 & 7 \end{pmatrix}$,    $\begin{pmatrix} 2 & 4 & 6 \\ 3 & 5 & 7 \end{pmatrix}$.

9. $\begin{pmatrix} 1 & 0 & 0 \\ 0 & 1 & 1 \\ 0 & 0 & 0 \end{pmatrix}$,    $\begin{pmatrix} 1 & 0 & 0 \\ 1 & 1 & 0 \\ 0 & 0 & 0 \end{pmatrix}$.

10. $\begin{pmatrix} 1 & 0 & 0 & 0 \\ 0 & 1 & 0 & 0 \\ 0 & 0 & 1 & 0 \\ 0 & 0 & 0 & 1 \end{pmatrix}$,    $\begin{pmatrix} 1 & 0 & 0 \\ 0 & 1 & 0 \\ 0 & 0 & 1 \end{pmatrix}$.

11. If

$$\begin{pmatrix} x_{11} & x_{12} \\ x_{21} & x_{22} \end{pmatrix} = \begin{pmatrix} 3 & 2 \\ 5 & 0 \end{pmatrix},$$

find $x_{11}, x_{12}, x_{21}, x_{22}$.

12. If

$$\begin{pmatrix} y_{11} & 5 \\ 7 & y_{21} \end{pmatrix} = \begin{pmatrix} 7 & z_{12} \\ z_{21} & -3 \end{pmatrix},$$

find $y_{11}, y_{21}, z_{12}, z_{21}$.

*Perform the indicated operations in Exercises 13-22 using the matrices shown below. If the indicated operation is not possible, give reasons why.*

$$A = \begin{pmatrix} 5 & 4 \\ -3 & 0 \end{pmatrix}, \quad B = \begin{pmatrix} 8 & -3 \\ 7 & -1 \end{pmatrix}, \quad C = \begin{pmatrix} 0 & 1 \\ 1 & 0 \end{pmatrix},$$

$$D = \begin{pmatrix} 5 & 4 & 1 \\ 2 & 0 & 1 \end{pmatrix}, \quad E = \begin{pmatrix} 6 & -7 \\ 1 & 1 \\ 0 & 3 \end{pmatrix} \quad F = \begin{pmatrix} 7 & 5 & 1 \\ 0 & 4 & 2 \end{pmatrix},$$

$$G = \begin{pmatrix} 1 & 0 & 1 \\ 0 & 1 & -1 \\ 1 & 5 & 0 \end{pmatrix}, \quad H = \begin{pmatrix} 2 & 8 & 14 \\ 4 & 10 & 16 \\ 6 & 12 & 18 \end{pmatrix}.$$

13. $A + B$.
14. $B + A$.
15. $C - B$.
16. $B - C$.
17. $D + E$.
18. $D + F$.
19. $G + H$.
20. $A + (B + C)$.
21. $(A + B) + C$.
22. $A + (B - C)$.

23. If

$$\begin{pmatrix} 4 & 3 \\ -1 & 3 \end{pmatrix} + \begin{pmatrix} -3 & 7 \\ 10 & -5 \end{pmatrix} = \begin{pmatrix} z_{11} & z_{12} \\ z_{21} & z_{22} \end{pmatrix},$$

find $z_{11}, z_{12}, z_{21}, z_{22}$.

24. If

$$\begin{pmatrix} -2 & -6 \\ 4 & 8 \end{pmatrix} - \begin{pmatrix} 3 & -5 \\ -7 & 9 \end{pmatrix} = \begin{pmatrix} c_{11} & c_{12} \\ c_{21} & c_{22} \end{pmatrix},$$

find $c_{11}, c_{12}, c_{21}, c_{22}$.

25. If

$$\begin{pmatrix} x_{11} & 3 \\ -1 & x_{22} \end{pmatrix} + \begin{pmatrix} -3 & 7 \\ y_{21} & -5 \end{pmatrix} = \begin{pmatrix} 6 & z_{12} \\ 5 & 7 \end{pmatrix},$$

find $x_{11}, x_{22}, y_{21}, z_{12}$.

26. If

$$\begin{pmatrix} 5 & a_{12} \\ a_{21} & 7 \end{pmatrix} - \begin{pmatrix} 7 & 4 \\ 3 & -6 \end{pmatrix} = \begin{pmatrix} c_{11} & 5 \\ 2 & c_{22} \end{pmatrix},$$

find $a_{12}, a_{21}, c_{11}, c_{22}$.

27. The following table gives the nonwhite population for the mid-Atlantic States, New York, New Jersey, and Pennsylvania, for the years 1950 and 1960.

| State | Negro | | Indian | | Japanese | | Chinese | |
|---|---|---|---|---|---|---|---|---|
| | 1960 | 1950 | 1960 | 1950 | 1960 | 1950 | 1960 | 1950 |
| New Jersey | 514,875 | 318,565 | 1,699 | 621 | 3,514 | 1,784 | 3,813 | 1,818 |
| New York | 1,417,511 | 918,191 | 16,491 | 10,640 | 8,702 | 3,893 | 37,573 | 20,171 |
| Pennsylvania | 825,750 | 638,485 | 2,122 | 1,141 | 2,348 | 1,029 | 3,741 | 2,258 |

a. Write a matrix, $M_{1960}$, to represent the nonwhite populations of the states in the table in 1960.

b. Write a matrix, $M_{1950}$, to represent the nonwhite populations of the states in the table in 1950.

c. Use matrix subtraction to find the matrix $C$ which gives the change in nonwhite populations of the states in the table from 1950 to 1960.

28. The following table gives the egg production (in millions of eggs) for the western states, Alaska, California, Hawaii, Oregon and Washington in 1965 and 1966.

| State | 1965 | 1966 |
|---|---|---|
| Alaska | 9 | 10 |
| California | 7,406 | 7,664 |
| Hawaii | 190 | 188 |
| Oregon | 498 | 512 |
| Washington | 1,062 | 1,007 |

a. Write a matrix that shows the egg production in 1965 and 1966 for the five states in the table.

b. Write a vector that shows the total egg production for all of the western states in 1965 and 1966.

c. Write a vector that shows the total egg production in 1965 and 1966 for each of the five western states.

## ——3-4  Matrix Multiplication

Now let us return to the population matrix $P$ of the last section.

$$\begin{array}{c} \\ \text{Purple} \\ \text{Lavender} \\ \text{Pink} \end{array} \begin{array}{cccc} \text{Mars} & \text{Venus} & \text{Neptune} & \text{Saturn} \\ \begin{pmatrix} 17 & 13 & 11 & 3 \\ 28 & 7 & 10 & 8 \\ 3 & 12 & 7 & 71 \end{pmatrix} \end{array} = P.$$

Suppose we find that the population of each group on each planet doubled in the period between 1984 and 2084. The population matrix for 2084 is then:

$$\begin{array}{c} \\ \text{Purple} \\ \text{Lavender} \\ \text{Pink} \end{array} \begin{array}{cccc} \text{Mars} & \text{Venus} & \text{Neptune} & \text{Saturn} \\ \begin{pmatrix} 17 \cdot 2 & 13 \cdot 2 & 11 \cdot 2 & 3 \cdot 2 \\ 28 \cdot 2 & 7 \cdot 2 & 10 \cdot 2 & 8 \cdot 2 \\ 3 \cdot 2 & 12 \cdot 2 & 7 \cdot 2 & 71 \cdot 2 \end{pmatrix} \end{array} = \begin{pmatrix} 34 & 26 & 22 & 6 \\ 56 & 14 & 20 & 16 \\ 6 & 24 & 14 & 142 \end{pmatrix}.$$

Every entry in the matrix $P$ would be multiplied by 2.

In general, we multiply a matrix $A$ by a real number $c$ by multiplying every element in $A$ by $c$. So,

$$cA = c \begin{pmatrix} a_{11} & a_{12} & \cdots & a_{1n} \\ a_{21} & a_{22} & \cdots & a_{2n} \\ \vdots & \vdots & \vdots & \vdots \\ a_{m1} & a_{m2} & \cdots & a_{mn} \end{pmatrix} = \begin{pmatrix} ca_{11} & ca_{12} & \cdots & ca_{1n} \\ ca_{21} & ca_{22} & \cdots & ca_{2n} \\ \vdots & \vdots & \vdots & \vdots \\ ca_{m1} & ca_{m2} & \cdots & ca_{mn} \end{pmatrix}.$$

Some other examples of multiplying a matrix by a real number follow.

$$2\begin{pmatrix} 1 & 0 \\ 0 & 1 \end{pmatrix} = \begin{pmatrix} 2 \cdot 1 & 2 \cdot 0 \\ 2 \cdot 0 & 2 \cdot 1 \end{pmatrix} = \begin{pmatrix} 2 & 0 \\ 0 & 2 \end{pmatrix};$$

$$^-\tfrac{1}{2}\begin{pmatrix} 6.2 & 8 \\ ^-10 & ^-12 \\ 14 & 16 \end{pmatrix} = \begin{pmatrix} ^-\tfrac{1}{2} \cdot & 6.2 & ^-\tfrac{1}{2} \cdot & 8 \\ ^-\tfrac{1}{2} \cdot & ^-10 & ^-\tfrac{1}{2} \cdot & ^-12 \\ ^-\tfrac{1}{2} \cdot & 14 & ^-\tfrac{1}{2} \cdot & 16 \end{pmatrix} = \begin{pmatrix} ^-3.1 & ^-4 \\ 5 & 6 \\ ^-7 & ^-8 \end{pmatrix};$$

$$0\begin{pmatrix} ^-16 & 0.5 \\ 0.5 & ^-16 \end{pmatrix} = \begin{pmatrix} 0 \cdot ^-16 & 0 \cdot & 0.5 \\ 0 \cdot & 0.5 & 0 \cdot ^-16 \end{pmatrix} = \begin{pmatrix} 0 & 0 \\ 0 & 0 \end{pmatrix}.$$

Suppose in our example the purple people on each planet doubled in population, the lavender people quadrupled in population, and the pink people tripled in population between 1984 and 2084. To find the new total population on Mars we would make the following calculation:

Mars:    $2 \cdot 17 + 4 \cdot 28 + 3 \cdot 3 = 34 + 112 + 9 = 155.$

Similarly, to find the total population on each of the other planets we would perform the next calculations:

$$
\begin{array}{lll}
\text{Venus:} & 2 \cdot 13 + 4 \cdot 7 \ + 3 \cdot 12 = 26 + 28 + \ \ 36 = \ \ 90; \\
\text{Neptune:} & 2 \cdot 11 + 4 \cdot 10 + 3 \cdot 7 \ = 22 + 40 + \ \ 21 = \ \ 83; \\
\text{Saturn:} & 2 \cdot 3 \ \ + 4 \cdot 8 \ \ + 3 \cdot 71 = \ \ 6 + 32 + 213 = 251;
\end{array}
$$

The preceding calculations are suggested by the product of a row vector and a matrix having the form

$$
\begin{aligned}
(2 \quad 4 \quad 3) &\begin{pmatrix} 17 & 13 & 11 & 3 \\ 28 & 7 & 10 & 8 \\ 3 & 12 & 7 & 71 \end{pmatrix} \\
&= (2 \cdot 17 + 4 \cdot 28 + 3 \cdot 3, \quad 2 \cdot 13 + 4 \cdot 7 + 3 \cdot 12, \\
&\qquad\qquad\qquad\qquad\quad 2 \cdot 11 + 4 \cdot 10 + 3 \cdot 7, \quad 2 \cdot 3 + 4 \cdot 8 + 3 \cdot 71) \\
&= (155 \quad 90 \quad 83 \quad 251).
\end{aligned}
$$

We see that the new total populations on Mars, Venus, Neptune, and Saturn are 155 million, 90 million, 83 million, and 251 million respectively. Each of these figures is the result of multiplying the row vector by one of the columns in the matrix as shown by the arrows.

Suppose that by 2084 the population on Mars doubled, the population on Venus increased by a factor of 1.5, the population of Neptune tripled, and the population of Saturn doubled. Suppose also that these increases were proportional among the three "races" on each planet. Then the following calculations would give the total number of purple people, the total number of lavender people and the total number of pink people on all of the four planets combined.

$$
\begin{array}{lll}
\text{Purple:} & 2 \cdot 17 + 1.5 \cdot 13 + 3 \cdot 11 + 2 \cdot 3 \ \ = \ \ 92.5; \\
\text{Lavender:} & 2 \cdot 28 + 1.5 \cdot 7 \ + 3 \cdot 10 + 2 \cdot 8 \ = 112.5; \\
\text{Pink:} & 2 \cdot 3 \ \ + 1.5 \cdot 12 + 3 \cdot 7 \ + 2 \cdot 71 = 187.0.
\end{array}
$$

These calculations are suggested by the product of the matrix and column vector that follow.

$$
\begin{pmatrix} 17 & 13 & 11 & 3 \\ 28 & 7 & 10 & 8 \\ 3 & 12 & 7 & 71 \end{pmatrix} \begin{pmatrix} 2 \\ 1.5 \\ 3 \\ 2 \end{pmatrix} =
$$

$$
\begin{pmatrix} 17 \cdot 2 + 13 \cdot 1.5 + 11 \cdot 3 + \ \ 3 \cdot 2 \\ 28 \cdot 2 + \ \ 7 \cdot 1.5 + 10 \cdot 3 + \ \ 8 \cdot 2 \\ 3 \cdot 2 + 12 \cdot 1.5 + \ \ 7 \cdot 3 + 71 \cdot 2 \end{pmatrix} = \begin{pmatrix} 92.5 \\ 112.5 \\ 187.0 \end{pmatrix}.
$$

These calculations show that there are 92.5 million purple people on all four planets, 112.5 million lavender people, and 187.0 million pink people. These numbers are the result of multiplying the column vector by each row of the matrix, as shown by the arrows.

With the preceding two models in mind we shall adopt, in general, the following definitions for the multiplication of an $m$-component row vector $\mathbf{x}$ by an $m \times n$ matrix $A$ and for the multiplication of an $m \times n$ matrix $A$ by an $n$-component column vector $\mathbf{y}$.

$$\mathbf{x} \cdot A = (x_1 \quad x_2 \cdots x_m) \begin{pmatrix} a_{11} & a_{12} \cdots a_{1n} \\ a_{21} & a_{22} \cdots a_{2n} \\ \vdots & \vdots \quad \vdots \quad \vdots \\ a_{m1} & a_{m2} \cdots a_{mn} \end{pmatrix}$$

$$= (x_1 a_{11} + x_2 a_{21} + \cdots + x_m a_{m1}, \quad x_1 a_{12} + x_2 a_{22} + \cdots + x_m a_{m2},$$

$$\ldots, \quad x_1 a_{1n} + x_2 a_{2n} + \cdots + x_m a_{mn});$$

$$A \cdot \mathbf{y} = \begin{pmatrix} a_{11} & a_{12} \cdots a_{1n} \\ a_{21} & a_{22} \cdots a_{2n} \\ \vdots & \vdots \quad \vdots \quad \vdots \\ a_{m1} & a_{m2} \cdots a_{mn} \end{pmatrix} \begin{pmatrix} y_1 \\ y_2 \\ \vdots \\ y_n \end{pmatrix}$$

$$= \begin{pmatrix} a_{11} y_1 + a_{12} y_2 + \cdots + a_{1n} y_n \\ a_{21} y_1 + a_{22} y_2 + \cdots + a_{2n} y_n \\ \vdots \quad \vdots \quad \vdots \quad \vdots \\ a_{m1} y_1 + a_{m2} y_2 + \cdots + a_{mn} y_n \end{pmatrix}.$$

Note that in order to multiply a row vector by a matrix the number of components of the vector must equal the number of rows of the matrix. Similarly, to multiply a matrix by a column vector, the number of columns of the matrix must equal the number of components of the vector. Thus, the following multiplications are not defined.

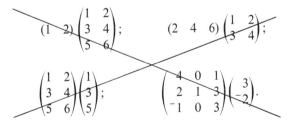

It is also important to note that the product of a row vector and a matrix is a row vector and the product of a matrix and a column vector is a column vector. Some numerical examples of the multiplication of vectors and matrices are:

$$(1 \quad 2 \quad 3)\begin{pmatrix} 1 & 0 & 1 \\ 3 & 1 & 1 \\ 0 & 0 & 1 \end{pmatrix} = (1 \cdot 1 + 2 \cdot 3 + 3 \cdot 0, \quad 1 \cdot 0 + 2 \cdot 1 + 3 \cdot 0,$$
$$1 \cdot 1 + 2 \cdot 1 + 3 \cdot 1)$$

$$= (7 \quad 2 \quad 6);$$

$$\begin{pmatrix} 1 & 2 & 3 \\ 4 & 5 & 6 \end{pmatrix}\begin{pmatrix} 1 \\ 0 \\ -1 \end{pmatrix} = \begin{pmatrix} 1 \cdot 1 + 2 \cdot 0 + 3 \cdot {}^-1 \\ 4 \cdot 1 + 5 \cdot 0 + 6 \cdot {}^-1 \end{pmatrix} = \begin{pmatrix} {}^-2 \\ {}^-2 \end{pmatrix}.$$

Under certain conditions it is possible to multiply two matrices $A$ and $B$ together, where neither of the matrices is a vector, to form a product matrix $C$. Each entry in the new matrix is the product of one of the rows of $A$ by one of the columns of $B$. We carry out the step-by-step computation of such a product below. The squares in the product matrix $C$ indicate entries to be filled in.

$$A \cdot B = \begin{pmatrix} 1 & 2 & 3 \\ 4 & 5 & 6 \end{pmatrix}\begin{pmatrix} {}^-1 & 0 \\ 4 & 3 \\ 1 & {}^-2 \end{pmatrix} = \begin{pmatrix} c_{11} & \square \\ \square & \square \end{pmatrix} = C,$$

$$A \cdot B = \begin{pmatrix} 1 & 2 & 3 \\ 4 & 5 & 6 \end{pmatrix}\begin{pmatrix} {}^-1 & 0 \\ 4 & 3 \\ 1 & {}^-2 \end{pmatrix} = \begin{pmatrix} c_{11} & c_{12} \\ \square & \square \end{pmatrix} = C,$$

$$A \cdot B = \begin{pmatrix} 1 & 2 & 3 \\ 4 & 5 & 6 \end{pmatrix}\begin{pmatrix} {}^-1 & 0 \\ 4 & 3 \\ 1 & {}^-2 \end{pmatrix} = \begin{pmatrix} c_{11} & c_{12} \\ c_{21} & \end{pmatrix} = C,$$

$$A \cdot B = \begin{pmatrix} 1 & 2 & 3 \\ 4 & 5 & 6 \end{pmatrix}\begin{pmatrix} {}^-1 & 0 \\ 4 & 3 \\ 1 & {}^-2 \end{pmatrix} = \begin{pmatrix} c_{11} & c_{12} \\ c_{21} & c_{22} \end{pmatrix} = C.$$

Therefore,

$$A \cdot B =$$

$$\begin{pmatrix} 1 & 2 & 3 \\ 4 & 5 & 6 \end{pmatrix} \cdot \begin{pmatrix} {}^-1 & 0 \\ 4 & 3 \\ 1 & {}^-2 \end{pmatrix} = \begin{pmatrix} 1 \cdot {}^-1 + 2 \cdot 4 + 3 \cdot 1 & 1 \cdot 0 + 2 \cdot 3 + 3 \cdot {}^-2 \\ 4 \cdot {}^-1 + 5 \cdot 4 + 6 \cdot 1 & 4 \cdot 0 + 5 \cdot 3 + 6 \cdot {}^-2 \end{pmatrix}$$

$$= \begin{pmatrix} 10 & 0 \\ 22 & 3 \end{pmatrix}.$$

Note that to get the element in the *first row* and *first column* of the resulting matrix, we multiply the *first row* of the first matrix by the *first column* of the second matrix. Similarly, to obtain the element in the *first row, second column* of the resulting matrix we multiply the *first row* of the first matrix by the *second column* of the second matrix.

In general, if $A$ is an $m \times r$ matrix and $B$ is an $r \times n$ matrix, the product matrix $C = A \cdot B$ is an $m \times n$ matrix whose components are

$$c_{ij} = (a_{i1} \quad a_{i2} \cdots a_{ik}) \begin{pmatrix} b_{1j} \\ b_{2j} \\ \vdots \\ b_{kj} \end{pmatrix}$$

$$= a_{i1} b_{1j} + a_{i2} b_{2j} + \cdots + a_{ik} b_{kj}.$$

Taking $i = 1$ and $j = 1$, we compute the entry $c_{ij} = c_{11}$ in the above example as follows:

$$c_{11} = a_{11} b_{11} + a_{12} b_{21} + a_{13} b_{31}.$$

This is the result of multiplying the first row of $A$ by the first column of $B$:

$$\begin{matrix} a_{11} & a_{12} & a_{13} \\ \downarrow & \downarrow & \downarrow \\ (1 & 2 & 3) \end{matrix} \begin{pmatrix} -1 \\ 4 \\ 1 \end{pmatrix} \begin{matrix} \leftarrow b_{11} \\ \leftarrow b_{21} \\ \leftarrow b_{31} \end{matrix}$$

So,

$$c_{11} = 1 \cdot {}^-1 + 2 \cdot 4 + 3 \cdot 1 = 10.$$

Incidentally, the multiplication of two vectors or of a vector and a matrix can now be interpreted as simply a special case of matrix multiplication.

It is important to notice that the method of matrix multiplication requires that the first of the two matrices being multiplied must have the same number of columns as the second matrix has rows. If this is not so, it is impossible to multiply. Consider, for instance, the two matrices

$$C = \begin{pmatrix} 1 & 2 \\ 3 & 4 \end{pmatrix} \quad \text{and} \quad D = \begin{pmatrix} 1 & 0 \\ 0 & 1 \\ 2 & 4 \end{pmatrix}.$$

To multiply $C$ and $D$ we would first multiply the first row of $C$ by the first column of $D$.

$$C \cdot D = \begin{pmatrix} 1 & 2 \\ 3 & 4 \end{pmatrix} \begin{pmatrix} 1 & 0 \\ 0 & 1 \\ 2 & 4 \end{pmatrix} = \begin{pmatrix} \square & \\ & \end{pmatrix}.$$

But upon attempting to multiply we run into a problem.

$$(1 \quad 2)\begin{pmatrix}1\\0\\2\end{pmatrix} = 1 \cdot 1 + 2 \cdot 0 + ? \cdot 2.$$

With this idea in mind consider the following matrices. It is not possible to obtain their products.

$$\begin{pmatrix}2 & 0\\0 & 1\end{pmatrix}\cancel{\begin{pmatrix}1 & 22 & 3\\4 & 5 & 6\\8 & 10 & 12\end{pmatrix}}, \qquad \cancel{\begin{pmatrix}1 & 2 & 3\\4 & 5 & 6\end{pmatrix}\begin{pmatrix}1 & 2 & 3\\4 & 5 & 6\end{pmatrix}}, \qquad \cancel{\begin{pmatrix}^-1 & 2 & 0\\3 & 5 & 7\end{pmatrix}\begin{pmatrix}1 & 0\\0 & 1\end{pmatrix}}.$$

However, the following are examples of possible matrix multiplications.

$$\begin{pmatrix}1 & 2\\3 & 0\end{pmatrix}\begin{pmatrix}1 & 0 & 1\\^-1 & 2 & 3\end{pmatrix} = \begin{pmatrix}1\cdot1+2\cdot{}^-1 & 1\cdot0+2\cdot2 & 1\cdot1+2\cdot3\\3\cdot1+0\cdot{}^-1 & 3\cdot0+0\cdot2 & 3\cdot1+0\cdot3\end{pmatrix}$$

$$= \begin{pmatrix}^-1 & 4 & 7\\3 & 0 & 3\end{pmatrix},$$

and

$$\begin{pmatrix}2 & 0 & 2\\1 & ^-1 & 3\\0 & 1 & 0\end{pmatrix}\begin{pmatrix}1 & 2\\3 & 4\\5 & 6\end{pmatrix} = \begin{pmatrix}2\cdot1+ & 0\cdot3+2\cdot5 & 2\cdot2+ & 0\cdot4+2\cdot6\\1\cdot1+ & ^-1\cdot3+3\cdot5 & 1\cdot2+ & ^-1\cdot4+3\cdot6\\0\cdot1+ & 1\cdot3+0\cdot5 & 0\cdot2+ & 1\cdot4+0\cdot6\end{pmatrix}$$

$$= \begin{pmatrix}12 & 16\\13 & 16\\3 & 4\end{pmatrix}.$$

Sociologists have used matrices having only entries of 0 and 1 to analyze the structure of dominance relations in groups of humans or animals We shall use the notation $T_1$ d $T_2$ to means $T_1$ "dominates" $T_2$. For example, if $T_1$ and $T_2$ are teams $T_1$ d $T_2$ means $T_1$ beats $T_2$; if $T_1$ and $T_2$ are chickens, $T_1$ d $T_2$ means $T_1$ pecks $T_2$.

We shall call a relation d a *dominance relation* if it satisfies two conditions:

(1)  $T$ d $T$ is false; in other words, an individual cannot dominate himself.

(2)  For every pair of individuals $T_1$ and $T_2$ either $T_1$ d $T_2$ or $T_2$ d $T_1$, but not both. That is, for each pair one and only one individual dominates.

Notice that the transitive property does not hold for dominance. That is, if $T_1$ d $T_2$ and $T_2$ d $T_3$ it is not necessarily true that $T_1$ d $T_3$. For instance, in a series of tennis matches if individual $T_1$ beats individual $T_2$, and individual $T_2$ beats individual $T_3$, it is not necessarily true that $T_1$ beats $T_3$.

Now consider the two dominance matrices below,

$$
\begin{array}{c}
 & \begin{array}{ccc} T_1 & T_2 & T_3 \end{array} \\
\begin{array}{c} T_1 \\ T_2 \\ T_3 \end{array} & \begin{pmatrix} 0 & 0 & 1 \\ 1 & 0 & 0 \\ 0 & 1 & 0 \end{pmatrix}
\end{array}
\qquad
\begin{array}{c}
 & \begin{array}{ccc} T_1 & T_2 & T_3 \end{array} \\
\begin{array}{c} T_1 \\ T_2 \\ T_3 \end{array} & \begin{pmatrix} 0 & 1 & 0 \\ 0 & 0 & 1 \\ 1 & 0 & 0 \end{pmatrix}
\end{array}.
$$

$$\text{(a)} \qquad\qquad\qquad \text{(b)}$$

An entry of 1 in the row of individual $T_i$ and the column of individual $T_j$ means that $T_i$ dominates $T_j$. In Example (a), for instance, $T_1$ d $T_3$ since there is a 1 in the row of individual $T_1$ and the column of individual $T_3$:

$$
\begin{array}{c}
 & \begin{array}{ccc} T_1 & T_2 & T_3 \end{array} \\
\begin{array}{c} T_1 \\ T_2 \\ T_3 \end{array} & \begin{pmatrix} 0 & 0 & ① \\ 1 & 0 & 0 \\ 0 & 1 & 0 \end{pmatrix}.
\end{array}
$$

Note that each entry on the *main diagonal* (drawn from upper left to lower right) of each dominance matrix is 0. For instance in example (b) we have:

$$
\begin{array}{c}
 & \begin{array}{ccc} T_1 & T_2 & T_3 \end{array} \\
\begin{array}{c} T_1 \\ T_2 \\ T_3 \end{array} & \begin{pmatrix} 0 & 1 & 0 \\ 0 & 0 & 1 \\ 1 & 0 & 0 \end{pmatrix}.
\end{array}
$$

This results from requirement (1) that an individual may not dominate himself.

Notice that the entries that are in opposing locations with reference to the main diagonal are different. That is, if an entry above the main diagonal is 0, the entry in the opposing location below the diagonal is 1. We can see this in example (b), where pairs of entries in opposing locations are indicated.

$$
\begin{array}{c}
 & \begin{array}{ccc} T_1 & T_2 & T_3 \end{array} \\
\begin{array}{c} T_1 \\ T_2 \\ T_3 \end{array} & \begin{array}{ccc} 0 & ① & ⓪ \\ ⓪ & 0 & ① \\ ① & ⓪ & 0 \end{array}
\end{array}
$$

The 0 entry in the second row, first column means $T_2$ does not dominate $T_1$.

The 1 entered in the opposing position above the main diagonal in the first row, second column means that $T_1$ dominates $T_2$. These different entries result from requirement (2) that in a pair of individuals one and only one of the pair may dominate the other.

Any dominance matrix, say $D$, is always square, so we can raise $D$ to powers. Let us consider the dominance matrix

$$D = \begin{array}{c} \\ T_1 \\ T_2 \\ T_3 \end{array} \begin{array}{ccc} T_1 & T_2 & T_3 \\ \begin{pmatrix} 0 & 0 & 1 \\ 1 & 0 & 0 \\ 0 & 1 & 0 \end{pmatrix} \end{array}.$$

For $D^2$ we would have:

$$D^2 = D \cdot D = \begin{pmatrix} 0 & 0 & 1 \\ 1 & 0 & 0 \\ 0 & 1 & 0 \end{pmatrix} \begin{pmatrix} 0 & 0 & 1 \\ 1 & 0 & 0 \\ 0 & 1 & 0 \end{pmatrix} = \begin{pmatrix} 0 & 1 & 0 \\ 0 & 0 & 1 \\ 1 & 0 & 0 \end{pmatrix}.$$

To find if $D^2$ has any significance, examine an entry of $D^2$. Arbitrarily let $D^2 = T$ and let us examine the entry $t_{12}$ in the first row, second column of $D^2$.

$$\begin{array}{c} \\ T_1 \\ T_2 \\ T_3 \end{array} \begin{array}{ccc} T_1 & T_2 & T_3 \\ \begin{pmatrix} 0 & \boxed{1} & 0 \\ 0 & 0 & 1 \\ 1 & 0 & 0 \end{pmatrix} \end{array} = D^2 = T.$$

We obtained $t_{12}$ by multiplying the *first* row of $D$ by the *second* column of $D$:

$$\begin{pmatrix} 0 & 0 & 1 \\ 1 & 0 & 0 \\ 0 & 1 & 0 \end{pmatrix} \begin{pmatrix} 0 & 0 & 1 \\ 1 & 0 & 0 \\ 0 & 1 & 0 \end{pmatrix} = \begin{pmatrix} — & 0 \cdot 0 + 0 \cdot 0 + 1 \cdot 1 & — \\ — & — & — \\ — & — & — \end{pmatrix}$$

$$= \begin{pmatrix} — & 1 & — \\ — & — & — \\ — & — & — \end{pmatrix}.$$

That is,

$$t_{12} = d_{11} d_{12} + d_{12} d_{22} + d_{13} d_{32}$$
$$= 0 \cdot 0 \quad + 0 \cdot 0 \quad + 1 \cdot 1$$
$$= 1.$$

Note that a product $d_{ik}d_{kj}$ affects $t_{ij}$ only if it is nonzero. This only occurs if both factors are nonzero; in such a case they are both 1. If $d_{ik} = 1$, then $T_i$ d $T_k$ and if $d_{kj} = 1$, then $T_k$ d $T_j$. This means $T_i$ d $T_k$ d $T_j$. This sort of dominance is called a *two-stage dominance* to distinguish it from a *one-stage dominance* such as $T_i$ d $T_k$.

So from this example we see that the entry $t_{ij}$ in the matrix $T = D^2$ gives the number of two-stage dominances that individual $T_i$ has over $T_j$.

Examining our matrix

$$D^2 = \begin{pmatrix} 0 & 1 & 0 \\ 0 & 0 & 1 \\ 1 & 0 & 0 \end{pmatrix},$$

we see that

$T_1$ has one two-stage dominance over $T_2$,
$T_2$ has one two-stage dominance over $T_3$, and
$T_3$ has one two-stage dominance over $T_1$.

In other words, $T_1$ dominates $T_3$ and $T_3$, in turn, dominates $T_2$ ($T_1$ d $T_3$ d $T_2$); $T_2$ dominates $T_1$ which dominates $T_3$ ($T_2$ d $T_1$ d $T_3$); and $T_3$ dominates $T_2$ which dominates $T_1$ ($T_3$ d $T_2$ d $T_1$). Be certain to note that it is not true that $T_3$ d $T_1$ even though $T_3$ d $T_2$ d $T_1$.

## EXERCISES

*Compute the product in Exercises 1-10, using the matrices below. If the indicated operation is not possible, give reasons.*

$$A = \begin{pmatrix} 2 \\ -1 \\ 3 \end{pmatrix}, \qquad B = (5 \quad -3), \qquad C = \begin{pmatrix} 2 & 3 \\ -1 & 1 \end{pmatrix},$$

$$D = \begin{pmatrix} 5 & 4 & 3 \\ 0 & 1 & 2 \\ 1 & -2 & 1 \end{pmatrix}, \quad E = \begin{pmatrix} 2 & 1 \\ 3 & -2 \\ 6 & 0 \end{pmatrix}, \quad F = \begin{pmatrix} 5 & 0 & 4 \\ 3 & -1 & 2 \end{pmatrix},$$

$$G = \begin{pmatrix} 2 & 0 & 1 \\ 0 & 2 & 1 \\ -1 & 3 & 2 \end{pmatrix}.$$

1. $3A$.          2. $^-4C$.     3. $2D$.     4. $D \cdot A$.     5. $B \cdot C$.
6. $E \cdot F$.        7. $F \cdot E$.     8. $D \cdot G$.     9. $C \cdot F$.     10. $B \cdot F$.
11. If $A$ is a $3 \times 2$ matrix and $B$ is a $2 \times 5$ matrix is it possible to find $A \cdot B$? If so, what are the dimensions of $A \cdot B$?
12. If $X$ is a $5 \times 1$ matrix and $Y$ is a $5 \times 1$ matrix, is it possible to find $X \cdot Y$? If so, what are the dimensions of $X \cdot Y$?

13. The following matrix gives the vitamin contents of a breakfast in conveniently chosen units.

Vitamin

|  | A | $B_1$ | $B_2$ | C |
|---|---|---|---|---|
| Orange juice | 500 | 0.2 | 0 | 129 |
| Cantaloupe | 12,000 | 0 | 0 | 65 |
| Oatmeal | 0 | 0.2 | 0 | 0 |
| Milk | 1,560 | 0.32 | 1.7 | 6 |
| Biscuit | 0 | 0 | 0 | 0 |
| Butter | 460 | 0 | 0 | 0 |

If we have 1 unit of orange juice, $\frac{1}{2}$ unit of cantaloupe, 1 unit of oatmeal $\frac{1}{4}$ unit milk, 2 units of biscuits, and 2 units of butter, find the matrix that tells how much of each type of vitamin we have consumed.

14. The following table shows the prices of the stocks of the four companies shown for the months of January, February, and March.

| *Company* | *Price* | | |
|---|---|---|---|
|  | January | February | March |
| Hamburger Haven | 12 | 8 1/4 | 11 |
| Dunkin' Donuts | 16 1/2 | 20 | 23 3/8 |
| Acme Aircraft | 37 1/2 | 36 | 41 |
| Household Finance | 17 3/4 | 19 | 18 1/2 |

   a. Write a matrix P summarizing the information in the first column.

   b. Suppose the investor bought each month, 100 shares of Hamburger Haven, 50 shares of Dunkin' Donuts, 150 shares of Acme Aircraft, and 50 shares of Household Finance. Write a matrix Q to represent these facts.

   c. Use matrix multiplication to find a matrix showing the total amount the investor spent on stock each month.

   d. Suppose the investor bought 120 shares of each stock in January, 100 shares of each stock in February, and 200 shares of each stock in March. Write a matrix, R, to represent these facts.

   e. Use matrix multiplication to find a matrix showing the total amount the investor spent on each stock for the three-month period.

15. Write the dominance matrix for each of the given situations:

   a. Team A beats team B.
      Team B beats team C.
      Team C beats team A.

   b. Team A beats teams B and C.
      Team B beats team C.

16. a and b.  Find the two stage dominances that exist for each of the domin-
    ance matrices in 15 a and b.

*In dominance matrix theory there is a theorem that says:*

*Let d be a dominance relation on a set of n individuals, $T_1, T_2, \ldots, T_n$. Then
there exists at least one individual who can dominate in either one or two stages
every other individual in the group. There also exists at least one individual
who is dominated in either one or two stages by every other individual in the
group.*

*Using matrix language this theorem means that if $C = D + D^2$, then
there is at least one row and one column of C having all but the diagonal entry
nonzero.*

17. a and b.  Verify the preceding theorem for each of the dominance
    matrices in 15 a and b.  For each matrix name the individual(s) that
    dominates every other individual in the group.

*In a dominance situation the power of an individual is defined as the total
of one-stage and two-stage dominances that he can exert. The total of one-stage
dominances exerted by $T_i$ is the sum of the entries in the ith row of matrix D,
and the total number of two-stage dominances exerted by $T_i$ is the sum of the
entries in the ith row of the matrix, $D^2$. So the power of $T_i$ may be expressed as*

  *power $T_i$ = sum of entries in the ith row of matrix $C = D + D^2$.*

18. For the following dominance matrix,

$$D = \begin{pmatrix} 0 & 1 & 0 & 1 \\ 0 & 0 & 0 & 0 \\ 1 & 1 & 0 & 0 \\ 0 & 1 & 1 & 0 \end{pmatrix},$$

    determine the power of each of the individuals by computing the
    matrix $C = D + D^2$.

19. The following are the results of a certain football season.

        UC beats Stanford,
        USC beats Stanford, UC, UCLA,
        UCLA beats UC, Stanford.

    a. Write the dominance matrix corresponding to the results.
    b. Determine the power of each of the teams and rank them using the
       results obtained.

20. If $D$ is any dominance matrix give an interpretation of the entries in the
    matrix, $D^3$.  Also give an interpretation of the row and column sums
    of $D^3$ as well as of the entries and row and column sums of the matrix
    $S = D + D^2 + D^3$.

## ——3-5  Properties of Matrix Addition and Multiplication

In this section we will discuss the properties that matrices have under the operations of addition and multiplication. Some of these properties have come up already; others are not as self-evident. A careful examination of the properties to follow will make possible many shortcuts in working with matrices.

First, we will consider matrix addition. Does it matter in what order we add two matrices? To answer this question let us examine an example. Take, for instance, the two matrices

$$A = \begin{pmatrix} 2 & 1 \\ 0 & 3 \end{pmatrix} \quad \text{and} \quad B = \begin{pmatrix} -1 & 0 \\ -3 & 1 \end{pmatrix}.$$

Does $A + B = B + A$? Adding, we find

$$A + B = \begin{pmatrix} 2 & 1 \\ 0 & 3 \end{pmatrix} + \begin{pmatrix} -1 & 0 \\ -3 & 1 \end{pmatrix} = \begin{pmatrix} 1 & 1 \\ -3 & 4 \end{pmatrix},$$

and

$$B + A = \begin{pmatrix} -1 & 0 \\ -3 & 1 \end{pmatrix} + \begin{pmatrix} 2 & 1 \\ 0 & 3 \end{pmatrix} = \begin{pmatrix} 1 & 1 \\ -3 & 4 \end{pmatrix}.$$

Yes! $A + B = B + A$ *in our example.*

However, we cannot make a generalization from one example. Let us add two general matrices $C$ and $D$ and see whether $C + D = D + C$. Remember that we have agreed that two matrices must have the same dimensions for addition to be permissible.

Let

$$C = \begin{pmatrix} c_{11} & c_{12} & \cdots & c_{1n} \\ c_{21} & c_{22} & \cdots & c_{2n} \\ c_{31} & c_{32} & \cdots & c_{3n} \\ \vdots & \vdots & \vdots & \vdots \\ c_{m1} & c_{m2} & \cdots & c_{mn} \end{pmatrix},$$

and

$$D = \begin{pmatrix} d_{11} & d_{12} & \cdots & d_{1n} \\ d_{21} & d_{22} & \cdots & d_{2n} \\ d_{31} & d_{32} & \cdots & d_{3n} \\ \vdots & \vdots & \vdots & \vdots \\ d_{m1} & d_{m2} & \cdots & d_{mn} \end{pmatrix}.$$

Then we have

$$C + D = \begin{pmatrix} c_{11} + d_{11} & c_{12} + d_{12} & \cdots & c_{1n} + d_{1n} \\ c_{21} + d_{21} & c_{22} + d_{22} & \cdots & c_{2n} + d_{2n} \\ c_{31} + d_{31} & c_{32} + d_{32} & \cdots & c_{3n} + d_{3n} \\ \vdots & \vdots & \vdots & \vdots \\ c_{m1} + d_{m1} & c_{m2} + d_{m2} & \cdots & c_{mn} + d_{mn} \end{pmatrix}.$$

We already know that addition of any two real numbers is commutative.

Therefore, since all of the entries of $C$ and $D$ are real numbers, we have

$$C + D = \begin{pmatrix} d_{11} + c_{11} & d_{12} + c_{12} & \cdots & d_{1n} + c_{1n} \\ d_{21} + c_{21} & d_{22} + c_{22} & \cdots & d_{2n} + c_{2n} \\ d_{31} + c_{31} & d_{32} + c_{32} & \cdots & d_{3n} + c_{3n} \\ \vdots & \vdots & \vdots & \vdots \\ d_{m1} + c_{m1} & d_{m2} + c_{m2} & \cdots & d_{mn} + c_{mn} \end{pmatrix}.$$

However, this matrix is exactly the matrix we would obtain if we had added $D$ and $C$; so we see,

$$C + D = D + C.$$

That is to say, the order in which we add two matrices does not matter. We say, more formally, that addition of matrices is *commutative*.

Now, let us see whether it matters how we group when we add matrices. That is, for three matrices, $A$, $B$, and $C$, of the same size, is it always true that

$$A + (B + C) = (A + B) + C?$$

(Here the parentheses are used to indicate grouping. That is, $A + (B + C)$ means add $B$ and $C$, then add $A$ to the result.)

As before, let us take a simple numerical example using $2 \times 2$ matrices. Let

$$A = \begin{pmatrix} 1 & 2 \\ 3 & 4 \end{pmatrix}$$

$$B = \begin{pmatrix} {}^-4 & 3 \\ 2 & {}^-1 \end{pmatrix}$$

and

$$C = \begin{pmatrix} 2 & 1 \\ 5 & {}^-3 \end{pmatrix}.$$

Then

$$A + (B + C) = \begin{pmatrix} 1 & 2 \\ 3 & 4 \end{pmatrix} + \left[ \begin{pmatrix} {}^-4 & 3 \\ 2 & {}^-1 \end{pmatrix} + \begin{pmatrix} 2 & 1 \\ 5 & {}^-3 \end{pmatrix} \right]$$

$$= \begin{pmatrix} 1 & 2 \\ 3 & 4 \end{pmatrix} + \begin{pmatrix} {}^-2 & 4 \\ 7 & {}^-4 \end{pmatrix},$$

hence

$$A + (B + C) = \begin{pmatrix} {}^-1 & 6 \\ 10 & 0 \end{pmatrix}.$$

Now find $(A + B) + C$.

$$(A + B) + C = \left[ \begin{pmatrix} 1 & 2 \\ 3 & 4 \end{pmatrix} + \begin{pmatrix} {}^-4 & 3 \\ 2 & {}^-1 \end{pmatrix} \right] + \begin{pmatrix} 2 & 1 \\ 5 & {}^-3 \end{pmatrix}$$

$$= \begin{pmatrix} {}^-3 & 5 \\ 5 & 3 \end{pmatrix} + \begin{pmatrix} 2 & 1 \\ 5 & {}^-3 \end{pmatrix},$$

hence

$$(A + B) + C = \begin{pmatrix} {}^-1 & 6 \\ 10 & 0 \end{pmatrix}.$$

For our example, then, it is true that $A + (B + C) = (A + B) + C$.

Can we show that this is true in general? Let us write $A$, $B$, and $C$ as general matrices of the same dimensions and see.

Let

$$A = \begin{pmatrix} a_{11} & a_{12} & \cdots & a_{1n} \\ a_{21} & a_{22} & \cdots & a_{2n} \\ a_{31} & a_{32} & \cdots & a_{3n} \\ \vdots & \vdots & \vdots & \vdots \\ a_{m1} & a_{m2} & \cdots & a_{mn} \end{pmatrix},$$

$$B = \begin{pmatrix} b_{11} & b_{12} & \cdots & b_{1n} \\ b_{21} & b_{22} & \cdots & b_{2n} \\ b_{31} & b_{32} & \cdots & b_{3n} \\ \vdots & \vdots & \vdots & \vdots \\ b_{m1} & b_{m2} & \cdots & b_{mn} \end{pmatrix},$$

and

$$C = \begin{pmatrix} c_{11} & c_{12} & \cdots & c_{1n} \\ c_{21} & c_{22} & \cdots & c_{2n} \\ c_{31} & c_{32} & \cdots & c_{3n} \\ \vdots & \vdots & \vdots & \vdots \\ c_{m1} & c_{m2} & \cdots & c_{mn} \end{pmatrix}.$$

Then we find

$$A + (B + C) = \begin{pmatrix} a_{11} & a_{12} & \cdots & a_{1n} \\ a_{21} & a_{22} & \cdots & a_{2n} \\ a_{31} & a_{32} & \cdots & a_{3n} \\ \vdots & \vdots & \vdots & \vdots \\ a_{m1} & a_{m2} & \cdots & a_{mn} \end{pmatrix} + \begin{pmatrix} b_{11}+c_{11} & b_{12}+c_{12} & \cdots & b_{1n}+c_{1n} \\ b_{21}+c_{21} & b_{22}+c_{22} & \cdots & b_{2n}+c_{2n} \\ b_{31}+c_{31} & b_{32}+c_{32} & \cdots & b_{3n}+c_{3n} \\ \vdots & \vdots & \vdots & \vdots \\ b_{m1}+c_{m1} & b_{m2}+c_{m2} & \cdots & b_{mn}+c_{mn} \end{pmatrix}$$

$$= \begin{pmatrix} a_{11}+b_{11}+c_{11} & a_{12}+b_{12}+c_{12} & \cdots & a_{1n}+b_{1n}+c_{1n} \\ a_{21}+b_{21}+c_{21} & a_{22}+b_{22}+c_{22} & \cdots & a_{2n}+b_{2n}+c_{2n} \\ a_{31}+b_{31}+c_{31} & a_{32}+b_{32}+c_{32} & \cdots & a_{3n}+b_{3n}+c_{3n} \\ \vdots & \vdots & \vdots & \vdots \\ a_{m1}+b_{m1}+c_{m1} & a_{m2}+b_{m2}+c_{m2} & \cdots & a_{mn}+b_{mn}+c_{mn} \end{pmatrix}.$$

Also,

$$(A + B) + C = \begin{pmatrix} a_{11}+b_{11} & a_{12}+b_{12} & \cdots & a_{1n}+b_{1n} \\ a_{21}+b_{21} & a_{22}+b_{22} & \cdots & a_{2n}+b_{2n} \\ a_{31}+b_{31} & a_{32}+b_{32} & \cdots & a_{3n}+b_{3n} \\ \vdots & \vdots & \vdots & \vdots \\ a_{m1}+b_{m1} & a_{m2}+b_{m2} & \cdots & a_{mn}+b_{mn} \end{pmatrix} + \begin{pmatrix} c_{11} & c_{12} & \cdots & c_{1n} \\ c_{21} & c_{22} & \cdots & c_{2n} \\ c_{31} & c_{32} & \cdots & c_{3n} \\ \vdots & \vdots & \vdots & \vdots \\ c_{m1} & c_{m2} & \cdots & c_{mn} \end{pmatrix}.$$

Continuing, we find that

$$(A + B) + C = \begin{pmatrix} a_{11} + b_{11} + c_{11} & a_{12} + b_{12} + c_{12} & \cdots & a_{1n} + b_{1n} + c_{1n} \\ a_{21} + b_{21} + c_{21} & a_{22} + b_{22} + c_{22} & \cdots & a_{2n} + b_{2n} + c_{2n} \\ a_{31} + b_{31} + c_{31} & a_{32} + b_{32} + c_{32} & \cdots & a_{3n} + b_{3n} + c_{3n} \\ \vdots & \vdots & \vdots & \vdots \\ a_{m1} + b_{m1} + c_{m1} & a_{m2} + b_{m2} + c_{m2} & \cdots & a_{mn} + b_{mn} + c_{mn} \end{pmatrix}.$$

So we see that $A + (B + C) = (A + B) + C$. We say that addition of matrices is *associative*.

So far we have seen that addition of matrices is both commutative and associative. Next we shall investigate the question of whether or not there exists a matrix $Z$ such that, for any given $m \times n$ matrix $A$, $A + Z = A$. Consider, as an example,

$$A = \begin{pmatrix} 4 & ^-2 \\ 3 & 1 \\ 0 & 5 \end{pmatrix}.$$

Is there a matrix $Z$ such that $A + Z = A$? To begin with we notice that such a matrix $Z$ would have to be of the form

$$\begin{pmatrix} z_{11} & z_{12} \\ z_{21} & z_{22} \\ z_{31} & z_{32} \end{pmatrix}$$

in order to make addition to $A$ possible. So we are looking for a matrix $Z_{3 \times 2}$ so that we will have

$$A + Z = \begin{pmatrix} 4 & ^-2 \\ 3 & 1 \\ 0 & 5 \end{pmatrix} + \begin{pmatrix} z_{11} & z_{12} \\ z_{21} & z_{22} \\ z_{31} & z_{32} \end{pmatrix}$$

$$= \begin{pmatrix} 4 + z_{11} & ^-2 + z_{12} \\ 3 + z_{21} & 1 + z_{22} \\ 0 + z_{31} & 5 + z_{32} \end{pmatrix}$$

$$= \begin{pmatrix} 4 & ^-2 \\ 3 & 1 \\ 0 & 5 \end{pmatrix}.$$

From our definition of equality of matrices, this means that we would like to find values for the entries of $Z$ so that

$$4 + z_{11} = 4, \qquad ^-2 + z_{12} = ^-2,$$
$$3 + z_{21} = 3, \qquad 1 + z_{22} = 1,$$
$$0 + z_{31} = 0, \qquad 5 + z_{32} = 5.$$

It is easy to see that all of the entries of $Z$ must be zero! We say that

$$Z = \begin{pmatrix} 0 & 0 \\ 0 & 0 \\ 0 & 0 \end{pmatrix}$$

is the $3 \times 2$ *zero* or *identity* matrix which, when added to any $3 \times 2$ matrix $A$, will yield $A$. In terms of our example,

$$\begin{pmatrix} 4 & ^-2 \\ 3 & 1 \\ 0 & 5 \end{pmatrix} + \begin{pmatrix} 0 & 0 \\ 0 & 0 \\ 0 & 0 \end{pmatrix} = \begin{pmatrix} 4 & ^-2 \\ 3 & 1 \\ 0 & 5 \end{pmatrix}.$$

In general, we can say that for any dimensions $m$ and $n$ there can be found an identity matrix $Z_{m \times n}$ so that for any matrix $A_{m \times n}$,

$$A + Z = Z + A = A.$$

Now we know such an identity matrix $Z_{m \times n}$ exists. The next question is whether we can find for each matrix $A_{m \times n}$ a matrix $B$ such that $A_{m \times n} + B = Z_{m \times n}$. Once again, let

$$A = \begin{pmatrix} 4 & ^-2 \\ 3 & 1 \\ 0 & 5 \end{pmatrix}.$$

We know the identity matrix, $Z$, corresponding to $A$ is

$$\begin{pmatrix} 0 & 0 \\ 0 & 0 \\ 0 & 0 \end{pmatrix},$$

so we must find

$$B = \begin{pmatrix} b_{11} & b_{12} \\ b_{21} & b_{22} \\ b_{31} & b_{32} \end{pmatrix}$$

so that

$$A + B = \begin{pmatrix} 4 & ^-2 \\ 3 & 1 \\ 0 & 5 \end{pmatrix} + \begin{pmatrix} b_{11} & b_{12} \\ b_{21} & b_{22} \\ b_{31} & b_{32} \end{pmatrix}$$

$$= \begin{pmatrix} 4 + b_{11} & ^-2 + b_{12} \\ 3 + b_{21} & 1 + b_{22} \\ 0 + b_{31} & 5 + b_{32} \end{pmatrix} = \begin{pmatrix} 0 & 0 \\ 0 & 0 \\ 0 & 0 \end{pmatrix}.$$

From our definition of equality of matrices this means we must have corresponding components equal:

$$4 + b_{11} = 0, \qquad {}^-2 + b_{12} = 0,$$
$$3 + b_{21} = 0, \qquad 1 + b_{22} = 0,$$
$$0 + b_{31} = 0, \qquad 5 + b_{32} = 0.$$

It then follows that

$$b_{11} = {}^-4, \qquad b_{12} = \phantom{-}2,$$
$$b_{21} = {}^-3, \qquad b_{22} = {}^-1,$$
$$b_{31} = \phantom{-}0, \qquad b_{32} = {}^-5,$$

so our desired matrix $B$ is

$$\begin{pmatrix} {}^-4 & 2 \\ {}^-3 & {}^-1 \\ 0 & {}^-5 \end{pmatrix}.$$

In general, a matrix such as $B$ above which, when added to a given matrix $A_{m \times n}$ yields the identity matrix $Z_{m \times n}$, is called the *additive inverse* of $A$. This inverse is denoted by ${}^-A$. There exists an additive inverse matrix ${}^-A$ for *any* given matrix $A$. From our example, it is clearly seen that the entries of ${}^-A$ are simply the negatives of the corresponding entries of $A$.

So far we have shown that matrix addition is commutative and associative. We have also shown that there is an additive identity matrix $Z_{m \times n}$ for every matrix $A_{m \times n}$, and that for each matrix $A_{m \times n}$ there is an additive inverse $-A$. Do there exist corresponding properties and matrices for the operation of multiplication?

First, let us consider a simple example to get a feel for whether matrix multiplication is commutative. Suppose

$$A = \begin{pmatrix} 1 & 2 \\ 3 & 4 \end{pmatrix} \quad \text{and} \quad B = \begin{pmatrix} 0 & {}^-1 \\ 3 & 2 \end{pmatrix}.$$

Is it true that $A \cdot B = B \cdot A$? Let us check.

$$A \cdot B = \begin{pmatrix} 1 & 2 \\ 3 & 4 \end{pmatrix}\begin{pmatrix} 0 & {}^-1 \\ 3 & 2 \end{pmatrix} = \begin{pmatrix} 6 & 3 \\ 12 & 5 \end{pmatrix},$$

$$B \cdot A = \begin{pmatrix} 0 & {}^-1 \\ 3 & 2 \end{pmatrix}\begin{pmatrix} 1 & 2 \\ 3 & 4 \end{pmatrix} = \begin{pmatrix} {}^-3 & {}^-4 \\ 9 & 14 \end{pmatrix}.$$

$A \cdot B \neq B \cdot A$! This one case serves as a counterexample to the statement that matrix multiplication is commutative. Order *does* matter when two matrices are multiplied. In Exercises 7-12 we will examine a class of matrices for which matrix multiplication is commutative.

Next, we would like to decide whether matrix multiplication has the property of associativity. Again, we take a simple example to use as a guideline. Let

$$A = \begin{pmatrix} 1 & 0 \\ 2 & -1 \end{pmatrix}, \qquad B = \begin{pmatrix} 2 & -4 \\ 6 & 1 \end{pmatrix}, \qquad \text{and} \qquad C = \begin{pmatrix} 3 & 1 \\ 2 & 0 \end{pmatrix}.$$

We want to know whether $(A \cdot B)C = A(B \cdot C)$. We have

$$(A \cdot B)C = \left[ \begin{pmatrix} 1 & 0 \\ 2 & -1 \end{pmatrix} \begin{pmatrix} 2 & -4 \\ 6 & 1 \end{pmatrix} \right] \begin{pmatrix} 3 & 1 \\ 2 & 0 \end{pmatrix}$$

$$= \begin{pmatrix} 2 & -4 \\ -2 & -9 \end{pmatrix} \begin{pmatrix} 3 & 1 \\ 2 & 0 \end{pmatrix}$$

$$= \begin{pmatrix} -2 & 2 \\ -24 & -2 \end{pmatrix}$$

and

$$A(B \cdot C) = \begin{pmatrix} 1 & 0 \\ 2 & -1 \end{pmatrix} \left[ \begin{pmatrix} 2 & -4 \\ 6 & 1 \end{pmatrix} \begin{pmatrix} 3 & 1 \\ 2 & 0 \end{pmatrix} \right]$$

$$= \begin{pmatrix} 1 & 0 \\ 2 & -1 \end{pmatrix} \begin{pmatrix} -2 & 2 \\ 20 & 6 \end{pmatrix}$$

$$= \begin{pmatrix} -2 & 2 \\ -24 & -2 \end{pmatrix}.$$

We see that, *in this case*,

$$(A \cdot B)C = A(B \cdot C).$$

Although we shall not prove it here, it can be shown that the preceding equality holds for any three matrices, $A$, $B$, and $C$, which have the proper number of rows and columns required for matrix multiplication. We define the product $A \cdot B \cdot C$ to be the common value of $(A \cdot B)C$ and $A(B \cdot C)$. That is,

$$(A \cdot B)C = A(B \cdot C) = A \cdot B \cdot C.$$

Our next concern is whether there exists an *identity element* for matrix multiplication. Let us again take a simple $2 \times 2$ matrix

$$A = \begin{pmatrix} 2 & 3 \\ 1 & -4 \end{pmatrix}.$$

We would like to find an identity matrix $I$ for $A$ such that $A \cdot I = I \cdot A = A$. It must be of the form

$$I = \begin{pmatrix} i_{11} & i_{12} \\ i_{21} & i_{22} \end{pmatrix}$$

in order for both products $A \cdot I$ and $I \cdot A$ to be possible. Since we would like $A \cdot I = A$ we have

$$\begin{pmatrix} 2 & 3 \\ 1 & -4 \end{pmatrix}\begin{pmatrix} i_{11} & i_{12} \\ i_{21} & i_{22} \end{pmatrix} = \begin{pmatrix} 2i_{11} + 3i_{21} & 2i_{12} + 3i_{22} \\ i_{11} - 4i_{21} & i_{12} - 4i_{22} \end{pmatrix} = \begin{pmatrix} 2 & 3 \\ 1 & -4 \end{pmatrix}.$$

This means we must have

$$2i_{11} + 3i_{21} = 2, \tag{1}$$

$$i_{11} - 4i_{21} = 1, \tag{2}$$

$$2i_{12} + 3i_{22} = 3, \tag{3}$$

$$i_{12} - 4i_{22} = {}^-4. \tag{4}$$

By inspection, Equations (1) and (2) imply $i_{11} = 1$ and $i_{21} = 0$, since

$$2(1) + 3(0) = 2 + 0 = 2,$$

and

$$1 - 4(0) = 1 - 0 = 1.$$

Similarly, Equations (3) and (4) imply that $i_{12} = 0$ and $i_{22} = 1$, since

$$2(0) + 3(1) = 0 + 3 = 3,$$

and

$$0 - 4(1) = 0 - 4 = {}^-4.$$

These results combined tell us that, if there is a multiplicative identity matrix $I$ for $A$, it must be of the form

$$I = \begin{pmatrix} i_{11} & i_{12} \\ i_{21} & i_{22} \end{pmatrix} = \begin{pmatrix} 1 & 0 \\ 0 & 1 \end{pmatrix}.$$

Checking the products $I \cdot A$ and $A \cdot I$ we find that

$$I \cdot A = A \cdot I = A.$$

Our example is rather special, since $A$ is a square matrix. How does our search for a multiplicative identity matrix work out for a nonsquare matrix $M$? Suppose, for example that

$$M = \begin{pmatrix} 2 & 3 & 4 \\ 5 & 6 & 7 \end{pmatrix}.$$

A candidate for the multiplicative identity matrix for $M$ is

$$I = \begin{pmatrix} 1 & 0 & 0 \\ 0 & 1 & 0 \\ 0 & 0 & 1 \end{pmatrix},$$

since

$$M \cdot I = \begin{pmatrix} 2 & 3 & 4 \\ 5 & 6 & 7 \end{pmatrix}\begin{pmatrix} 1 & 0 & 0 \\ 0 & 1 & 0 \\ 0 & 0 & 1 \end{pmatrix} = \begin{pmatrix} 2 & 3 & 4 \\ 5 & 6 & 7 \end{pmatrix}.$$

That is,

$$M \cdot I = M.$$

However notice that $I \cdot M$ cannot be found since it is not possible to multiply a $3 \times 3$ matrix by a $2 \times 3$ matrix. This difficulty arises because $M$ is not square. Therefore, since we would like $I \cdot M = M \cdot I = M$, we will speak only of the multiplicative identity matrices of square matrices.

It can be shown that the matrix $I_n$ which is of the form

$$I_n = \begin{pmatrix} 1 & 0 & 0 \cdots 0 \\ 0 & 1 & 0 \cdots 0 \\ 0 & 0 & 1 \cdots \\ \phantom{0} & 0 & 0 \phantom{0} \\ \vdots & \vdots & \vdots & \vdots & \vdots \\ 0 & 0 & \cdots 0 & 1 \end{pmatrix}$$

acts for multiplication of $n \times n$ matrices in the same way that the number 1 acts for real number multiplication. That is, for any square matrix $A_{n \times n}$

$$I_n \cdot A = A \cdot I_n = A.$$

Our next task is to decide whether for any square matrix $A_{n \times n}$ there exists a square matrix $Y_{n \times n}$ so that

$$A \cdot Y = I_n,$$

where $I_n$ is the $n \times n$ multiplicative identity matrix. A matrix $Y$ with this property is called the *multiplicative inverse matrix* for $A$, denoted $A^{-1}$. However, before we can discuss such matrices we must turn to the topic of determinants in the next section.

*EXERCISES* ─────────────────────────────────

*Using the matrices below verify the following properties.*

$$A = \begin{pmatrix} 1 & 4 & ^-1 \\ 2 & ^-2 & 0 \\ 1 & 0 & 3 \end{pmatrix}, \quad B = \begin{pmatrix} 8 & 1 & ^-3 \\ 9 & 0 & 0 \\ 3 & 1 & 1 \end{pmatrix}, \quad C = \begin{pmatrix} 1 & 0 & 1 \\ 3 & 1 & 0 \\ 4 & 3 & ^-1 \end{pmatrix}.$$

1. The commutative property of matrix addition.
2. The associative property of matrix addition.
3. The existence of an additive identity element for $3 \times 3$ matrices.
4. The existence of an additive inverse element for each matrix.
5. The associative property of matrix multiplication.
6. The existence of a multiplicative identity element for $3 \times 3$ matrices.

*Find the products in Exercises 7-12, using the matrices below.*

$$A = \begin{pmatrix} 1 & 0 & 0 \\ 0 & 1 & 0 \\ 0 & 0 & 1 \end{pmatrix}, \qquad B = \begin{pmatrix} 3 & 0 & 0 \\ 0 & 3 & 0 \\ 0 & 0 & 3 \end{pmatrix}, \qquad C = \begin{pmatrix} 7 & 6 & 5 \\ ^-1 & 0 & 2 \\ 3 & 1 & 2 \end{pmatrix}.$$

7.  $A \cdot C$.

8.  $C \cdot A$.

9.  $B \cdot C$.

10. $C \cdot B$.

11. $A \cdot B$.

12. $B \cdot A$.

13. We have shown in this section that matrix multiplication is not, in general, commutative. Using the results of Exercises 7-12 as a guide, describe a class of matrices which is an exception to this generality concerning matrix multiplication.

14. If $A$ is a matrix such that

$$A \cdot \begin{pmatrix} 5 & 6 & 7 \\ 8 & 9 & 10 \\ 11 & 12 & 13 \end{pmatrix} = \begin{pmatrix} n \cdot 5 & n \cdot 6 & n \cdot 7 \\ n \cdot 8 & n \cdot 9 & n \cdot 10 \\ n \cdot 11 & n \cdot 12 & n \cdot 13 \end{pmatrix},$$

where $n$ is some fixed number, find $A$.

## ——3-6   Determinants

Corresponding to every square matrix is a *number* called a *determinant*. First, let us consider $2 \times 2$ matrices of the form

$$M = \begin{pmatrix} a_{11} & a_{12} \\ a_{21} & a_{22} \end{pmatrix}.$$

The determinant of such a matrix $M$ is denoted by $|M|$ or, written out more fully, by

$$\begin{vmatrix} a_{11} & a_{12} \\ a_{21} & a_{22} \end{vmatrix}.$$

By definition,

$$\begin{vmatrix} a_{11} & a_{12} \\ a_{21} & a_{22} \end{vmatrix} = a_{11} a_{22} - a_{21} a_{12}.$$

Notice that this result is obtained simply by first multiplying the diagonal elements in the upper-left and lower-right corners to get $a_{11} a_{22}$

$$\begin{vmatrix} a_{11} & a_{12} \\ a_{21} & a_{22} \end{vmatrix}$$

and then multiplying the elements on the other diagonal to get $a_{21} a_{12}$

$$\begin{vmatrix} a_{11} & a_{12} \\ a_{21} & a_{22} \end{vmatrix}.$$

Then the second product is subtracted from the first product to obtain the determinant.

Using this method we can obtain the determinants of the following $2 \times 2$ matrices

$$\begin{vmatrix} 1 & 2 \\ 3 & 4 \end{vmatrix} = 1 \cdot 4 - 3 \cdot 2 = 4 - 6 = {}^-2,$$

$$\begin{vmatrix} 3 & 2 \\ {}^-6 & {}^-4 \end{vmatrix} = 3 \cdot {}^-4 - {}^-6 \cdot 2 = {}^-12 + 12 = 0,$$

$$\begin{vmatrix} {}^-13 & {}^-5 \\ 6 & 2 \end{vmatrix} = {}^-13 \cdot 2 - 6 \cdot {}^-5 = {}^-26 + 30 = 4.$$

Note that the determinant of a square matrix may be positive, negative or zero, and do not confuse the determinant notation with that for absolute value.

So far, we have only discussed finding determinants of $2 \times 2$ matrices. Finding determinants of larger square matrices is not as simple. Before we can find the determinant of a square matrix of order larger than two we must know how to find the *minor* of each element in a matrix. Consider the $3 \times 3$ matrix

$$M = \begin{pmatrix} 1 & 2 & {}^-3 \\ 0 & {}^-4 & 5 \\ 3 & 2 & 4 \end{pmatrix}.$$

In order to find the minor of the element 1 which is in the first row and first column we cross out the first row and first column:

$$\begin{pmatrix} 1 & 2 & {}^-3 \\ 0 & {}^-4 & 5 \\ 3 & 2 & 4 \end{pmatrix}.$$

The determinant of the remaining *submatrix*

$$\begin{pmatrix} {}^-4 & 5 \\ 2 & 4 \end{pmatrix}$$

is the minor of the element 1. Thus, the minor of 1 is

$$\begin{vmatrix} {}^-4 & 5 \\ 2 & 4 \end{vmatrix} = {}^-4 \cdot 4 - 2 \cdot 5 = {}^-26.$$

Similarly, let us find the minor of 5, the element in the second row and third column of $M$. To find this minor we first cross out the second row and third column of $M$:

$$\begin{pmatrix} 1 & 2 & {}^-3 \\ 0 & {}^-4 & 5 \\ 3 & 2 & 4 \end{pmatrix}.$$

Then we compute the determinant of the remaining submatrix

$$\begin{pmatrix} 1 & 2 \\ 3 & 2 \end{pmatrix}.$$

The minor of 5, then, is

$$\begin{vmatrix} 1 & 2 \\ 3 & 2 \end{vmatrix} = 1 \cdot 2 - 3 \cdot 2 = {}^-4.$$

In general, the minor of the element in the $r$th row and $s$th column of a matrix of any order $n$ is the determinant of the matrix of order $n - 1$ obtained by crossing out all the elements in the $r$th row and $s$th column in the original matrix.

Corresponding to every element of a square matrix there is a number called a *cofactor*. The cofactor of an element $a_{rs}$ of matrix $M$ is formed by multiplying the minor of $a_{rs}$ by 1 or $^-1$. To find out easily which factor (1 or $^-1$) to use, consider again our sample matrix $M$ and the corresponding checkerboard pattern of signs:

$$\begin{pmatrix} 1 & 2 & ^-3 \\ 0 & ^-4 & 5 \\ 3 & 2 & 4 \end{pmatrix} \leftrightarrow \begin{pmatrix} + & - & + \\ - & + & - \\ + & - & + \end{pmatrix}.$$

This pattern tells us by what factor to multiply the minor of each element to get the corresponding cofactor. For example, when we multiply the minor of 1 by the factor 1 as follows, we obtain the cofactor of 1.

$$\begin{pmatrix} 1 & 2 & ^-3 \\ 0 & ^-4 & 5 \\ 3 & 2 & 4 \end{pmatrix} \leftrightarrow \begin{pmatrix} \oplus & - & + \\ - & + & - \\ + & - & + \end{pmatrix}$$

We found previously that the minor of 1 is $^-26$. Thus the cofactor of 1 is $1 \cdot {}^-26 = {}^-26$.

Similarly, we previously found that the minor of 5 is $^-4$. Referring again to the checkerboard pattern we see a negative sign corresponding to 5.

$$\begin{pmatrix} 1 & 2 & ^-3 \\ 0 & ^-4 & 5 \\ 3 & 2 & 4 \end{pmatrix} \leftrightarrow \begin{pmatrix} + & - & + \\ - & + & \ominus \\ + & - & + \end{pmatrix};$$

so the cofactor of 5 is $^-1 \cdot {}^-4 = 4$.

In general, the cofactor of the element in the $r$th row and $s$th column of a determinant can be found by the law

$$\text{cofactor} = (^-1)^{r+s}(\text{minor}).$$

The checkerboard pattern we have used is simply a mnemonic device.

Now we return to our original problem of finding the determinant of our example matrix, $M$. We may find the number which is the determinant of $M$ by finding the sum of the products of the elements of the first row and their corresponding cofactors:

$$|M| = 1 \cdot (^-1)^{1+1} \begin{vmatrix} ^-4 & 5 \\ 2 & 4 \end{vmatrix} + 2 \cdot (^-1)^{1+2} \begin{vmatrix} 0 & 5 \\ 3 & 4 \end{vmatrix} + (^-3)(^-1)^{1+3} \begin{vmatrix} 0 & ^-4 \\ 3 & 2 \end{vmatrix}$$

$$= 1 \cdot 1 \cdot {}^-26 + 2 \cdot {}^-1 \cdot {}^-15 + {}^-3 \cdot 1 \cdot 12$$

$$= {}^-26 + 30 + {}^-36 = {}^-32.$$

That is, $|M| = {}^-32$. The above computation is called *expanding* $|M|$ *by the first row of M*.

In fact, it may be verified that the determinant of a square matrix is the sum of the products of the elements of *any row* or *any column* and their corresponding cofactors. To illustrate, let us find $|M|$ expanding by the *second* row, this time using the checkerboard pattern to associate either 1 or $^-1$ with each minor. We have

$$|M| = 0 \cdot {}^-1 \cdot \begin{vmatrix} 2 & ^-3 \\ 2 & 4 \end{vmatrix} + {}^-4 \cdot 1 \cdot \begin{vmatrix} 1 & ^-3 \\ 3 & 4 \end{vmatrix} + 5 \cdot {}^-1 \cdot \begin{vmatrix} 1 & 2 \\ 3 & 2 \end{vmatrix}$$

$$= 0 + {}^-4 \cdot 13 + {}^-5 \cdot {}^-4 = {}^-32.$$

Notice that this is the same result we obtained by expanding $|M|$ by the first row.

Finally, let us find $|M|$ by expanding by the second column. We have

$$|M| = 2 \cdot {}^-1 \cdot \begin{vmatrix} 0 & 5 \\ 3 & 4 \end{vmatrix} + {}^-4 \cdot 1 \cdot \begin{vmatrix} 1 & ^-3 \\ 3 & 4 \end{vmatrix} + 2 \cdot {}^-1 \cdot \begin{vmatrix} 1 & ^-3 \\ 0 & 5 \end{vmatrix}$$

$$= {}^-2 \cdot {}^-15 + {}^-4 \cdot 13 + {}^-2 \cdot 5 = {}^-32.$$

This is in agreement with our earlier values for $|M|$.

We may use cofactors and the expansion by any row or any column to find the determinant of a square matrix of any order. As a final example let us find the determinant of the fourth order matrix $N$.

$$|N| = \begin{vmatrix} 1 & 0 & 1 & 0 \\ ^-1 & 1 & 0 & 3 \\ 0 & 0 & 4 & 1 \\ 2 & ^-2 & 3 & 0 \end{vmatrix}.$$

Again we may use a checkerboard pattern to determine by which factor (1 or $^-1$) to multiply each minor to get the corresponding cofactor. We have the pattern:

$$\begin{vmatrix} 1 & 0 & 1 & 0 \\ ^-1 & 1 & 0 & 3 \\ 0 & 0 & 4 & 1 \\ 2 & ^-2 & 3 & 0 \end{vmatrix} \leftrightarrow \begin{vmatrix} + & - & + & - \\ - & + & - & + \\ + & - & + & - \\ - & + & - & + \end{vmatrix}.$$

Let us find $|N|$ by expanding by the first row:

$$|N| = 1 \cdot 1 \cdot \begin{vmatrix} 1 & 0 & 3 \\ 0 & 4 & 1 \\ ^-2 & 3 & 0 \end{vmatrix} + 0 \cdot {}^-1 \cdot \begin{vmatrix} ^-1 & 0 & 3 \\ 0 & 4 & 1 \\ 2 & 3 & 0 \end{vmatrix} + 1 \cdot 1 \cdot \begin{vmatrix} ^-1 & 1 & 3 \\ 0 & 0 & 1 \\ 2 & ^-2 & 0 \end{vmatrix} +$$

$$0 \cdot {}^-1 \cdot \begin{vmatrix} ^-1 & 1 & 0 \\ 0 & 0 & 4 \\ 2 & ^-2 & 3 \end{vmatrix}.$$

Note that two terms drop out due to multiplication by 0. We must now evaluate two third-order determinants to find $|N|$. Evaluating each using its first column we have

$$|N| = 1 \cdot \left[ 1 \cdot 1 \cdot \begin{vmatrix} 4 & 1 \\ 3 & 0 \end{vmatrix} + 0 \cdot {}^-1 \cdot \begin{vmatrix} 0 & 3 \\ 3 & 0 \end{vmatrix} + {}^-2 \cdot 1 \cdot \begin{vmatrix} 0 & 3 \\ 4 & 1 \end{vmatrix} \right]$$

$$+ 1 \cdot \left[ {}^-1 \cdot 1 \cdot \begin{vmatrix} 0 & 1 \\ -2 & 0 \end{vmatrix} + 0 \cdot {}^-1 \cdot \begin{vmatrix} 1 & 3 \\ -2 & 0 \end{vmatrix} + 2 \cdot 1 \begin{vmatrix} 1 & 3 \\ 0 & 1 \end{vmatrix} \right]$$

$$= 1 \cdot [1 \cdot {}^-3 + 0 \cdot {}^-9 + {}^-2 \cdot {}^-12] + 1 \cdot [{}^-1 \cdot 2 + 0 \cdot 6 + 2 \cdot 1]$$

$$= 1 \cdot 21 + 1 \cdot 0.$$

That is, $|N| = 21$.

Determinants may be used to solve a system of $n$ equations in $n$ unknowns using what is known as Cramer's Rule. Consider the following system of $n$ equations in $n$ unknowns: (The coefficients are indicated by $b_{ij}$, while the $x_j$'s are the unknowns and the $c_i$ are constants.)

$$b_{11} x_1 + b_{12} x_2 + \cdots b_{1n} x_n = c_1$$
$$b_{21} x_1 + b_{22} x_2 + \cdots b_{2n} x_n = c_2$$
$$\vdots \qquad \vdots \qquad \vdots \qquad \vdots$$
$$b_{n1} x_1 + b_{n2} x_2 + \cdots b_{nn} x_n = c_n$$

The array of the coefficient $b_{ij}$ (ignoring the unknowns $x_j$) is called the *coefficient matrix* of this system of equations, and the column of $c_i$'s may be viewed as a vector.

CRAMER'S RULE. *If the determinant D of the coefficient matrix of a system of n linear equations in n unknowns is not zero, then the equations have a unique solution. In the solution the value of the unknown $x_j$ is the fraction whose denominator is D and whose numerator is the determinant of the matrix* *obtained by replacing the jth column of the coefficient matrix with the vector of the constants* $c_i$.

Let us use an example to illustrate this statement of Cramer's Rule. Consider the following system of three equations in three unknowns.

$$\begin{aligned} x + y + z &= 10, \\ 2x - y &= 3, \\ x + 2y - 3z &= 5. \end{aligned}$$

The determinant $D$ of the coefficient matrix is

$$D = \begin{vmatrix} 1 & 1 & 1 \\ 2 & {}^-1 & 0 \\ 1 & 2 & {}^-3 \end{vmatrix}.$$

We may find the solution for $x$ by forming the fraction whose denominator is $D$ and whose numerator is the determinant of the matrix obtained by replacing the first column of $D$ by the vector

$$\begin{pmatrix} 10 \\ 3 \\ 5 \end{pmatrix}.$$

Thus,

$$x = \frac{\begin{vmatrix} 10 & 1 & 1 \\ 3 & {}^-1 & 0 \\ 5 & 2 & {}^-3 \end{vmatrix}}{\begin{vmatrix} 1 & 1 & 1 \\ 2 & {}^-1 & 0 \\ 1 & 2 & {}^-3 \end{vmatrix}}.$$

Evaluating each of the determinants in the preceding fraction we find that

$$x = \frac{50}{14} = \frac{25}{7}.$$

Similarly, we may find the solutions for $y$ and $z$:

$$y = \frac{\begin{vmatrix} 1 & 10 & 1 \\ 2 & 3 & 0 \\ 1 & 5 & {}^-3 \end{vmatrix}}{14} = \frac{58}{14} = \frac{29}{7},$$

$$z = \frac{\begin{vmatrix} 1 & 1 & 10 \\ 2 & {}^-1 & 3 \\ 1 & 2 & 5 \end{vmatrix}}{14} = \frac{32}{14} = \frac{16}{7}.$$

We may check these solutions by substituting them into the three original equations:

$$\frac{25}{7} + \frac{29}{7} + \frac{16}{7} = \frac{70}{7} = 10, \qquad \text{Check}$$

$$2\left(\frac{25}{7}\right) - \frac{29}{7} = \frac{21}{7} = 3, \qquad \text{Check}$$

$$\frac{25}{7} + 2\left(\frac{29}{7}\right) - 3\left(\frac{16}{7}\right) = \frac{35}{7} = 5. \qquad \text{Check}$$

Note that Cramer's Rule applies only when the determinant of the co-efficient matrix of the system of equations is nonzero. This is most important. Some systems that have coefficient matrices with determinants of zero have an infinite number of solutions while the remaining systems cannot be solved at all. Such systems will not be discussed here.

*EXERCISES* ——————————————————————————

*Find the determinants of the matrices in Exercises 1-10.*

1. $\begin{pmatrix} 2 & 3 \\ 4 & -1 \end{pmatrix}$.

2. $\begin{pmatrix} -1 & 3 \\ 4 & -2 \end{pmatrix}$.

3. $\begin{pmatrix} 6 & \frac{1}{2} \\ 6 & \frac{1}{2} \end{pmatrix}$.

4. $\begin{pmatrix} 3 & 2 \\ 3 & 2 \end{pmatrix}$.

5. $\begin{pmatrix} 1 & 0 & 1 \\ 3 & 4 & 5 \\ -1 & 0 & 1 \end{pmatrix}$.

6. $\begin{pmatrix} 2 & 0 & 0 \\ 4 & -1 & 2 \\ -4 & 3 & 1 \end{pmatrix}$.

7. $\begin{pmatrix} 2 & 4 & 6 \\ 0 & 0 & 3 \\ 2 & 4 & 6 \end{pmatrix}$.

8. $\begin{pmatrix} 5 & 1 & 5 \\ 2 & 0 & 2 \\ 3 & -4 & 3 \end{pmatrix}$.

9. $\begin{pmatrix} 3 & 2 & 0 & -1 \\ 0 & 4 & 9 & 1 \\ 6 & 8 & -3 & 4 \\ 1 & 6 & 0 & 8 \end{pmatrix}$.

10. $\begin{pmatrix} 3 & 6 & -3 & 3 \\ 5 & -9 & 8 & 0 \\ 8 & 5 & -8 & 2 \\ 2 & 9 & 5 & 0 \end{pmatrix}$.

11. Verify using the two matrices below that if a matrix $A$ has two rows or columns alike, $|A| = 0$.

a. $\begin{pmatrix} 3 & 5 \\ 3 & 5 \end{pmatrix}$.

b. $\begin{pmatrix} 1 & 4 & 1 \\ 2 & 5 & 2 \\ 3 & 6 & 3 \end{pmatrix}$.

12. A square matrix, $A$, is said to be *nonsingular* if and only if $|A| \neq 0$. Classify the following matrices as singular or nonsingular.

a. $\begin{pmatrix} 3 & -1 \\ 0 & 4 \end{pmatrix}$.

b. $\begin{pmatrix} 6 & 5 & 4 \\ 6 & 5 & 10 \\ 0 & 0 & 1 \end{pmatrix}$.

   *A square matrix, M, is said to be triangular if all entries above (or below) the main diagonal are zero. For each of the matrices below, a. find the value of the determinant by expansion; b. verify that the value of the determinant of a triangular matrix is the product of the elements on the main diagonal.*

13. $\begin{pmatrix} 1 & 1 \\ 0 & 2 \end{pmatrix}$.

14. $\begin{pmatrix} -3 & 0 & 0 \\ 1 & 2 & 0 \\ 5 & 4 & 1 \end{pmatrix}$.

15. $\begin{pmatrix} 6 & 2 & 0 & 1 \\ 0 & -3 & 3 & -4 \\ 0 & 0 & 5 & 2 \\ 0 & 0 & 0 & 1 \end{pmatrix}$.

16. $\begin{pmatrix} 0 & 0 & 0 \\ 18 & 0 & 0 \\ 3 & -5 & 4 \end{pmatrix}$.

   *If $f(t)$, $g(t)$, $h(t)$, $j(t)$ are functions of $t$ we may form the determinant*

$$\begin{vmatrix} f(t) & g(t) \\ h(t) & j(t) \end{vmatrix}$$

*just as with numbers. Find the values of the following determinants.*

17. $\begin{vmatrix} \sin t & \cos t \\ -\cos t & \sin t \end{vmatrix}$.

18. $\begin{vmatrix} t+1 & -1 \\ t & t-1 \end{vmatrix}$.

19. $\begin{vmatrix} 0 & x & y \\ -x & 0 & z \\ -y & -z & 0 \end{vmatrix}$.

   *Solve each of the following systems of equations using Cramer's Rule.*

20. $2a - b = 5,$
    $a + 2b = 8,$

21. $x + y = 7,$
    $3x - 2y = 10.$

22. $2r - t = 1,$
    $2r + 4s - t = 1,$
    $r - 8s - 3t = {}^-2.$

23. $x - y + 2z = 2,$
    $2y - 3z = {}^-2,$
    $3x - 2y + 4z = 5.$

24. $a + 2b + 2c + 2d = 1,$
    $a + \phantom{2}b + 2c + 2d = 2,$
    $a + \phantom{2}b + \phantom{2}c + 2d = 3,$
    $a + \phantom{2}b + \phantom{2}c + \phantom{2}d = 4.$

25. $2r + \phantom{2}s + \phantom{2}t + \phantom{2}v = 1,$
    $\phantom{2}r + 2s + \phantom{2}t + \phantom{2}v = 0,$
    $\phantom{2}r + \phantom{2}s + 2t + \phantom{2}v = 1,$
    $\phantom{2}r + \phantom{2}s + \phantom{2}t + 2v = 0.$

26. Using

$$A = \begin{pmatrix} 5 & 4 \\ 3 & 2 \end{pmatrix} \quad \text{and} \quad B = \begin{pmatrix} {}^-1 & 2 \\ 3 & 4 \end{pmatrix},$$

verify that

$$|A \cdot B| = |A| \cdot |B|.$$

## ——3-7   The Multiplicative Inverse

Now let us return to the question of whether there exists for every $n \times n$ matrix $A$ a multiplicative inverse matrix $A^{-1}$ such that

$$A \cdot A^{-1} = A^{-1} \cdot A = I,$$

where $I$ is the $n \times n$ identity matrix.

In order to find the inverse of a square matrix we must know how to find three things that correspond to the matrix in question:

1.  The determinant of the matrix.
2.  The matrix whose elements are the cofactors of the corresponding elements of the original matrix.
3.  The transpose of the matrix of cofactors found in condition 2.

We have already discussed in the previous section the method of finding the determinant of any square matrix. Also, we know from the preceding section how to find the cofactor of any element in a matrix. Now we must obtain the matrix whose elements are the cofactors of the corresponding elements in the original matrix. Let us take some examples to illustrate how to do this.

Consider the $2 \times 2$ matrix

$$A = \begin{pmatrix} 1 & {}^-1 \\ 3 & 2 \end{pmatrix}.$$

To find the element in the first row and first column of the matrix of the cofactors of $A$ we find the cofactor of 1

$$\begin{pmatrix} 1 & {}^-1 \\ 3 & 2 \end{pmatrix},$$

which is 2. So we know that 2 belongs in the first row and first column of the matrix we shall call cofactor $A$. We have, then,

$$A = \begin{pmatrix} 1 & ^-1 \\ 3 & 2 \end{pmatrix} \rightarrow (\text{cofactor } A) = \begin{pmatrix} 2 & \\ & \end{pmatrix},$$

$$A = \begin{pmatrix} 1 & ^-1 \\ 3 & 2 \end{pmatrix} \rightarrow (\text{cofactor } A) = \begin{pmatrix} 2 & ^-3 \\ & \end{pmatrix}.$$

(Remember the checkerboard pattern, which tells us to take the negative of 3 here.)

$$A = \begin{pmatrix} 1 & ^-1 \\ 3 & 2 \end{pmatrix} \rightarrow (\text{cofactor } A) = \begin{pmatrix} 2 & ^-3 \\ 1 & \end{pmatrix}.$$

(We must take the negative of $^-1$ here, too, because of the checkerboard pattern.)

$$A = \begin{pmatrix} 1 & ^-1 \\ 3 & 2 \end{pmatrix} \rightarrow (\text{cofactor } A) = \begin{pmatrix} 2 & ^-3 \\ 1 & 1 \end{pmatrix}.$$

Let us now find the matrix consisting of the cofactors of the 3 × 3 matrix

$$B = \begin{pmatrix} 2 & 0 & ^-1 \\ 1 & ^-2 & 3 \\ 0 & 1 & 1 \end{pmatrix}.$$

For the element of the first row and first column of the matrix (cofactor $B$), we find the cofactor of 2, the element in the first row and first column of $B$.

$$B = \begin{pmatrix} 2 & 0 & ^-1 \\ 1 & ^-2 & 3 \\ 0 & 1 & 1 \end{pmatrix} \rightarrow (\text{cofactor } B) = \begin{pmatrix} ^-5 & & \\ & & \\ & & \end{pmatrix}.$$

The entry in the first row and first column of (cofactor $B$) is $^-5$, since

$$1 \cdot \begin{vmatrix} ^-2 & 3 \\ 1 & 1 \end{vmatrix} = ^-5.$$

We obtain other elements of the matrix (cofactor $B$) as follows:

$$B = \begin{pmatrix} 2 & 0 & ^-1 \\ 1 & ^-2 & 3 \\ 0 & 1 & 1 \end{pmatrix} \rightarrow (\text{cofactor } B) = \begin{pmatrix} ^-5 & ^-1 & \\ & & \\ & & \end{pmatrix},$$

$$B = \begin{pmatrix} 2 & 0 & ^-1 \\ 1 & ^-2 & 3 \\ 0 & 1 & 1 \end{pmatrix} \rightarrow (\text{cofactor } B) = \begin{pmatrix} ^-5 & ^-1 & 1 \\ & & \\ & & \end{pmatrix},$$

$$B = \begin{pmatrix} 2 & 0 & ^-1 \\ 1 & ^-2 & 3 \\ 0 & 1 & 1 \end{pmatrix} \rightarrow (\text{cofactor } B) = \begin{pmatrix} ^-5 & ^-1 & 1 \\ ^-1 & & \\ & & \end{pmatrix}, \ldots .$$

Continuing in this manner we obtain the complete (cofactor $B$) matrix:

$$(\text{cofactor } B) = \begin{pmatrix} -5 & -1 & 1 \\ -1 & 2 & -2 \\ -2 & -7 & -4 \end{pmatrix}.$$

So far in our quest for a method of finding the inverse of a given square matrix we know how to find the determinant of the matrix in question as well as the matrix of the cofactors of the given matrix. We need only to find the *transpose* of this matrix of cofactors. In general, the transpose of a given matrix $M$, denoted $M^T$, is the matrix formed by making the first *row* of $M$ the first *column* of $M^T$, the second row of $M$ the second column of $M^T$, .... Thus, if our given matrix is

$$M = \begin{pmatrix} 2 & 4 & 6 \\ 8 & 10 & 12 \\ 14 & 16 & 18 \end{pmatrix},$$

we have

$$M = \begin{pmatrix} 2 & 4 & 6 \\ 8 & 10 & 12 \\ 14 & 16 & 18 \end{pmatrix} \rightarrow M^T = \begin{pmatrix} 2 \\ 4 \\ 6 \end{pmatrix}$$

and so on. The final result would be

$$M^T = \begin{pmatrix} 2 & 8 & 14 \\ 4 & 10 & 16 \\ 6 & 12 & 18 \end{pmatrix}.$$

As another example, consider the matrix (cofactor $B$) that we found previously in this section:

$$(\text{cofactor } B) = \begin{pmatrix} -5 & -1 & 1 \\ -1 & 2 & -2 \\ -2 & -7 & -4 \end{pmatrix}.$$

The transpose of this matrix would be

$$(\text{cofactor } B)^T = \begin{pmatrix} -5 & -1 & -2 \\ -1 & 2 & -7 \\ 1 & -2 & -4 \end{pmatrix}.$$

Now let us go back to our example matrix, $B$. We now know enough to find the inverse of $B$, $B^{-1}$. We assert that

$$B^{-1} = \frac{(\text{cofactor } B)^T}{|B|}.$$

By the method of the previous section we have

$$|B| = {}^-11.$$

By the above assertion, then,

$$B^{-1} = \frac{\begin{pmatrix} {}^-5 & {}^-1 & {}^-2 \\ {}^-1 & 2 & {}^-7 \\ 1 & {}^-2 & {}^-4 \end{pmatrix}}{{}^-11},$$

$$B^{-1} = \begin{pmatrix} 5/11 & 1/11 & 2/11 \\ 1/11 & {}^-2/11 & 7/11 \\ {}^-1/11 & 2/11 & 4/11 \end{pmatrix}.$$

If this matrix for $B^{-1}$ is correct, we should have

$$B \cdot B^{-1} = B^{-1} \cdot B = I = \begin{pmatrix} 1 & 0 & 0 \\ 0 & 1 & 0 \\ 0 & 0 & 1 \end{pmatrix}.$$

We find that this value of $B^{-1}$ checks, since

$$B \cdot B^{-1} = \begin{pmatrix} 2 & 0 & {}^-1 \\ 1 & {}^-2 & 3 \\ 0 & 1 & 1 \end{pmatrix} \begin{pmatrix} 5/11 & 1/11 & 2/11 \\ 1/11 & {}^-2/11 & 7/11 \\ {}^-1/11 & 2/11 & 4/11 \end{pmatrix} = \begin{pmatrix} 1 & 0 & 0 \\ 0 & 1 & 0 \\ 0 & 0 & 1 \end{pmatrix},$$

and

$$B^{-1} \cdot B = \begin{pmatrix} 5/11 & 1/11 & 2/11 \\ 1/11 & {}^-2/11 & 7/11 \\ {}^-1/11 & 2/11 & 4/11 \end{pmatrix} \begin{pmatrix} 2 & 0 & {}^-1 \\ 1 & {}^-2 & 3 \\ 0 & 1 & 1 \end{pmatrix} = \begin{pmatrix} 1 & 0 & 0 \\ 0 & 1 & 0 \\ 0 & 0 & 1 \end{pmatrix}.$$

To summarize, the inverse of an *n*-by-*n* matrix $A$ is the *n*-by-*n* matrix

$$A^{-1} = \frac{(\text{cofactor } A)^T}{|A|}.$$

It is extremely important to note that the inverse of a square matrix, $A$, *does not exist* if $|A| = 0$, since a division by 0 would occur during the process of finding $A^{-1}$. However, if $|A| \neq 0$, then $A^{-1}$ always exists.

We conclude by saying *a square matrix has a multiplicative inverse if and only if its determinant is nonzero.*

EXERCISES —————————————————————————————————

1. Find the matrix of the cofactors of each of the following matrices

a. $A = \begin{pmatrix} 1 & 2 \\ 3 & 2 \end{pmatrix}$.

b. $B = \begin{pmatrix} 3 & 4 \\ -9 & -12 \end{pmatrix}$.

c. $C = \begin{pmatrix} 3 & 0 & 4 \\ 1 & 2 & -3 \\ 5 & 4 & 1 \end{pmatrix}$.

2. a–c.   Find the transpose of the matrices resulting in Exercise 1, a–c.

3. a–c.   Find, if possible, the inverse of each matrix in Exercise 1, a–c.

4. If $xz - wy \neq 0$, find the inverse of the matrix

$$\begin{pmatrix} x & y \\ w & z \end{pmatrix}.$$

5. Suppose

$$M = \begin{pmatrix} 1 & 2 \\ 3 & 4 \end{pmatrix}.$$

a.   Find $M^{-1}$.
b.   Find $M^2$.
c.   Find $M^{-2}$, the inverse of $M^2$.
d.   Show $(M^{-1})^2 = M^{-2}$.
e.   Find $M^3$.
f.   Find $M^{-3}$, the inverse of $M^3$.
g.   Show $(M^{-1})^3 = M^{-3}$.
h.   Generalize the preceding for any square matrix $A$.

6. If $X$ and $Y$ are two $2 \times 2$ matrices,

$$X = \begin{pmatrix} 1 & 2 \\ 3 & -1 \end{pmatrix} \quad \text{and} \quad Y = \begin{pmatrix} 5 & 4 \\ 0 & 3 \end{pmatrix}$$

a.   Find $X \cdot Y$.
b.   Show $(X \cdot Y)^{-1} = Y^{-1} \cdot X^{-1}$.

—————3-8  An Application of the Multiplicative Inverse

In this section we will examine an application of the process of finding the inverse of a square matrix. To begin with, consider the following equations:

$$2x + 3y = 8,$$
$$2x - y = 12.$$

These two equations form *a system of two equations in two unknowns.* Similarly, the equations.

$$x + y + z = 8,$$
$$2x \quad\quad - 3z = 12,$$
$$10x + 2y - 3z = 10$$

form a *system of three equations in three unknowns* (the coefficient of the $y$ term in the second equation is 0); and the equations

$$2x + 3y + z = 10,$$
$$x - y - 2z = 3$$

form a system of *two equations in three unknowns.*

In this section we will be applying the inverse of the coefficient matrix of such systems. But since only square matrices can have inverses, we will confine ourselves to solving systems of $n$ equations in $n$ unknowns. Now let us go back to our example of two equations in two unknowns.

$$2x + 3y = 8,$$
$$2x - y = 12.$$

This system of equations may be written in an equivalent way using the *matrix equation*

$$\begin{pmatrix} 2 & 3 \\ 2 & -1 \end{pmatrix} \begin{pmatrix} x \\ y \end{pmatrix} = \begin{pmatrix} 8 \\ 12 \end{pmatrix}.$$

The matrix

$$\begin{pmatrix} 2 & 3 \\ 2 & -1 \end{pmatrix}$$

is, of course, the coefficient matrix of the above system of equations. To see that the above matrix equation is equivalent to the given system of equations, we perform the indicated multiplication on the left to obtain

$$\begin{pmatrix} 2x + 3y \\ 2x - y \end{pmatrix} = \begin{pmatrix} 8 \\ 12 \end{pmatrix}.$$

By the definition of equal vectors this means that

$$2x + 3y = 8$$

and
$$2x - y = 12.$$

Thus, we may say that

$$2x + 3y = 8, \qquad \text{is equivalent to} \qquad \begin{pmatrix} 2 & 3 \\ 2 & -1 \end{pmatrix}\begin{pmatrix} x \\ y \end{pmatrix} = \begin{pmatrix} 8 \\ 12 \end{pmatrix}.$$
$$2x - y = 12$$

Similarly, we see that the following system of three equations in three unknowns

$$x + y - z = 12$$
$$3x - y \phantom{+ 4z} = 1$$
$$2x - 3y + 4z = 3$$

is equivalent to the matrix equation

$$\begin{pmatrix} 1 & 1 & ^-1 \\ 3 & ^-1 & 0 \\ 2 & ^-3 & 4 \end{pmatrix}\begin{pmatrix} x \\ y \\ z \end{pmatrix} = \begin{pmatrix} 12 \\ 1 \\ 3 \end{pmatrix}.$$

Here,

$$\begin{pmatrix} 1 & 1 & ^-1 \\ 3 & ^-1 & 0 \\ 2 & ^-3 & 4 \end{pmatrix}$$

is the coefficient matrix of the given system.

How, then, can we solve systems of equations of this type? Once again, let us consider the system

$$2x + 3y = 8$$
$$2x - y = 12$$

and its equivalent matrix equation form

$$\begin{pmatrix} 2 & 3 \\ 2 & -1 \end{pmatrix}\begin{pmatrix} x \\ y \end{pmatrix} = \begin{pmatrix} 8 \\ 12 \end{pmatrix}.$$

Let us find the inverse of the coefficient matrix

$$C = \begin{pmatrix} 2 & 3 \\ 2 & -1 \end{pmatrix}.$$

Using the method of the previous section we see that the inverse is

$$C^{-1} = \frac{\begin{pmatrix} ^-1 & ^-3 \\ ^-2 & 2 \end{pmatrix}}{\begin{vmatrix} 2 & 3 \\ 2 & ^-1 \end{vmatrix}} = \frac{\begin{pmatrix} ^-1 & ^-3 \\ ^-2 & 2 \end{pmatrix}}{^-8} = \begin{pmatrix} \dfrac{1}{8} & \dfrac{3}{8} \\ \dfrac{1}{4} & ^-\dfrac{1}{4} \end{pmatrix}.$$

If we multiply both sides of the matrix equation

$$\begin{pmatrix} 2 & 3 \\ 2 & ^-1 \end{pmatrix} \begin{pmatrix} x \\ y \end{pmatrix} = \begin{pmatrix} 8 \\ 12 \end{pmatrix}$$

by

$$\begin{pmatrix} \dfrac{1}{8} & \dfrac{3}{8} \\[2mm] \dfrac{1}{4} & \dfrac{^-1}{4} \end{pmatrix},$$

the inverse of its coefficient matrix, we obtain by matrix multiplication:

$$\begin{pmatrix} \frac{1}{8} & \frac{3}{8} \\ \frac{1}{4} & -\frac{1}{4} \end{pmatrix} \begin{pmatrix} 2 & 3 \\ 2 & ^-1 \end{pmatrix} \begin{pmatrix} x \\ y \end{pmatrix} = \begin{pmatrix} \frac{1}{8} & \frac{3}{8} \\ \frac{1}{4} & -\frac{1}{4} \end{pmatrix} \begin{pmatrix} 8 \\ 12 \end{pmatrix},$$

$$\begin{pmatrix} 1 & 0 \\ 0 & 1 \end{pmatrix} \begin{pmatrix} x \\ y \end{pmatrix} = \begin{pmatrix} 8 \cdot \frac{1}{8} + 12 \cdot \frac{3}{8} \\ 8 \cdot \frac{1}{4} + 12 \cdot ^-\frac{1}{4} \end{pmatrix},$$

$$\begin{pmatrix} x \\ y \end{pmatrix} = \begin{pmatrix} 5\frac{1}{2} \\ ^-1 \end{pmatrix}.$$

By equality of vectors we have our solution to the system of equations

$$2x + 3y = 8,$$
$$2x - y = 12.$$

It is $x = 5\frac{1}{2}, y = ^-1$.

This solution may be checked by substituting $x = 5\frac{1}{2}$ and $y = ^-1$ into the two equations that make up the system. For the first equation we have:

$$2(5\frac{1}{2}) + 3(^-1) \overset{?}{=} 8,$$
$$11 - \quad 3 \overset{?}{=} 8,$$
$$8 = 8. \qquad \text{Check}$$

And for the second equation we have

$$2(5\frac{1}{2}) - (^-1) \overset{?}{=} 12,$$
$$11 + \quad 1 \overset{?}{=} 12,$$
$$12 = 12. \qquad \text{Check}$$

Using this method let us now solve the following system of three equations in three unknowns:

$$2x + 3y - z = 8,$$
$$x + y + z = 7,$$
$$2y - z = 3.$$

Corresponding to this system we have the matrix equation

$$\begin{pmatrix} 2 & 3 & ^-1 \\ 1 & 1 & 1 \\ 0 & 2 & ^-1 \end{pmatrix} \begin{pmatrix} x \\ y \\ z \end{pmatrix} = \begin{pmatrix} 8 \\ 7 \\ 3 \end{pmatrix}.$$

We must now find the inverse of the coefficient matrix

$$C = \begin{pmatrix} 2 & 3 & ^-1 \\ 1 & 1 & 1 \\ 0 & 2 & ^-1 \end{pmatrix}.$$

Using the method of the previous section we find

$$C^{-1} = \frac{\begin{pmatrix} ^-3 & 1 & 2 \\ 1 & ^-2 & ^-4 \\ 4 & ^-3 & ^-1 \end{pmatrix}^T}{\begin{vmatrix} 2 & 3 & ^-1 \\ 1 & 1 & 1 \\ 0 & 2 & ^-1 \end{vmatrix}} = \frac{\begin{pmatrix} ^-3 & 1 & 4 \\ 1 & ^-2 & ^-3 \\ 2 & ^-4 & ^-1 \end{pmatrix}}{^-5},$$

$$C^{-1} = \begin{pmatrix} 3/5 & ^-1/5 & ^-4/5 \\ ^-1/5 & 2/5 & 3/5 \\ ^-2/5 & 4/5 & 1/5 \end{pmatrix}.$$

Next we multiply both sides of our matrix equation by $C^{-1}$:

$$\begin{pmatrix} 3/5 & ^-1/5 & ^-4/5 \\ ^-1/5 & 2/5 & 3/5 \\ ^-2/5 & 4/5 & 1/5 \end{pmatrix} \begin{pmatrix} 2 & 3 & ^-1 \\ 1 & 1 & 1 \\ 0 & 2 & ^-1 \end{pmatrix} \begin{pmatrix} x \\ y \\ z \end{pmatrix} = \begin{pmatrix} 3/5 & ^-1/5 & ^-4/5 \\ ^-1/5 & 2/5 & 3/5 \\ ^-2/5 & 4/5 & 1/5 \end{pmatrix} \begin{pmatrix} 8 \\ 7 \\ 3 \end{pmatrix}.$$

We obtain

$$\begin{pmatrix} 1 & 0 & 0 \\ 0 & 1 & 0 \\ 0 & 0 & 1 \end{pmatrix} \begin{pmatrix} x \\ y \\ z \end{pmatrix} = \begin{pmatrix} 1 \\ 3 \\ 3 \end{pmatrix},$$

$$\begin{pmatrix} x \\ y \\ z \end{pmatrix} = \begin{pmatrix} 1 \\ 3 \\ 3 \end{pmatrix}.$$

Our solutions are $x = 1$, $y = 3$, $z = 3$. Checking each of the three equations by substitution we have

$$2(1) + 3(3) - 3 = 8, \qquad \text{Check}$$
$$1 + 3 + 3 = 7, \qquad \text{Check}$$
$$2(3) - 3 = 3. \qquad \text{Check}$$

These methods may be generalized to any system of $n$ equations in $n$ unknowns as long as the determinant of the coefficient matrix is not 0, for if the coefficient matrix has a nonzero determinant, the inverse of the coefficient matrix exists.

*EXERCISES* ————————————————————————

*Using the method of this section solve the following systems of equations, if possible.*

1.  $3a + 2b = 7,$
    $a - b = 5.$

2.  $3x + 4y = 8,$
    $9x - 2y = 12.$

3.  $x + y + z = 3,$
    $2x \quad - z = 12,$
    $3x - 2y + 4z = 16.$

4.  $r + s - 2t = 7,$
    $2r - s \quad = 10,$
    $4r - 3s + 6t = 8.$

5.  $x + y \quad = 7,$
    $y - z + w = 5,$
    $x - y + z + w = 6,$
    $y \quad - w = 10.$

# An Introduction to Probability    4

What is Probability?

" The chance of rain is 10% today, increasing to 40% tonight." " Chances are, I'll be able to contact my brother before noon." " He will probably win the election." " I may get a B in math this quarter." Each of these commonly heard statements refers to a situation in which we are not sure of the outcome. However, we can often make a prediction about the outcome and feel relatively sure that our prediction will be verified.

Although probability applies to a variety of practical situations, an understanding of the subject will be made much easier if it is first applied to nonpractical situations, such as those arising in games of chance.

To gain a feel for probability consider the simple repetitive experiment of tossing a coin twice. In this experiment there are four possible outcomes:

TH, HT, HH, TT.

This set of possible outcomes is called the *sample space*. Here, for example, the symbol TH means that a tail T is obtained on the first toss and a head H on the second toss.

Another simple repetitive experiment is the following: from an urn containing four red (R) marbles, four white (W) marbles and four blue (B) marbles, draw one marble, note its color, return it to the urn, and draw a second marble. The set of possible outcomes, or the *sample space*, is:

RR, RW, RB, WR, WW, WB, BR, BW, BB.

In each of these two experiments it seems reasonable to assume that all of the outcomes are *equally likely*. In other words, each side of the coin has an equal chance of turning up in the first experiment and each color has an equal chance of being drawn in the second. Experiments such as these in which all outcomes are equally likely are called *random*.

In experiments like the ones we have just described, there is a way to assign a *measure* to the likelihood or expected relative frequency of a certain outcome. In our coin-tossing experiment, for instance, we see that since there are four equally likely outcomes, there is one chance in four of having the outcome HH. So we say that the measure of the chance, or the *probability*, that an outcome of HH results is $\frac{1}{4}$. That is, if we were to conduct the experiment a large number of times we would obtain the result HH *about* $\frac{1}{4}$ of the time. If we were to increase the number of trials more and more, the number of occurrences of the outcome HH divided by the total number of trials would get closer and closer to $\frac{1}{4}$.

Similarly, we say that the probability that we will obtain one head and one tail in the experiment is $\frac{2}{4}$ or $\frac{1}{2}$ since there are two chances out of four of tossing a head and a tail: HT and TH.

In the second experiment involving drawing marbles we see that the probability of drawing a red marble and a blue marble is $\frac{2}{9}$ since there are two possibilities, RB and BR, out of nine. Similarly, the probability of drawing two marbles of different colors is $\frac{6}{9}$ or $\frac{2}{3}$. Finally, the probability of drawing one red marble and one green marble is $\frac{0}{9}$ or 0. (Why?)

In experiments involving chance we are often interested in obtaining a certain set of outcomes, not just one particular outcome. For example, suppose we pitch a die with six faces numbered 1, 2, 3, 4, 5, and 6. What is the probability that we will get a 3? There are six possible outcomes in this case, only one of which is a *favorable outcome* (getting a 3). Thus the probability of throwing a 3 is $\frac{1}{6}$. What is the probability that the outcome will be greater than 2? In this situation there are six possible outcomes, four of which are favorable (getting a 3, 4, 5, or 6). The probability of obtaining a value greater than 2 is thus $\frac{4}{6}$ or $\frac{2}{3}$. If we let E denote the set of favorable outcomes, then we say $P(E)$ denotes the probability of obtaining an outcome in E. In the case when E is the set of outcomes favorable to rolling a number greater than 2 on a single die, we thus have

$$P(E) = \frac{2}{3}.$$

This is read "the probability of E is $\frac{2}{3}$." The set E of favorable outcomes is also called the *event* E.

In general, the probability of the occurrence of a *favorable outcome* is described as follows:

If an experiment can result in any one of $n$ different, equally likely outcomes, and if $f$ of these outcomes are favorable, then

$$P \text{ (a favorable outcome)} = \frac{f}{n}.$$

In an experiment if all outcomes are favorable, then $f = n$ and we have for E, the event of all favorable outcomes

$$P(\text{E}) = \frac{n}{n} = 1.$$

For instance, if there are three orange balls in a box the probability of the event E of drawing an orange ball is

$$P(\text{E}) = \frac{f}{n} = \frac{3}{3} = 1.$$

Such an event is called *certain*.

On the other hand, if there are no favorable outcomes for an event E (such as drawing a quarter from an urn containing only dimes) then we have $f = 0$, so

$$P(\text{E}) = \frac{0}{n} = 0.$$

An event of this sort is said to be *impossible*.

It should now be clear that for any event E,

$$0 \leqslant P(\text{E}) \leqslant 1.$$

Let us turn to an experiment that involves drawing marbles from an urn containing two red (R) marbles and two green (G) marbles. As in the preceding example, we draw one marble, note its color, return it to the urn, and draw a second marble. This is called *drawing with replacement*. There are four possible outcomes:

$$\text{RR, RG, GR, GG.}$$

The probability of the event E of drawing two red marbles is

$$P(\text{E}) = \frac{1}{4},$$

where $f = 1$ and $n = 4$. The probability of the event of not drawing two red marbles, denoted by $\sim\text{E}$, is

$$P(\sim\text{E}) = \frac{3}{4},$$

where $f = 3$ and $n = 4$. Here,

$$P(E) + P(\sim E) = 1,$$

where in both instances E is the event "red is drawn twice."

In fact, it is always true that for any event E

$$P(E) + P(\sim E) = 1.$$

(Here read $P(\sim E)$ as "the probability of not E.") Therefore, if you know the probability of an event E, you also know the probability of the event $\sim E$, since

$$P(\sim E) = 1 - P(E).$$

The concepts of $P(E)$ and $P(\sim E)$ are used when we speak of *odds*: "The odds are three to one that he will receive the Democratic nomination at the convention."

"The odds are four to three that Native Dancer will win tomorrow's race."

These two statements simply mean that

$$\frac{P(E)}{P(\sim E)} = \frac{3}{1}$$

and

$$\frac{P(E)}{P(\sim E)} = \frac{4}{3},$$

respectively. So, for instance, if the probability of rain on Tuesday is 1/5, then the odds for rain that day are

$$\frac{P(\text{rain})}{P\sim(\text{rain})} = \frac{1/5}{4/5} = \frac{1}{4},$$

Generally, we say that if an event E may or may not occur then the ratio

$$\frac{P(E)}{P(\sim E)}$$

gives the *odds in favor of* the occurrence of E.

In this section we have discussed probability problems by analyzing the corresponding sample spaces (sets of possible outcomes). We assumed equally likely outcomes. For instance, we assumed a coin will fall heads just as likely as it will fall tails. However, we did not actually toss a coin to obtain the probability that heads will fall when a coin is tossed. Instead we found the probability *theoretically*. On the other hand, we could have tossed a coin thousands of times to see whether heads turn up as often as tails. Our answer would turn out to be an *estimate* of the probability rather than the exact ratio we obtained in our theoretical solution. A solution that is obtained by experimenting is an *empirical* solution. In some situations involving probability, it is desirable to check theoretical answers with experimental results. See Exercises 1 through 4, for example.

## EXERCISES

1. If a coin were tossed what is the probability that a tail would turn up?

2. Conduct at least five experiments in which a coin is tossed 25 times. Record your results in the table below and compute the actual ratio of the number of tails that turned up to the total number of tosses. ($t'$ and $n'$ represent "total number of trials" and "total number of tails," respectively.) Is the ratio about what you expected?

| Experiment | Number of tosses $t$ | Number of times a tail turned up $n$ | $\dfrac{n}{t}$ |
|:---:|:---:|:---:|:---:|
| 1 | | | |
| 2 | | | |
| 3 | | | |
| 4 | | | |
| 5 | | | |
| Totals | $t' =$ | $n' =$ | $\dfrac{n'}{t'} =$ |

3. Consider an experiment in which each trial consists of tossing a coin twice. Find theoretically the following probabilities.
   a. $P(HH)$.        b. $P(HT)$.
   c. $P(TT)$.        d. $P(TH)$.

4. Now conduct 100 trials of the experiment described in Exercise 3 and compute the following ratios.

   a. $\dfrac{\text{Number of times HH turned up}}{100}$.

   b. $\dfrac{\text{Number of times HT turned up}}{100}$.

   c. $\dfrac{\text{Number of times TT turned up}}{100}$.

   d. $\dfrac{\text{Number of times TH turned up}}{100}$.

   Are your results about what you would have expected, based on your solution of Exercise 3?

*For each of the experiments in Exercises 5 to 9 find the sample space.*

5. Drawing with replacement of two marbles from an urn containing two red marbles, two blue marbles, and two white marbles.

6. a. Drawing with replacement of three marbles from an urn containing three red marbles, and one blue marble.
   b. Drawing *without* replacement of three marbles from the urn of Part a.

7. Picking one integer from the digits 0, 1, 2, 3, 4, 5.

8. Picking two integers without replacement from the digits 2, 4, 6, 8, 10. (Use the notation $(a, b)$ to indicate that the digits $a$ and $b$ are picked.)

9. Tossing of two dice. (See comment on notation in Exercise 8.)

10. a. What is the probability of picking a king from a 52-card bridge deck?
    b. What is the probability of picking a king of spades from a 52-card bridge deck?
    c. What is the probability of picking a spade from a 52-card bridge deck?

11. a. What is the probability of tossing a sum of two with two dice?
    b. What is the probability of tossing a sum of eight with two dice?

12. What is the probability that the two children in a family are:
    a. Two boys?
    b. Two girls?
    c. A boy and a girl?

13. What is the probability that a family of four children will consist of two girls and two boys?

14. Suppose that in an election one of the two candidates for an office received $m$ votes and the other received $n$ votes, where $m > n$. Mathematicians have shown that the probability that the eventual winner was always ahead during the counting of election returns is

$$\frac{m - n}{m + n}.$$

Using this result compute the probability that the incumbent governor was always ahead during the counting of election returns if he received a total of 112,252 votes and his challenger received a total of 102,752.

15. If the probability of rain on Tuesday is $\frac{1}{10}$, what is the probability that it will not rain that day?

16. a. What is the probability that you will win the door prize at a party attended by 125 people including yourself?
    b. What is the probability that you will not win?

17. Of 100,000 people alive at age 20, 95,709 will live to the age of 25 and 71,383 will live to the age of 60. If you are 25 what is your chance of living till 60?

18. What are the odds that the last digit of a phone number is 5.

19. If twelve people are seated at random around a circular dining room table, what are the odds that a certain man and his wife in the group will be seated next to each other?

20. The odds are 5:4 that the San Francisco Giants will win the pennant. What is the probability that the Giants will win the pennant?

## ——4-2  The Addition Rule

Quite often we are interested in finding the probability of the occurrence of two or more events rather than just one. For instance, for two events $E_1$ and $E_2$ we might want to know the probability that both $E_1$ and $E_2$ occur. This probability is denoted by $P(E_1$ and $E_2)$. Or we might wonder whether at least one of the events $E_1$ or $E_2$ will occur when an experiment is performed. The probability of such an event is written $P(E_1$ or $E_2)$. Here " or " means either $E_1$ occurs, but not $E_2$, $E_2$ occurs but not $E_1$, or both $E_1$ and $E_2$ occur. If two events $E_1$ and $E_2$ have the property that the occurrence of one of the events prevents the occurrence of the other, then the two events are called *mutually exclusive*. For instance, if $E_1$ is the event of drawing a red ball from an urn on a given trial and $E_2$ is the event of drawing a blue ball from the urn on the same trial, then $E_1$ and $E_2$ are *mutually exclusive*.

Now suppose we are rolling a die. Let $E_1$ be the event of getting a 6 and $E_2$ be the event of rolling a 1. Clearly, $E_1$ and $E_2$ are mutually exclusive events. There are six possible outcomes:

$$1, 2, 3, 4, 5, 6.$$

By counting favorable outcomes we find

$$P(E_1 \text{ or } E_2) = \frac{2}{6} = \frac{1}{3},$$

since $f = 2$ and $n = 6$. We could obtain the same result $\frac{1}{3}$ by writing

$$P(E_1 \text{ or } E_2) = \frac{1}{6} + \frac{1}{6} = P(E_1) + P(E_2) = \frac{1}{3}.$$

Take another example. Suppose that instead of the traditional cubes for dice we have tetrahedrons. (See Figure 4-1.) A tetrahedron has four faces and we will be interested in the number on the bottom when the tetrahedron is rolled. (We will pretend we are under a glass table looking up at the tetra-hedron and reading the number facing us.) We will have a red (R) tetrahedron and a white (W) tetrahedron. One face of each tetrahedron will show one dot, another face of each will show two dots, another face of each will show three

Figure 4-1.

dots, and the fourth face of each will show four dots. We summarize the sample space in Table 4-1.

| W \ R | 1 | 2 | 3 | 4 |
|---|---|---|---|---|
| 1 | (1, 1) | (1, 2) | (1, 3) | (1, 4) |
| 2 | (2, 1) | (2, 2) | (2, 3) | (2, 4) |
| 3 | (3, 1) | (3, 2) | (3, 3) | (3, 4) |
| 4 | (4, 1) | (4, 2) | (4, 3) | (4, 4) |

Table 4-1.

The entries in the table may be interpreted as follows. There is, for example, in the second row and third column the entry (2, 3). This means a 2 was rolled using the white tetrahedron and a 3 was rolled using the red tetrahedron. Similarly, the entry (3, 2) means a 3 was rolled using the white tetrahedron and a 2 was rolled using the red tetrahedron.

What is $P(4)$, the probability that the numbers we obtain when we throw the white and red tetrahedrons add up to 4? Since there are sixteen equally likely possible outcomes and there are three possible favorable outcomes, namely (2, 2), (3, 1), and (1, 3), we have

$$P(4) = \frac{3}{16}.$$

Using similar reasoning we find also that

$$P(5) = \frac{4}{16} = \frac{1}{4}.$$

What, then, is $P(4 \text{ or } 5)$? That is, what is the probability that we will get a 4 or a 5 when we roll the two tetrahedrons? (Notice that rolling a 4 and rolling a 5 are again mutually exclusive.) Since there are sixteen possible outcomes and seven possible favorable outcomes, (3, 1), (2, 2), (1, 3), (4, 1), (3, 2), (2, 3), (1, 4), we have

$$P(4 \text{ or } 5) = \frac{7}{16}.$$

Note that

$$P(4) + P(5) = \frac{3}{16} + \frac{4}{16} = \frac{7}{16}$$

as well. So,

$$P(4 \text{ or } 5) = P(4) + P(5).$$

In fact, we have, in general, that for two mutually exclusive events, $E_1$ and $E_2$,

$$\boxed{P(E_1 \text{ or } E_2) = P(E_1) + P(E_2).}$$

$P(E_1 \text{ or } E_2)$ can be written $P(E_1 \cup E_2)$, so the preceding can be written

$$\boxed{P(E_1 \cup E_2) = P(E_1) + P(E_2).}$$

Let us return to the example of rolling the red and the white tetrahedrons and consider two events that are not mutually exclusive. What is the probability that we will roll a 5 or that the white tetrahedron will show a 1? Let us denote the latter event $W_1$. Again, there are sixteen possible outcomes. There are four of these outcomes for which we get a 5: (4, 1), (3, 2), (2, 3), and (1, 4). There are four of these outcomes for which we have $W_1$: (1, 1), (1, 2), (1, 3), and (1, 4). The two events are not mutually exclusive, since *both* occur for the outcome (1, 4). Thus, we cannot write

$$\cancel{P(5 \text{ or } W_1) = P(5) + P(W_1) = \frac{4}{16} + \frac{4}{16} = \frac{8}{16}.}$$

Instead we must take into account the outcomes common to both events. In all there are seven favorable outcomes possible. The outcome (1, 4) is to be counted only once! We have

$$P(5 \text{ or } W_1) = \frac{4}{16} + \frac{4}{16} - \frac{1}{16} = \frac{7}{16}.$$

Now consider the event K of obtaining a king when drawing a card from a bridge deck and the event S of obtaining a spade when drawing a card from a bridge deck. These two events, like the two in the preceding example, are not mutually exclusive. What is $P(K \text{ or } S)$? Here again we cannot simply add $P(K)$ and $P(S)$. Instead, we must take into account any outcomes common to K and S, that is, outcomes in $K \cap S$. In all there are fifty-two possible outcomes. There are four favorable outcomes for K, namely drawing the king of hearts, the king of diamonds, the king of spades, and the king of clubs. There are thirteen favorable outcomes for S, since there are thirteen spades in a bridge deck. But one of these spades is a king of spades. We must avoid counting the king of spades twice. The number of favorable outcomes for (K or S) is thus $4 + 13 - 1$, where the $-1$ corrects for the extra time that the king of spades was counted in writing down $4 + 13$. We obtain

$$P(K \text{ or } S) = \frac{4 + 13 - 1}{52} = \frac{4}{52} + \frac{13}{52} - \frac{1}{52} = \frac{16}{52}.$$

It appears that the probability of (K or S), where K and S are not mutually exclusive, is just $P(K) + P(S) - P(K \cap S)$, where $K \cap S$ is the set of outcomes favorable to both K and S. In general, if two events $E_1$ and $E_2$ are not mutually exclusive,

$$\boxed{P(E_1 \cup E_2) = P(E_1) + P(E_2) - P(E_1 \cap E_2).}$$

In our first example of nonmutually exclusive events $E_1 \cap E_2$ was $(1, 4)$ and $P(E_1 \cap E_2)$ was $\frac{1}{16}$. In our second example of nonmutually exclusive events $E_1 \cap E_2$ was the king of spades and $P(E_1 \cap E_2)$ was $\frac{1}{52}$.

### EXERCISES

1. Find the probability of obtaining a sum of seven when rolling two dice.

2. A committee composed of a man and a woman is to be chosen at random from a group of seven men and four women. Mr. and Mrs. Edwards are in the group. What is the probability that at least one of them will be chosen to be on the committee?

3. What is the probability of getting a 2 or a 4 or a 6 when rolling a die?

4. What is the probability of getting a result less than three when rolling a die?

5. What is the probability of obtaining a sum less than three or greater than four when rolling two dice?

6. Find the probability of drawing a card less than 7 (6, 5, 4, 3, 2) or a picture card (ace, king, queen, jack) from a bridge deck of fifty-two cards.

7. What is the probability of drawing a white marble or a black marble from a container containing five white marbles, four gray marbles, and three black marbles?

8.  If the probability of Jackson's winning the vice presidential nomination is $\frac{1}{4}$ and the probability of Fairbanks' winning the nomination is $\frac{1}{5}$, what is the probability that either Jackson or Fairbanks will win the nomination?

9.  For two events $A$ and $B$ if $P(A \cup B) = 6/7$, $P(A) = 4/7$ and $P(B) = 5/7$, what is $P(A \cap B)$?

10. In a certain office of thirty people, fifteen voted for the Republican gubernatorial candidate and for the Democratic candidate for lieutenant governor; ten voted for the Democratic gubernatorial candidate, but for the Republican candidate for lieutenant governor; and five voted for both Republican candidates.
    a.  If a member of the office staff is chosen at random, what is the probability that he voted for only one Republican?
    b.  What is the probability that he voted for at least one Republican?

11. A red die and a green die are rolled. What is the probability that the sum will be seven or that the green die will show a 2?

12. Two dice are rolled.
    a.  What is the probability that the sum obtained will be between three and six or between four and nine?
    b.  What is the probability that the sum obtained will be neither between three and six nor between four and nine?
    c.  What is the probability that the sum obtained will be between three and six and between four and nine?

## ——4-3  The Multiplication Rule

In the last section we developed a method for finding $P(E_1 \text{ or } E_2)$ first for mutually exclusive events, then for nonmutually exclusive events. In this section we will develop a method to find $P(E_1 \text{ and } E_2)$. First, we must examine the notion of *conditional probability*, the probability that an event $E_2$ will occur if it is known that $E_1$ will occur. This is denoted $P(E_2 \mid E_1)$ (read "probability of $E_2$ given $E_1$"). For example: What is the probability that Mayor Smythe will be reelected if he decides to run? What is the probability that Charles will be dealt a king of diamonds if he already has been dealt the king of spades and the king of hearts?

We will assume that $E_1$ and $E_2$ are not mutually exclusive. As an illustration let us return to the example of the preceding section concerning the red and white tetrahedrons. What is the probability that the sum of numbers obtained in rolling the two tetrahedrons will be six, if it is known that the tetrahedrons show at least three points each? That is, what is

$$P(E_2 \mid E_1)$$

when $E_1$ is the event that each tetrahedron shows at least three points, and $E_2$ is the event that the sum of points obtained in rolling the two tetrahedrons is six? The sample space for this conditional probability problem is shown in Table 4-2.

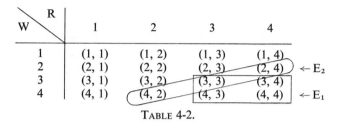

TABLE 4-2.

The possible outcomes for the events $E_1$ and $E_2$ are marked on the table. From the table we can see that (3, 3) is the favorable outcome for which we are looking, since each tetrahedron shows three points and together they show six points. Since $E_1$ must occur, the only experimental outcomes we need consider are in $E_1$; thus

$$P(E_2 \mid E_1) = \frac{1}{4},$$

where 1 is the number of elements in both $E_1$ and $E_2$ (here, (3, 3)), and 4 is the number of elements in $E_1$. What this means in an experimental sense is that if two tetrahedrons are repeatedly rolled and if all outcomes in which either tetrahedron shows a number less than 3 are discarded, then among those outcomes that are kept, the proportion of them that yields a total of six points will approach $\frac{1}{4}$ in the long run.

In general terms

$$P(E_2 \mid E_1) = \frac{N(E_1 \text{ and } E_2)}{N(E_1)}, \tag{1}$$

where $N(E_1 \text{ and } E_2)$ stands for the number of outcomes in both $E_1$ and $E_2$, $(E_1 \cap E_2)$, and $N(E_1)$ stands for the number of outcomes in $E_1$. Using these symbols we may write

$$P(E_1) = \frac{N(E_1)}{n}$$

or

$$nP(E_1) = N(E_1), \tag{2}$$

where $n =$ the total number of outcomes. We may also write

$$P(E_1 \text{ and } E_2) = \frac{N(E_1 \text{ and } E_2)}{n}$$

or $$nP(E_1 \text{ and } E_2) = N(E_1 \text{ and } E_2).$$ (3)

Substituting Equations (2) and (3) into Equation (1), we have

$$P(E_2 \mid E_1) = \frac{nP(E_1 \text{ and } E_2)}{nP(E_1)}.$$

Simplifying, we obtain the *multiplication rule for probability*:

$$P(E_1)P(E_2 \mid E_1) = P(E_1 \text{ and } E_2).$$

In words, the multiplication rule says that the probability that both of two events $E_1$ and $E_2$ will occur is equal to the probability that the first event will occur multiplied by the conditional probability that the second event will occur when it is known that the first event will definitely occur. For many pairs of events there is a definite time-order relationship so that it is easy to pick out which of the events should be considered the first event. However, for other pairs of events either event may be called the first event. Thus if you are throwing a die the event of rolling a 4 and the event of rolling a 5 have no time order. Either might be called the first event in finding the probability that you will throw a 4 if it is known that you will also throw a 5.

As an example let us use the multiplication rule to find the probability of drawing a white marble from a canister containing three white (W) marbles, two purple (P) marbles, and four green (G) marbles on each of two successive draws without replacement. Let $E_1$ be the event of drawing a white marble on the first draw and $E_2$ is the probability of drawing a white marble on the second draw. We have

$$P(E_1) = \frac{3}{9} = \frac{1}{3},$$

since $N(E_1) = 3$ and $n = 9$. To find $P(E_2 \mid E_1)$ it is necessary to consider only those experimental outcomes for which $E_1$ has already occurred. Since the white ball was not replaced, there are, after $E_1$ has occurred, only eight balls in the canister (two white, two purple, and four green), so

$$P(E_2 \mid E_1) = \frac{2}{8} = \frac{1}{4}.$$

Here 2 is the number of favorable outcomes (that is, white balls left) and 8 is the number of possible outcomes. Substituting these values of $P(E_1)$ and $P(E_2 \mid E_1)$ into the multiplication rule, we have

$$P(E_1 \text{ and } E_2) = \frac{1}{3} \cdot \frac{1}{4} = \frac{1}{12}.$$

As an example of an extension of the multiplication rule, consider the problem of finding the probability of drawing three white balls from the canister of the preceding example without replacement. Now instead of two events, we have three, $E_1$, $E_2$, and $E_3$ corresponding to drawing a white ball each time. To find $P(E_1$ and $E_2$ and $E_3)$, we may generalize the multiplication rule. However, it is much easier to take each stage of the experiment in order and multiply the appropriate probabilities together. For the first event $E_1$ we have

$$P(E_1) = \frac{3}{9},$$

since there are three possible favorable outcomes and nine possible outcomes. For the event $E_2$ there are two white balls remaining. So for the second stage of the experiment we have

$$P(E_2 \mid E_1) = \frac{2}{8}.$$

For the event $E_3$ there is one white ball left out of the seven remaining balls after $E_1$ and $E_2$ have occurred, so

$$P(E_3 \mid (E_1 \text{ and } E_2)) = \frac{1}{7}.$$

Thus we have

$$P(E_1 \text{ and } E_2 \text{ and } E_3) = P(E_1)P(E_2 \mid E_1)P(E_3 \mid (E_1 \text{ and } E_2))$$

$$= \frac{3}{9} \cdot \frac{2}{8} \cdot \frac{1}{7},$$

so

$$P(E_1 \text{ and } E_2 \text{ and } E_3) = \frac{1}{84}.$$

Chances are slim that three white balls will be drawn!

Such events as the event that the President of the United States will have chicken for dinner and the event that the stock market will go up that same day do not depend on each other. An event $E_2$ is said to be *independent* of an event $E_1$ if the occurrence of $E_2$ does not depend on the occurrence of $E_1$.

Since for independent events $E_1$ and $E_2$ we have

$$P(E_2 \mid E_1) = P(E_2),$$

we obtain

$$P(E_1 \text{ and } E_2) = P(E_1)P(E_2)$$

by substituting $P(E_2)$ for $P(E_2 \mid E_1)$ in the multiplication rule. From this result we can say that *two events are independent if and only if the probability of their both occurring is equal to the product of their individual probabilities.*

As an application of the preceding rule consider the following card problems.

Two cards are drawn from a bridge deck of fifty-two cards. The first card is replaced before the second card is drawn. What is the probability that both cards will be hearts? We are dealing with independent events, since the first card is replaced. So we have

$$P(E_1 \text{ and } E_2) = P(E_1)P(E_2) = \frac{13}{52} \cdot \frac{13}{52} = \frac{1}{16}.$$

What is the probability that both cards will be hearts if the first card is not replaced before the second is drawn? We are no longer dealing with independent events, so we must use the original multiplication rule:

$$P(E_1 \text{ and } E_2) = P(E_1)P(E_2 \mid E_1) = \frac{13}{52} \cdot \frac{12}{51} = \frac{1}{17}.$$

Thus, as would be expected, it is slightly more likely that the two cards drawn will be hearts if the first card is replaced before the second is drawn.

*EXERCISES*

1.  What is the probability that a sum of ten is rolled, if at least one of the two dice rolled is a 6?

2.  Suppose a red box holds ten white marbles and five black marbles and a green box holds six white marbles and four black marbles. What is the probability that a blindfolded person will draw a black marble from the green box?

3.  The probability that a man will live ten more years is $\frac{1}{3}$. The probability that his wife will live ten more years is $\frac{1}{2}$. What is the probability that both will be alive in ten years?

4.  Suppose two dice are tossed. What is the probability that one die shows a 5 and the other die shows an even number?

5.  A committee of five is to be chosen at random from a group of twenty people.
    a.  *A* is in the group. What is the probability that *A* is chosen to be on the committee?
    b.  *B* is in the group. What is the probability that *B* will be on the committee if *A* is on the committee?
    c.  What is the probability that neither *A* nor *B* is on the committee?

6.  Two coins and one die are tossed simultaneously. What is the probability that a head, a tail, and a 6 are obtained?

7. Two people are chosen at random from a class of thirty people.
   a. What is the probability that both were born on a Thursday?
   b. What is the probability that neither was born on a Thursday?
   c. What is the probability that at least one of the two was born on a Thursday?
   d. What is the probability that one was born on a Thursday and one was born on a Friday?

8. The probability that Sue will catch a certain bus is $\frac{2}{5}$ and the probability that Chris will catch the same bus is $\frac{1}{3}$.
   a. What is the probability that both will catch the bus?
   b. What is the probability that neither will catch the bus?
   c. What is the probability that at least one will catch the bus?

9. The probability that a child picked at random is a boy is $\frac{1}{2}$.
   a. What is the probability that at least two children in a family of five will be boys?
   b. What is the probability that the first three of the children will be boys and the last two girls?
   c. What is the probability that there will be exactly two boys in the family?

10. In a lottery 200 tickets were sold for four prizes. Mrs. Jensen bought four tickets.
    a. What is the probability that she will win exactly one prize?
    b. What is the probability that she will win at least one prize?
    c. What is the probability that she will win a prize, if three winning tickets have already been drawn and they were not hers?
    d. What is the probability that she will win no prizes?

11. A radio station calls phone numbers that are chosen at random from a list of 100,000 numbers. The recipient of the phone call is asked to name the amount in the jackpot. It is his if he guesses correctly.
    a. What is the probability that a particular phone number in the radio station's list will be called?
    b. The probability of knowing the jackpot was found to be 1/250. What is the probability that a person whose phone number is on the list will win the jackpot?

## —— 4-4    Permutations and Combinations

In the preceding sections we have found that, in a finite sample space of equally likely outcomes, the probability of an event $E$ is

$$P(E) = \frac{f}{n},$$

where $n$ is the total number of possible outcomes and $f$ is the total number of favorable outcomes in $E$. In this section we will discuss some counting schemes that will enable us to find $f$ and $n$ in certain kinds of probability problems.

In how many different orders can a salesman call on three different customers? This question deals with the number of ways in which a set of $n$ different occurrences can be arranged in a sequence. An arrangement of $n$ different objects (or occurrences) in a specified order is called a *permutation* of the $n$ objects. To *permute* a set of $n$ objects means to arrange them in a specific order.

Let us determine the number of permutations or sequences in which the salesman in the question posed above can visit his three customers. Call the customers $U$, $S$, and $A$. The salesman's first call can be to either $U$, $S$, or $A$; he has three choices. For his second call, the salesman has only two choices, and for his third call, there is only one choice left. Thus, altogether there are

$$3 \cdot 2 \cdot 1 = 3! \text{ or } 6$$

different ways in which the salesman can make his calls. We can picture this situation in the *tree diagram* in Figure 4-2. Notice that there are six different "branches" on our tree. One branch is shown in Figure 4-3. It is the permuta-

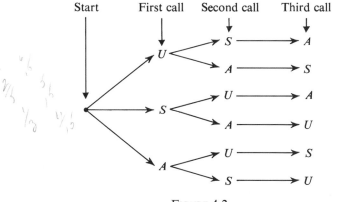

FIGURE 4-2.

tion $U$, $S$, then $A$, the case when the salesman calls on customer $U$ first, then customer $S$, then customer $A$.

Now suppose the salesman decides to visit customer $U$ first, then $S$, and then $A$. Also suppose that he can get to customer $U$ by car or train, to customer $S$ by ferry, car, bus, or plane, and to customer $A$ by train, bus, or plane. In how many ways can he visit his customers? To answer this question we can reason as follows: The salesman can get to customer $U$ in two ways, then to customer $S$ in four ways, and finally to customer $A$ in three ways. Thus, there are

$$2 \cdot 4 \cdot 3 = 24$$

ways in which the salesman can make his trip.

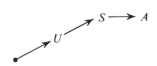

FIGURE 4-3.

In general, we can state the following principle, illustrated by our examples.

*If event A has m different outcomes and, after this event has occurred, event B has n different outcomes, then the event consisting of A, then B has m · n different outcomes.*

Of course, this principle can be applied to more than two events, as the examples above illustrate.

Now, instead of occurrences, let us deal with objects. Suppose we have five books and we want to put any three of them in a row on a display shelf. How many permutations or arrangements are possible? We will represent the number of permutations by

$$_5P_3.$$

This is read as "the number of permutations of five objects taken three at a time." Then we can use the principle stated above to find that

$$_5P_3 = 5 \cdot 4 \cdot 3 = 60,$$

since there are five different books we could choose for the first book in the row, four different books we could choose for the second book in the row, and three different books we could choose for the third book in the row. Thus $_5P_3$ is 60.

In general, we define $_nP_r$, the number of permutations of $n$ objects taken $r$ at a time, as

$$_nP_r = n(n-1)(n-2) \cdots (n-r+1),$$

where $r \leq n$.

This expression can be written

$$_nP_r = \frac{n(n-1)(n-2)\cdots(n-r+1)\cdot(n-r)\cdots 3\cdot 2\cdot 1}{(n-r)\cdots 3\cdot 2\cdot 1}$$

or

$$_nP_r = \frac{n!}{(n-r)!}.$$

In particular,

$$_nP_n = \frac{n!}{0!} = \frac{n!}{1} = n!.$$

Thus

$$_5P_3 = 5(4)(5-3+1) = 5\cdot 4\cdot 3 = 60,$$

as we have seen. Also,

$$_6P_4 = 6\cdot 5\cdot 4\cdot (6-4+1) = 6\cdot 5\cdot 4\cdot 3 = 360$$

and

$$_3P_3 = 3! = 6,$$

as we saw in this section's first example.

We can use permutations to solve certain types of probability problems. Suppose, for example, that an investment club chooses five people from whom they will select three to serve as presiding partner, financial partner, and trading partner. What is the probability of the event $A$ that Mr. Highberg will be elected presiding partner, Mr. Treffry will be elected financial partner, and Mr. Johns will be elected trading partner? (We are, of course, assuming that all possible choices of three members to fill these offices are equally likely. If in fact Mr. Johns is the village idiot, it is not very likely that he will be chosen trading partner.)

To answer this question we must know that the three officers can be chosen from a group of five candidates in

$$_5P_3 = \frac{5!}{2!} \quad \text{or} \quad 60$$

different ways. Only one of these ways is the listing in which we are interested. Therefore,

$$P(A) = \frac{1}{60}.$$

(Note: Do not confuse the $P$ in $P(A)$ standing for probability and the $P$ in $_5P_3$ standing for permutation.)

If we wish to find the number of distinct permutations possible with $n$ objects, when some of them are alike, we must make some adjustments in our expression for $_nP_n$. Suppose, for instance, that we would like to find the number of permutations $P$ of the letters

$$U, S, S, R.$$

If all the letters were different, the number of permutations would be

$$_4P_4 = 4!$$

Let us, for a moment, distinguish between the two $S$'s by calling them

$$S_1 \text{ and } S_2.$$

Then, corresponding to our original arrangement

$$U, S, S, R,$$

we obtain $2! = 2$ arrangements

$$U, S_1, S_2, R \text{ and } U, S_2, S_1, R$$

by permuting the now distinguishable letters $S_1$ and $S_2$ among themselves in all $2!$ possible ways. Any other distinct arrangement of $U$, $S$, $S$, and $R$ will also yield $2!$ corresponding arrangements of $U$, $S_1$, $S_2$ and $R$. Thus, if $x$ is the number of distinct arrangements of $U$, $S$, $S$, and $R$, then the number of distinct arrangements of $U$, $S_1$, $S_2$, and $R$ is

$$(2!)x.$$

However, we know that the number of permutations of $U$, $S_1$, $S_2$, and $R$ is

$$_4P_4 = 4!.$$

Thus

$$(2!)x = {_4P_4} = 4!,$$

and hence

$$x = \frac{_4P_4}{2!}.$$

We can generalize this example as follows:

The number of possible permutations of $n$ objects in which there are $n_1$ objects alike of one kind, $n_2$ objects alike of another kind, ..., $n_k$ objects alike of another kind is

$$\boxed{\frac{n!}{n_1!\, n_2! \cdots n_k!}},$$

where $n = n_1 + n_2 + \cdots + n_k$.

Thus, the number of permutations of the letters in the word Hawaii is

$$\frac{6!}{1!\,2!\,1!\,2!} = 180.$$

$$\uparrow \quad \uparrow \quad \uparrow \quad \uparrow$$

1h  2a's  1w  2i's

Next suppose we are interested in choosing $r$ objects from a set of $n$ different objects without being interested in how they are arranged. For instance, if we are choosing three employees from a group of four people, we will be interested in which people we picked, not the order in which we picked them. Such a selection is called a *combination*, as contrasted to a permutation, in which order matters. We shall denote the number of combinations of $r$ objects chosen from $n$ objects as

$$_nC_r \quad \text{or} \quad \binom{n}{r},$$

where, of course, $r \le n$. Let us call our four candidates for the job $A$, $B$, $C$, and $D$. How many combinations of three can we pick from this group of four? We see that there are four possible combinations of three from the group of four. They are

$$ABC, \ ABD, \ ACD, \ BCD.$$

From each of these selections we can get

$$_3P_3 = 3! = 6$$

different permutations, since each selection of three can be rearranged. See Table 4-3 for the $4 \times 3! = 24$ different permutations of four candidates taken three at a time.

| Combination | Permutations |
|---|---|
| ABC | ABC, ACB, BAC, BCA, CAB, CBA |
| ABD | ABD, ADB, BAD, BDA, DAB, DBA |
| ACD | ACD, ADC, CAD, CDA, DAC, DCA |
| BCD | BCD, BDC, CBD, CDB, DBC, DCB |

TABLE 4-3.

Thus, in our example,

(number of combinations) × 3! = number of permutations

or

$$(\text{number of combinations}) = \frac{\text{number of permutations}}{3!}.$$

Using numbers,

$$_4C_3 = \binom{4}{3} = \frac{_4P_3}{3!} = \frac{4 \cdot 3 \cdot 2}{3 \cdot 2 \cdot 1} = 4.$$

Just as this example hints, we can use this result to make the following generalization.

The number of combinations of $n$ different objects, taken $r$ at a time, is

$$_nC_r = \frac{_nP_r}{r!} = \frac{n!}{r!(n-r)!}.$$

Therefore, we can immediately say that

$$_{10}C_5 = \frac{10!}{5!5!} = \frac{10 \cdot 9 \cdot 8 \cdot 7 \cdot 6 \cdot 5!}{5 \cdot 4 \cdot 3 \cdot 2 \cdot 1 \cdot 5!} = 252.$$

For instance, 252 combinations of 5 different ice cream toppings can be chosen from a group of 10 sauces at an ice cream smorgasbord!

Combinations are especially useful in certain probability problems. Suppose, for instance, that a company has to lay off two supervisors from the Space Division and the Aircraft Division. The four supervisors in the Space Division and the six supervisors in the Aircraft Division are all equally qualified. Therefore, the company decides to pick the two to be laid off by random drawing.

The sample space consists of all possible choices of two men from the total group. There are $_{10}C_2$ such choices, so $n = {}_{10}C_2$. Let us determine probability of the event E which consists of all possible ways of choosing two men from the Space Division and no men from the Aircraft Division. There are $_4C_2 \cdot {}_6C_0$ possible favorable outcomes. Therefore,

$$P(E) = P(\text{both from Space Division}) = \frac{f}{n}$$

$$= \frac{_4C_2 \cdot {}_6C_0}{_{10}C_2}$$

$$= \frac{\dfrac{4!}{2!2!} \cdot \dfrac{6!}{0!6!}}{\dfrac{10!}{2!8!}}$$

$$= \frac{\dfrac{4 \cdot 3 \cdot 2 \cdot 1}{2 \cdot 1 \cdot 2 \cdot 1} \cdot \dfrac{6!}{1 \cdot 6!}}{\dfrac{10 \cdot 9 \cdot 8!}{2 \cdot 1 \cdot 8!}}$$

$$= \frac{6}{45} \quad \text{or} \quad \frac{2}{15}.$$

Similarly, the probability that both will be from the Aircraft Division is

$$P(\text{both from Aircraft Division}) = \frac{{}_4C_0 \cdot {}_6C_2}{{}_{10}C_2}$$

$$= \frac{\dfrac{4!}{0!\,4!} \cdot \dfrac{6!}{2!\,4!}}{\dfrac{10!}{2!\,8!}}$$

$$= \frac{\dfrac{4!}{1 \cdot 4!} \cdot \dfrac{6 \cdot 5 \cdot 4!}{2 \cdot 1 \cdot 4!}}{\dfrac{10 \cdot 9 \cdot 8!}{2!\,8!}}$$

$$= \frac{15}{45} \quad \text{or} \quad \frac{1}{3}.$$

As expected, $\frac{1}{3}$, the probability that both supervisors laid off will be from the Aircraft Division, is greater than $\frac{2}{15}$, the probability that both will be from the Space Division, since the Aircraft Division has more supervisors. (See Exercise 21.)

## EXERCISES

*Evaluate the expressions in Exercises 1–10.*

1.  $_5P_4.$

2.  $_4P_4.$

3.  $_3P_2.$

4.  $_5P_2.$

5.  $_nP_{n-3}.$

6.  $\binom{5}{5}.$

7.  $\binom{5}{4}.$

8.  $_5C_3.$

9.  $\binom{10}{6}.$

10.  $_nC_{n-2}.$

11.  Find the number of different permutations using all of the letters in the word Mississippi.

12.  Find the number of different permutations using all of the letters in the word Honolulu.

13.  How many different four-digit numerals can be made using the numerals in 1776?

14.  There were 10 seats at the head table for the 10 honored guests at the Presidential Banquet for the first men to land on the moon. How many different seating arrangements were possible?

15.  A city council is made up of the mayor and six councilmen.

    a.  How many different committees of three can be formed?

    b.  How many different committees of three can be formed with the mayor on no committee?

    c.  How many different committees of three can be formed with the mayor on all committees?

16. If there are 3 doors into the cafeteria and 4 lines, how many different "routes" are there to take when buying a meal?

17. The all-male Ivy League College, Elay, has decided to admit 250 girls to the freshman class this year. The admissions office has chosen 500 of the most qualified of the 2,000 applicants. How many different groups of 250 girls can be chosen from these 500? (Obtain an expression for the answer, but do not evaluate it.)

18. A program is to consist of 5 presentations of awards and 4 musical interludes. In how many different ways can the program be arranged so that the program will begin and end with music?

19. All license plates in King County must begin with the letter A. How many license numbers are available, if each license consists of three letters, followed by any three-digit number?

20. The ten directors of XPERT Corporation must elect a president, vice-president, and treasurer at their next meeting.
    a. How many arrangements of the officers are possible?
    b. What is the probability that a given director will be elected president?
    c. What is the probability that a given director will be chosen as an officer?

21. In the last example of this section, what is the probability that one supervisor in the Space Division and one in the Aircraft Division will be laid off?

22. The May draft call for Selective Service Districts A and B is a total of 10. Selective Service District A has 20 young men in the most eligible category and Selective Service District B has 25 men in the most eligible category.
    a. What is the probability that all of the men drafted will be from District A?
    b. What is the probability that all of the men drafted will be from District B?
    c. What is the probability that five of the men drafted will be from District A and five from District B?

## —— 4-5   Binomial Probability

In this section we will discuss probability in connection with binomial experiments. In such experiments there are two possible outcomes for each trial. One outcome is usually favorable to some event $E$ in which we are interested, while the other is not. If $E$ occurs, the outcome is called a *success*; if $E$ does not occur, the outcome is called a *failure*.

A coin-tossing experiment is an example of a binomial experiment. For instance, the experiment might consist of tossing a coin three times. We might define success as getting a tail and failure as getting a head. What is the probability of tossing a certain number of tails? The possible outcomes of this experiment are shown in Table 4-4 along with $x$, the number of tails

| Outcome | TTT | HTT | THT | TTH | HHT | THH | HTH | HHH |
|---|---|---|---|---|---|---|---|---|
| Number of tails $x$ | 3 | 2 | 2 | 2 | 1 | 1 | 1 | 0 |

TABLE 4-4.

resulting from each outcome. Note that there are 8 possible outcomes. If we denote by $P(x)$ the probability of tossing $x$ tails, the results in Table 4-4 tell us that

$$P(3) = \frac{1}{8},$$

since of the 8 possible outcomes there is only one outcome, namely TTT, in which 3 tails occur. Similarly,

$$P(2) = \frac{3}{8},$$

$$P(1) = \frac{3}{8},$$

and

$$P(0) = \frac{1}{8}.$$

We can also say that

$$P(x > 0) = \frac{7}{8}.$$

That is, the probability of tossing at least one tail is $\frac{7}{8}$. In other words, the probability of at least one success is $\frac{7}{8}$. Similarly, the probability of tossing two or more (at least two) tails is

$$P(x \geq 2) = \frac{4}{8} = \frac{1}{2},$$

and the probability of tossing less than two tails is

$$P(x < 2) = \frac{4}{8} = \frac{1}{2}.$$

Next suppose that we conduct an experiment which consists of drawing two marbles from a bowl containing 4 blue (B) marbles, 3 white (W) marbles, and 2 green (G) marbles. After each draw assume that the marble picked is replaced. This is not a binomial experiment, since there are three possible outcomes for each draw, not two. However, if we are interested in whether or not we draw a blue marble in each trial, the experiment can be considered a binomial experiment in which we designate picking a blue marble as success S and picking a white or green marble as failure F. Table 4-5 shows the possible outcomes along with the probabilities computed for each. There $x$ stands for the number of blue marbles drawn. Since we assume that the marble drawn is replaced each time, each drawing is considered an independent event. Thus, from Section 4-3 we know, for instance, that

$$P(SF) = P(S) \cdot P(F) = \frac{4}{9} \cdot \frac{5}{9} = \frac{20}{81}.$$

| Outcome | SS | SF | FS | FF |
|---|---|---|---|---|
| $x$ | 2 | 1 | 1 | 0 |
| Probability | $\frac{4}{9} \cdot \frac{4}{9} = \frac{16}{81}$ | $\frac{4}{9} \cdot \frac{5}{9} = \frac{20}{81}$ | $\frac{5}{9} \cdot \frac{4}{9} = \frac{20}{81}$ | $\frac{5}{9} \cdot \frac{5}{9} = \frac{25}{81}$ |

TABLE 4-5.

The sample space {SS, SF, FS, FF} in Table 4-5 can now be simplified to the sample space for the variable $x$, now {0, 1, 2}. We can now find the probabilities of the composite events corresponding to each value of $x$. For example, the event $x = 1$ corresponds to the events SF and FS. Thus, from Section 4-2 we have

$$P(1) = P(SF \cup FS)$$

$$= P(SF) \cup P(FS) - P(SF \cap FS)$$

$$= \frac{20}{81} + \frac{20}{81} - 0$$

$$= \frac{40}{81}.$$

(Note that SF ∩ FS = ∅, so $P(SF \cap FS) = 0$.) Table 4-6 gives the probabilities for each value of $x$.

| $x$ | 0 | 1 | 2 |
|---|---|---|---|
| $P(x)$ | $\left(\frac{5}{9}\right)^2 = \frac{25}{81}$ | $2 \cdot \frac{4}{9} \cdot \frac{5}{9} = \frac{40}{81}$ | $\left(\frac{4}{9}\right)^2 = \frac{16}{81}$ |

TABLE 4-6.

The two binomial experiments we have examined above have certain characteristics that are common to all binomial experiments. To be considered a binomial experiment,

1.  The experiment must have a certain fixed number of trials.
2.  Each trial must result in either a success or a failure.
3.  The trials must be independent.
4.  The probability of success in each trial must be the same.

In the two examples above we followed these steps to find the probability that $x$, the number of successes in the binomial experiment, will have value $c$:

1.  Construction of sample space for the complete experiment.
2.  Calculation of the probability for each member of the sample spaces.
3.  Association of the appropriate value of $x$ to each member of the sample space.
4.  Summation of the probabilities of those members of the sample space which correspond to $x = c$.

It is convenient to have a formula when a binomial experiment arises. Suppose we let $p$ denote the probability that a trial will result in a success and $q$ denote the probability that a trial will result in a failure. Remember that from Section 4-1 that $p + q = 1$, since for an event E, $P(E) + P(\sim E) = 1$. (Note that if the event E is success, the event $\sim E$ is failure.)

Further suppose that the experiment consists of $n$ trials, and denote by $x$ the number of successes obtained in these $n$ trials. Then $n - x$ is the number of failures obtained. One sequence of outcomes for trials of this experiment might be

$$\underbrace{SSS\cdots S}_{x} \quad \underbrace{FFF\cdots F}_{+ \quad n-x} = n.$$

Some others are

$$\underbrace{F}_{1} + \underbrace{SSS\cdots S}_{x} \quad \underbrace{FFF\cdots F}_{+ n-x-1} = n$$

and

$$\underbrace{FF}_{2} + \underbrace{SSS\cdots S}_{x} \quad \underbrace{FFF\cdots F}_{+ n-x-2} = n.$$

Since each trial of the experiment is independent, the probabilities of obtaining the three results above are, respectively,

$$p \cdot p \cdot p \cdots p \cdot q \cdot q \cdot q \cdots q = p^x q^{n-x},$$

$$\underbrace{q}_{1} \cdot \underbrace{p \cdot p \cdot p \cdots p}_{x} \cdot \underbrace{q \cdot q \cdot q \cdots q}_{n-x-1} = qp^x q^{n-x-1} = p^x q^{n-x},$$

and

$$\underbrace{q \cdot q}_{2} \cdot \underbrace{p \cdot p \cdot p \cdots p}_{x} \cdot \underbrace{q \cdot q \cdot q \cdots q}_{n-x-2} = q^2 p^x q^{n-x-2} = p^x q^{n-x}.$$

Thus the probabilities for these three sequences are the same. In fact, they will be the same for every sequence with $x$ successes and $n - x$ failures.

The number of different ways that the event can occur is the number of different sequences that can be written down involving $x$ successes S and $n - x$ failures F. We know from Section 4-4 that this is the number of ways of choosing $x$ positions for $S$ out of $n$ possible positions. Thus, the number of sequences that will produce exactly $x$ successes is

$$_nC_x = \binom{n}{x} = \frac{n!}{x!(n-x)!}.$$

Since each of these sequences gives one mutually exclusive way in which the event can occur, and each sequence has the same probability of occurring, namely $p^x q^{n-x}$, the probability $P$ of obtaining $x$ successes in $n$ trials of a binomial experiment is

$$\boxed{P(x) = \frac{n!}{x!(n-x)!} p^x q^{n-x}.}$$

We can apply this formula to the two examples at the beginning of this section. For instance, in the coin-tossing experiment, where $n = 3$ and $p = q = \frac{1}{2}$, we have for $x = 2$

$$P(2) = \frac{3!}{2!(3-2)!} \cdot \left(\frac{1}{2}\right)^2 \left(\frac{1}{2}\right)^{3-2}$$

$$= \frac{3 \cdot 2 \cdot 1}{2 \cdot 1 \cdot 1} \cdot \frac{1}{4} \cdot \frac{1}{2}$$

$$= \frac{3}{8},$$

the result we obtained before.

For the marble-drawing experiment, where $n = 2$, $p = \frac{4}{9}$, and $q = 1 - \frac{4}{9} = \frac{5}{9}$, we have for $x = 1$

$$P(1) = \frac{2!}{1!(2-1)!} \left(\frac{4}{9}\right)^1 \cdot \left(\frac{5}{9}\right)^{2-1}$$

$$= \frac{2 \cdot 1}{1 \cdot 1} \cdot \frac{4}{9} \cdot \frac{5}{9}$$

$$= \frac{40}{81},$$

just as Table 4-6 shows. Similarly, we have for the probability of less than two successes

$$P(<2) = P(0) + P(1)$$

$$= \frac{2!}{0!(2-0)!}\left(\frac{4}{9}\right)^0\left(\frac{5}{9}\right)^{2-0} + \frac{2!}{1!(2-1)!}\left(\frac{4}{9}\right)^1\left(\frac{5}{9}\right)^{2-1}$$

$$= \frac{2 \cdot 1}{1 \cdot 2 \cdot 1} \cdot 1 \cdot \frac{25}{81} + \frac{2 \cdot 1}{1 \cdot 1} \cdot \frac{4}{9} \cdot \frac{5}{9}$$

$$= \frac{25}{81} + \frac{40}{81}$$

$$= \frac{65}{81}.$$

Chances are quite good that at least one blue marble will be drawn.

So far, the binomial experiments we have considered have been related to games of chance. Experiments such as these, which consist of repetitions of independent trials with only two possible outcomes, are mathematical models for real life problems in a variety of fields. Two examples follow.

The probability that the children in a certain family will have brown eyes is $\frac{3}{4}$. If there are five children in the family, what is the probability that exactly three of them will have brown eyes?

Before we may apply the formula for binomial probability, we must check that this problem meets the four requirements of a binomial experiment as given above. First, there is a fixed number of trials (the birth of each child), namely $n = 5$. Second, each trial results in either a success (the birth of a brown-eyed child) or a failure (the birth of a child who has eyes of a color other than brown). Third, each trial (birth) is certainly independent. And, fourth, the probability of success for each birth is the same due to basic laws of heredity.

Now that we are satisfied that the problem fits the model of a binomial distribution, we can apply the formula for binomial probability where $n = 5$, $p = \frac{3}{4}$, $q = 1 - \frac{3}{4} = \frac{1}{4}$, and $x = 3$. We have

$$P(3) = \frac{5!}{3!(5-3)!}\left(\frac{3}{4}\right)^3\left(\frac{1}{4}\right)^{5-3}$$

$$= \frac{5 \cdot 4 \cdot 3!}{3! \cdot 2 \cdot 1} \cdot \frac{27}{64} \cdot \frac{1}{16}$$

$$= \frac{135}{512}.$$

Therefore, the probability that the family in question will have exactly three brown-eyed children is $\frac{135}{512}$.

In business sampling is used to rate batches of certain products. For instance, suppose among cans of pineapple produced by a certain company it has been found that about one in 100 cans contains sour pineapple. If from a large shipment 10 cans are selected, what is the probability that less than 2 cans of sour pineapple will be found?

We can solve this problem by using the formula for binomial probability. (You should check that the conditions for a binomial experiment are satisfied.) Here $n = 10$, $p = \frac{1}{100}$, and $q = 1 - \frac{1}{100} = \frac{99}{100}$. Thus,

$$P(\text{less than 2 successes}) = P(0) + P(1)$$

$$= \frac{10!}{0!(10-0)!}\left(\frac{1}{100}\right)^0\left(\frac{99}{100}\right)^{10}$$

$$+ \frac{10!}{1!(10-1)!}\left(\frac{1}{100}\right)^1\left(\frac{99}{100}\right)^9$$

$$\approx 0.904 + 0.091$$

$$= 0.995.$$

In the process of obtaining an answer to the preceding problem we did not compute $P(0)$ and $P(1)$ by hand! The factors $\left(\frac{99}{100}\right)^{10}$ and $\left(\frac{99}{100}\right)^9$ would have made this a long, dreary task. Instead, we used a table such as that in Appendix III. That table gives the value of $\binom{n}{x}p^x q^{n-x}$, where $q = 1 - p$, for values of $p = 0.01, 0.05, 0.10, 0.20, 0.30, 0.40, 0.50, 0.60, 0.70, 0.80, 0.90,$ 0.95, and 0.99. In our example, $n = 10$ and $x = 0$ or 1, so to find the values of $P(0)$ and $P(1)$ we found the section corresponding to $n = 10$, $x = 0$ and 1 and $p = \frac{1}{100} = 0.01$ as shown in Table 4-7.

| $n$ | $x$ | .01 | .05 | $p$ |
|-----|-----|-----|-----|-----|
| | . | | . | |
| | . | | . | |
| | . | | . | |
| 10 | 0 | 904 | . . . | $P(0) = 0.904$ |
| | 1 | 091 | . . . | $P(1) = 0.091$ |
| | . | | . | |
| | . | | . | |
| | . | | . | |

TABLE 4-7.

To find $P$ (less than 2 successes) we might also have used the fact that

$$P \text{ (less than 2 successes)} = 1 - P \text{ (2 or more successes)}$$

and a table such as that shown in Appendix IV. That table gives the probability of observing $r$ or more successes in binomial experiments for certain values of $n$, $r$, and $p$. In other words, it gives

$$P(r \text{ or more successes}) = \binom{n}{r}p^r q^{n-r} + \binom{n}{r+1}p^{r+1}q^{n-r-1} + \cdots + \binom{n}{n}p^n q^0$$

$$= \sum_{x=r}^{n} \binom{n}{x}p^x q^{n-x}.$$

Thus, to find $P$ (less than 2 successes), where $n = 10$ and $r = 2$ in our example, we locate the section in Appendix IV corresponding to $n = 10$, $r = 2$, and

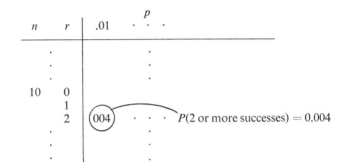

TABLE 4-8.

$p = 0.01$ as shown in Table 4-8. Thus,

$$P(\text{less than 2 successes}) = 1 - P \text{ (2 or more successes)}$$
$$= 1 - 0.004$$
$$= 0.996$$

This value for $P$(less than 2 successes) differs from the one found above (using Appendix III) by only 0.001.

A final comment should be made concerning the tables in Appendixes III and IV. It is possible to find the value of

$$\binom{n}{x}p^x q^{n-x} \quad \text{or} \quad \sum_{x=r}^{n} \binom{n}{x}p^x q^{n-x}$$

for values of $p$ other than the thirteen values 0.01, 0.05, ..., 0.99 listed. The procedure called *interpolation* must be used.

Suppose $p = 0.16$ and we want to find $P(2)$ for $n = 10$. Noting that $p = 0.16$ is between the listed $p$ values of 0.10 and 0.20, we could find the values listed in Table 4-9 from Appendix III. Since $p = 0.16$ is between

| $p$ | $P(2)$ |
|------|--------|
| 0.10 | 0.194 |
| 0.16 | $P(2) = ?$ |
| 0.20 | 0.302 |

TABLE 4-9.

$p = 0.10$ and $p = 0.20$, the corresponding value of $P(2)$ must be between the values of $P(2)$ corresponding to $p = 0.10$ and $p = 0.20$. By assuming linearity we can reason that the value of $P(2)$ when $n = 10$ and $p = 0.16$ must satisfy the following proportion:

$$\frac{0.16 - 0.10}{0.20 - 0.10} = \frac{P(2) - 0.194}{0.302 - 0.194}. \tag{1}$$

In words, the ratio of the difference between 0.16 and 0.10 to the difference between 0.20 and 0.10 must be equal to the ratio of the difference between $P(2)$ and 0.194 and 0.302 and 0.194. So, simplifying (1) and solving for $P(2)$ we obtain

$$\frac{0.06}{0.1} = \frac{P(2) - 0.194}{0.108},$$

$$\frac{6}{10} = \frac{P(2) - 0.194}{0.108},$$

$$\frac{6}{10}(0.108) = P(2) - 0.194,$$

$$0.0648 = P(2) - 0.194,$$

$$0.0648 + 0.194 = P(2),$$

$$0.2588 = P(2).$$

Hence, $P(2) = 0.2588$ when $n = 10$ and $p = 0.16$.

EXERCISES ─────────────────────────────────

Use the tables in Appendixes III and IV if necessary to solve the following problems.

1. Find the probability of obtaining exactly 3 successes in 5 trials of a binomial experiment in which the probability of success is $1/3$.
2. Find the probability of obtaining at least 3 successes in 5 trials of a binomial experiment in which the probability of success is $1/3$.

3. Find the probability of obtaining at most 3 successes in 5 trials of a binomial experiment in which the probability of success is 1/3.

4. The probability of obtaining 4 successes in 5 trials of a binomial experiment is 0.006. What is the probability of success? (*Hint*: Use Appendix III.)

5. The probability of obtaining at least 2 successes in 5 trials of a binomial experiment is 0.263. What is the probability of success? (*Hint:* Use Appendix IV).

*In Exercises 6 through 8 a fair die is tossed 5 times.*

6. Find the probability that exactly three ones are tossed.

7. Find the probability that at least three ones are tossed.

8. Find the probability that less than three ones are tossed.

*In Exercises 9 through 11, three pieces of fruit are picked at random with replacement from a bag containing two tangerines (T), three oranges (O), and four lemons (L).*

9. Find the probability that no lemons are picked.

10. Find the probability that at least one lemon is picked.

11. Find the probability that less than two lemons are picked.

*There are four children in the family of Exercises 12 and 13. Assume the probability of giving birth to a boy is 1/2.*

12. Find the probability that exactly two of the children are boys.

13. Find the probability that at least one of the children is a boy.

*Of the cars imported by a certain firm, 5% have been found to have faulty brakes. Ten cars in a large shipment are chosen at random for inspection in Exercises 14 through 17.*

14. Find the probability that no defective cars are discovered.

15. Find the probability that four of the cars are found to be defective.

16. Find the probability that more than one of the cars are found to be defective.

17. Find the probability that less than three of the cars are found to be defective.

18. A study of graduating classes of a small women's college in California shows that 95% of its graduates marry within five years of graduation. What is the probability that at least 15 members of the 20 members of the class of 1972 will be married by 1977?

19. It was discovered that 40% of all cranberry shipments were contaminated by an extremely poisonous insecticide. What is the probability that at least two uncontaminated shipments will be discovered after only three shipments are examined?

## —— 4-6 Expected Value

Suppose an experiment with $k$ possible outcomes is conducted $n$ times and the possible outcomes, which are given numerical values $a_1, a_2, \ldots, a_k$, occur $f_1, f_2, \ldots, f_k$ times. (The number of times each outcome occurs is called the *frequency* of the outcome.) The *arithmetic mean* or *average* of the outcome values which occurred during the $n$ trials is

$$\text{arithmetic average} = \frac{a_1 f_1 + a_2 f_2 + \cdots + a_k f_k}{n}.$$

Note that $f_1 + f_2 + \cdots + f_k = n$.

As an example consider the results of tossing a die 7 times as shown in Table 4-10.

| Outcome $a_i$ | Frequency $f_i$ |
|:---:|:---:|
| 1 | 1 |
| 2 | 0 |
| 3 | 2 |
| 4 | 1 |
| 5 | 2 |
| 6 | 1 |
|  | $\sum f_i = 7 = n$ |

TABLE 4-10.

Then we have

$$\text{arithmetic average} = \frac{1 \cdot 1 + 2 \cdot 0 + 3 \cdot 2 + 4 \cdot 1 + 5 \cdot 2 + 6 \cdot 1}{7}$$

$$= \frac{27}{7} \quad \text{or} \quad 3\frac{6}{7}.$$

If we rewrite the formula for arithmetic average in (1) as

$$\text{arithmetic average} = \frac{a_1 f_1}{n} + \frac{a_2 f_2}{n} + \cdots + \frac{a_k f_k}{n},$$

we know from our definition of probability in Section 4-1 that as $n$ becomes larger and larger each factor $f_i/n$ will approach $p_i$, the probability that the outcome $a_i$ occurs. We thus have the following definition.

If the possible outcomes of an experiment are given numerical values $a_1, a_2, \ldots, a_k$ and these outcomes occur with the probabilities $p_1, p_2, \ldots, p_k$ the *expected value* of the experiment is

$$E = a_1 p_1 + a_2 p_2 + \cdots + a_k p_k.$$

For our example $p_1 = p_2 = p_3 = p_4 = p_5 = p_6 = \frac{1}{6}$. Thus,

$$E = 1 \cdot \frac{1}{6} + 2 \cdot \frac{1}{6} + 3 \cdot \frac{1}{6} + 4 \cdot \frac{1}{6} + 5 \cdot \frac{1}{6} + 6 \cdot \frac{1}{6}$$

$$= \frac{21}{6} \text{ or } 3\frac{1}{2}.$$

This value for the expected value is close to the arithmetic average found above. This is not merely a coincidence! The arithmetic average of several trials and the expected value of an experiment will have, in general, *about* the same value. You must remember, however, that they are not the same, since $f_i/n$ is not exactly equal to $p_i$. As $n$, the number of trials increases, however, the arithmetic average should approach the expected value.

As another example of expected value, suppose a person bets $5 that a 6 will turn up when he tosses a die. (Of course it is a fair die!) Since the probability of tossing a 6 is $\frac{1}{6}$, and since the possible outcomes are the gain or loss of $5, the expected value is

$$E = \$5\left(\frac{1}{6}\right) + (-\$5)\left(\frac{5}{6}\right) = \frac{-\$20}{6} \text{ or } -\$3.33.$$

(Notice that the negative sign indicates the outcome "loss of $5.") If the person bets $5 that an even number will be tossed, the expected value is

$$E = \$5\left(\frac{3}{6}\right) + -\$5\left(\frac{3}{6}\right) = \$0,$$

where $\frac{3}{6}$ is the probability that an even number will be tossed and $1 - \frac{3}{6} = \frac{3}{6}$ is the probability that an odd number will be tossed. When the same person bets $5 that a multiple of two or three will be tossed, the expected value is

$$E = \$5\left(\frac{4}{6}\right) + (-\$5)\left(\frac{2}{6}\right) = \frac{\$10}{6} \text{ or } \$1.67,$$

where $\frac{4}{6}$ is the probability that a multiple of two or three will be tossed (namely 2, 3, 4, 6) and $1 - \frac{4}{6} = \frac{2}{6}$ is the probability that a multiple of two or three will not be tossed. These three examples should illustrate that the expected value of an experiment is *not* necessarily the value that will occur in a single trial of the experiment.

Furthermore, it should be noted that if an experiment with expected value $E$ is repeated many times and if we expect $a_1$ in $p_1$ of the trials (that is, with probability $p_1$), $a_2$ in $p_2$ of the trials, ..., $a_n$ in $p_n$ of the trials, then the average outcome per trial which can be expected is $E$. For instance, in a game $E$ can be interpreted as the average amount one may expect to win per play (trial) in a large number of plays. Thus in the example above the person would be foolish to bet \$5 per play that a 6 would turn up in a toss of a fair die, since in the long run he could expect to lose about \$3.33 per play. However, in the long run he could expect to break even if he bet \$5 that an even number would be tossed; and he could expect to win about \$1.67 per play in the long run if he repeatedly bet \$5 that a multiple of two or three would be tossed.

If a game has a positive expected value, it is called *favorable*. If it has a negative expected value, it is called *unfavorable*; and if it has an expected value of zero, then it is called *fair*. Each of these different types of games has been illustrated above.

From Section 4-5 we know that the probability of $x$ successes in $n$ independent trials when only two outcomes are possible is

$$\binom{n}{x} p^x q^{n-x},$$

where $p$ is the probability of success and $q$ is the probability of failure. If, in an experiment consisting of three tosses of a fair die, throwing a 6 is considered success, the expected value or number of successes is

(number of 6's)
↓

$$E = 0\binom{3}{0}\left(\frac{1}{6}\right)^0\left(\frac{5}{6}\right)^3 + 1\binom{3}{1}\left(\frac{1}{6}\right)^1\left(\frac{5}{6}\right)^2 + 2\binom{3}{2}\left(\frac{1}{6}\right)^2\left(\frac{5}{6}\right)^1 + 3\binom{3}{3}\left(\frac{1}{6}\right)^3\left(\frac{5}{6}\right)^0,$$

probability
of obtaining
0 6's

the sum of the products of the four possible numbers of successes (0, 1, 2, 3) and their corresponding probabilities. (Note that $p = \frac{1}{6}$ and $q = \frac{5}{6}$.) Thus,

$$E = 1 \cdot \frac{3 \cdot 2!}{1!\,2!} \cdot \frac{1}{6} \cdot \frac{25}{36} + 2 \cdot \frac{3 \cdot 2!}{2!\,1!} \cdot \frac{1}{36} \cdot \frac{5}{6} + 3 \cdot \frac{3!}{3!} \cdot \frac{1}{216} \cdot 1$$

$$= 3 \cdot \frac{25}{216} + 6 \cdot \frac{5}{216} + 3 \cdot \frac{1}{216}$$

$$= \frac{75}{216} + \frac{30}{216} + \frac{3}{216}$$

$$= \frac{108}{216} \quad \text{or} \quad \frac{1}{2}.$$

Note that $\frac{1}{2} = 3 \cdot \frac{1}{6} = np$.

In fact, it can be shown in general that in a two-outcome experiment consisting of $n$ independent trials with probability $p$ of success, the expected number of successes is $np$.

Applications of the concept of expected value are not confined to games of chance. For instance, expected value can be used to make business decisions. Suppose Locking Aircraft must choose between bidding on Contracts I and II. Table 4-11 summarizes for each of these contracts information concerning net

| Contract | Profit | Bid cost | Probability of winning bid |
|----------|--------|----------|----------------------------|
| I | $50,000 | $1,000 | 0.20 |
| II | $40,000 | $ 500 | 0.25 |

TABLE 4-11.

profit, cost of preparing the contract bid, and the estimated probability that Locking will win the bid. Using this information we find that

$$E_I = \$50,000(0.20) + (-\$1,000)(0.80) = \$9,200$$

and

$$E_{II} = \$40,000(0.25) + (-\$500)(0.75) = \$9,625.$$

These results suggest that Locking should bid on Contract II.

The preceding example is only one of many applications of the concept of expected value. Some others will be given in the exercises for this section and in the next section.

*EXERCISES*

1. The following table gives the approximate percent of blacks in schools with whites in 11 Southern states for the school years 1960–1961 to 1968–1969.

| School year | Percent |
|-------------|---------|
| 1960–1961 | 0.25% |
| 1961–1962 | 0.40% |
| 1962–1963 | 0.50% |
| 1963–1964 | 1.00% |
| 1964–1965 | 3.00% |
| 1965–1966 | 6.00% |
| 1966–1967 | 13.00% |
| 1967–1968 | 14.00% |
| 1968–1969 | 20.00% |

Find the arithmetic mean or average percent of blacks in schools with whites in 11 Southern states from 1960 to 1969.

2. The following table gives the quantities of wheat in millions of metric tons imported and exported by the Soviet Union during the years 1963 to 1968 inclusive.

| Year | Imports | Exports |
|------|---------|---------|
| 1963 | 3.00 | 4.00 |
| 1964 | 7.00 | 2.00 |
| 1965 | 6.25 | 1.75 |
| 1966 | 7.50 | 2.75 |
| 1967 | 2.00 | 5.00 |
| 1968 | 1.50 | 4.00 |

a. Find the average quantity of wheat imported by the Soviets during the period 1963–1968.
b. Find the average quantity of wheat exported by the Soviets during the period 1963–1968.

3. The following table gives the number of points scored by Ohio State during the 1967 football season.

| Points | Frequency |
|--------|-----------|
| 6 | 2 |
| 7 | 1 |
| 13 | 1 |
| 17 | 1 |
| 21 | 2 |
| 24 | 1 |
| 30 | 1 |

Find the average number of points scored per game by Ohio State in 1967.

4. Two coins are tossed.
   a. What is the probability that two heads will appear?
   b. What is the probability that one head will appear?
   c. What is the probability that no heads will appear?
   d. What is the expected value of this " game " to a person who will get $2.00 for each head which appears?

5. Jake's father agrees to give him $5.00 if he receives an A in English on his report card, $3.00 if he receives a B, and nothing if he receives a C. However, Jake must pay his father $3.00 if he receives a D and $5.00

if he receives an F. Jake estimates the following probabilities for obtaining the the given grades in English.

| Grade | Probability |
|-------|-------------|
| A | .05 |
| B | .10 |
| C | .20 |
| D | .30 |
| F | .35 |

How much money should Jake expect to make (or lose) on this agreement?

6. The probability that a man aged 21 will live for one year is 0.998. How much should he pay for a one-year insurance policy worth $10,000?

7. The probability that a man aged 40 will live to age 60 is 0.83. How much should he pay for a twenty-year insurance policy worth $10,000?

8. In a shipment of thirty items, five are known to be defective.
   a. If two items are picked at random, how many defective articles can one expect to find?
   b. If five items are picked at random, how many defective articles can one expect to find?

9. In a lottery 500 tickets are sold for $2 apiece. The first prize is worth $250, the second prize is worth $100, and the third prize is worth $50.
   a. If a person purchases 1 ticket, what is the expected net gain?
   b. If a person purchases 2 tickets, what is the expected net gain?

10. A shoe store stocks 5 kinds of winter boots denoted by the numbers 1–5. The table below gives the probability $p_i$ that a customer will select boot $i$ during the winter and the corresponding profits $pr_i$.

| Boot $i$ | Probability of sale $p_i$ | Profit $pr_i$ |
|----------|---------------------------|---------------|
| 1 | 0.40 | $4.00 |
| 2 | 0.20 | $5.00 |
| 3 | 0.25 | $2.00 |
| 4 | 0.10 | $3.00 |
| 5 | 0.05 | $8.00 |

What is the expected profit?

11. A company will make $10,000 profit if it wins a government contract. It estimates that it will cost $1,000 to prepare the proposal. If the probability of the company's winning the contract is $\frac{1}{4}$, what is the expected value of the contract?

12. Kent Construction Company must choose between bidding on contracts I, II, III, and IV. The table below gives the net profit, cost of preparing contract bid, and the estimated probability that Kent Construction Company will win the bid.
    a.  What is the expected value for each contract?
    b.  On which contract do the results suggest Kent Construction should bid?

| Contract | Profit | Bid Cost | Probability of Winning Contract |
|---|---|---|---|
| I | $100,000 | $20,000 | 0.30 |
| II | $150,000 | $40,000 | 0.25 |
| III | $ 50,000 | $ 1,000 | 0.50 |
| IV | $ 75,000 | $ 2,500 | 0.75 |

—— 4-7    Applying Expected Value in Business

In this section we will consider some additional applications of expected value in the field of business.

Expected value is especially useful when a business must decide on purchases of stock when certain unknowns, such as the number of items to be sold, are involved. When perishable items or items that lose their value, such as magazines, are involved, it is especially important that a businessman make wise decisions concerning purchases of stock.

Suppose as an example that Food King Supermarket purchases boxes containing twenty loaves of bread for $4.00 each and makes a profit of $1.00 on each twenty loaves of bread it sells. Since the bread gets stale after six days or so, Food King must decide carefully how many boxes of bread to order. Table 4-12 shows five quantities of bread (in numbers of boxes) and

| Number of boxes | Times sold | Probability |
|---|---|---|
| 100 | 4 | 4/30 = 2/15 |
| 80 | 6 | 6/30 = 1/5 |
| 60 | 12 | 12/30 = 2/5 |
| 40 | 6 | 6/30 = 1/5 |
| 20 | 2 | 2/30 = 1/15 |
| | Total: 30 | |

TABLE 4-12.

the frequency with which these quantities were sold during the last thirty 6-day periods. Also shown for each quantity is the probability that the quantity was sold. This probability is given by the ratio

$$\frac{\text{number of times the quantity sold}}{30}.$$

Using the information in Table 4-12 we can find the expected number of boxes of bread that will be sold from the next shipment if there is no reason (such as a bad storm, or a strike, or a government ban barring the use of calcium propionate as a preservative) to believe selling conditions will be altered. We have

$$E = 100\left(\frac{2}{15}\right) + 80\left(\frac{1}{5}\right) + 60\left(\frac{2}{5}\right) + 40\left(\frac{1}{5}\right) + 20\left(\frac{1}{15}\right)$$

$$= \frac{200}{15} + \frac{80}{5} + \frac{120}{5} + \frac{40}{5} + \frac{20}{15}$$

$$= \frac{940}{15} \quad \text{or} \quad 62\frac{2}{3} \text{ boxes.}$$

Thus, barring unforeseen circumstances, Food King can expect to sell $62\frac{2}{3}$ boxes (or about $20 \cdot 62\frac{2}{3}$ or 1,253 loaves) of bread during the next six-day period.

Food King should also analyze possible profits and losses before it places its bread order for the next six-day period. If, for instance, the store buys more bread than it can sell, it will lose the $4.00 already paid for each unsold box of bread. On the other hand, if the demand for bread is more than Food King has in stock, the store will lose a $1.00 profit for each box of bread not in stock. Should the store be conservative or take a chance when ordering?

To help answer this question information such as shown in Table 4-13 can be analyzed. There the profits possible for five combinations of boxes sold and boxes stocked are shown. Each entry is

$$\text{profit} - \text{loss from unsold stock}$$

at the end of the six-day period. For instance, if the store stocks 100 boxes of bread and sells 100 boxes of bread, it will have no stock left over. The profit is thus

$$\$1(100) - \$4(0) = \$100.$$

On the other hand, if the store stocks 100 boxes of bread and sells only 60 boxes, it will have 40 boxes of bread left over. In this case the profit is

$$\$1(60) - \$4(40) = {}^-\$100.$$

The store has a loss! (Notice that the figures in Table 4-13 do not take into

| Boxes sold \ Boxes stocked | 100 | 80 | 60 | 40 | 20 |
|---|---|---|---|---|---|
| 100 | $100 | $80 | $60 | $40 | $20 |
| 80 | 0 | 80 | 60 | 40 | 20 |
| 60 | $-100$ | $-20$ | 60 | 40 | 20 |
| 40 | $-200$ | $-120$ | $-40$ | 40 | 20 |
| 20 | $-300$ | $-220$ | $-140$ | $-60$ | 20 |

*Possible profits*

TABLE 4-13.

account the loss of business Food King sustains when the demand for bread is bigger than the stock on hand.)

For each possible quantity of stock the expected profit can be computed by combining the possible profits shown in Table 4-13 with the probability that each quantity will be sold as shown in Table 4-12. The expected profits for the five quantities considered in Table 4-12 and 4-13 are shown in Table 4-14. In particular, the expected profit when 100 boxes are stocked is the sum

| Number of boxes stocked | Expected profit |
|---|---|
| 100 | $\frac{2}{15}(100) + \frac{1}{5}(0) + \frac{2}{5}(-100) + \frac{1}{5}(-200) + \frac{1}{15}(-300) = -\frac{1300}{15}$ or $-$86.67 |
| 80 | $\frac{2}{15}(80) + \frac{1}{5}(80) + \frac{2}{5}(-20) + \frac{1}{5}(-120) + \frac{1}{15}(-220) = -\frac{100}{5}$ or $-$20.00 |
| 60 | $\frac{2}{15}(60) + \frac{1}{5}(60) + \frac{2}{5}(60) + \frac{1}{5}(-40) + \frac{1}{15}(-140) = \frac{400}{15}$ or $26.67 |
| 40 | $\frac{2}{15}(40) + \frac{1}{5}(40) + \frac{2}{5}(40) + \frac{1}{5}(40) + \frac{1}{15}(-60) = \frac{500}{15}$ or $33.33 |
| 20 | $\frac{2}{15}(20) + \frac{1}{5}(20) + \frac{2}{5}(20) + \frac{1}{5}(20) + \frac{1}{15}(20) = \frac{300}{15}$ or $20.00 |

TABLE 4-14.

of the products below:

P(100 boxes sold) × (Possible profit; 100 boxes sold, 100 boxes stocked),
P(80 boxes sold) × (Possible profit; 80 boxes sold, 100 boxes stocked),
P(60 boxes sold) × (Possible profit; 60 boxes sold, 100 boxes stocked),
P(40 boxes sold) × (Possible profit; 40 boxes sold, 100 boxes stocked),
P(20 boxes sold) × (Possible profit; 20 boxes sold, 100 boxes stocked).

Table 4-14 shows that in this case the store can expect a loss.

For the values shown in Table 4-14, the maximum profit can be expected when 40 boxes of bread are stocked. It is most important to notice that this expected value of $33.33 is only approximate! Chances are small that the store will make exactly this much profit if it stocks 40 boxes of bread. However, in the long run, *under similar conditions*, the store can expect an average profit of $33.33 if it purchases 40 boxes of bread.

Up to now, we have assumed that the bread is totally worthless after six days. Food King, however, may be able to sell any remaining bread at a price, called *salvage value*. Suppose the salvage value is $2 per box. Table 4-15

| Boxes sold \ Boxes stocked | 100 | 80 | 60 | 40 | 20 |
|---|---|---|---|---|---|
| 100 | $100 | $80 | $60 | $40 | $20 |
| 80 | 40 | 80 | 60 | 40 | 20 |
| 60 | -20 | 20 | 60 | 40 | 20 |
| 40 | -80 | -40 | 0 | 40 | 20 |
| 20 | -140 | -100 | -60 | -20 | 20 |

*Possible profits with salvage value*

TABLE 4-15.

gives the possible profits for the different combinations of boxes sold and boxes stocked given in Table 4-13 with the salvage value taken into account. Each entry is

Profit − loss from unsold stock + $2 (quantity of unsold stock).

For example, the entry for 40 boxes sold and 60 boxes stocked is

$$\$1(40) - \$4(20) + \$2(20) = 0.$$

Thus when the salvage value is taken into account, the possible profit when 40 boxes are sold and 60 are stocked is $0, as opposed to a loss of $40 when there is no salvage value. From the possible profits in Table 4-15 and the probabilities in Table 4-12 the expected profits with salvage value taken into account can be computed just as in Table 4-14. (See Exercise 1.)

Food King can also take into account possible losses for certain combinations of boxes of bread sold and stocked when it is trying to decide how much bread to stock. We have already discussed losses that occur when an item loses its value after a certain time. However, we have not yet taken into account losses caused by a shortage in stock when demand exists. Such a loss is called an *opportunity loss*. We can define it as follows:

> opportunity loss = greatest possible profit − profit.

In other words an opportunity loss is the difference between the profit actually made and the profit that could have been made if the supply of stock had been the same as the demand. With this interpretation of opportunity loss we can compute entries for a loss table as shown in Table 4-16. There

| Boxes sold \ Boxes stocked | 100 | 80 | 60 | 40 | 20 |
|---|---|---|---|---|---|
| 100 | $ 0 | $ 20 | $ 40 | $60 | $80 |
| 80 | 80 | 0 | 20 | 40 | 60 |
| 60 | 160 | 80 | 0 | 20 | 40 |
| 40 | 240 | 160 | 80 | 0 | 20 |
| 20 | 320 | 240 | 160 | 80 | 0 |

*Possible losses*

TABLE 4-16.

each entry is the largest profit for the corresponding number of boxes sold minus the profit actually made as shown in Table 4-13. For instance, the largest profit possible when 100 boxes are sold is $100. Thus, the possible loss for 100 boxes stocked is $100 − $100 or 0. For 80 boxes stocked, the possible loss is $100 − $80 or $20.

Unlike Table 4-13, Table 4-16 shows losses due to both understocking as well as overstocking. The losses from understocking are shown above the diagonal entries of zero in Table 4-16; the losses from overstocking are shown below the diagonal. (Note that the entries in this table assume that bread has no salvage value. See Exercise 2.)

We can now compute the expected loss for 100, 80, 60, 40 and 20 boxes of bread in stock using the probabilities for certain numbers of sales as computed in Table 4-12. These expected losses are shown in Table 4-17.

| Number of boxes stocked | Expected loss |
|---|---|
| 100 | $\frac{2}{15}(0) + \frac{1}{5}(80) + \frac{2}{5}(160) + \frac{1}{5}(240) + \frac{1}{15}(320) = \frac{448}{3}$ or $149.33 |
| 80 | $\frac{2}{15}(20) + \frac{1}{5}(0) + \frac{2}{5}(80) + \frac{1}{5}(160) + \frac{1}{15}(240) = \frac{248}{3}$ or $82.67 |
| 60 | $\frac{2}{15}(40) + \frac{1}{5}(20) + \frac{2}{5}(0) + \frac{1}{5}(80) + \frac{1}{15}(160) = \frac{108}{3}$ or $36.00 |
| 40 | $\frac{2}{15}(60) + \frac{1}{5}(40) + \frac{2}{5}(20) + \frac{1}{5}(0) + \frac{1}{15}(80) = \frac{88}{3}$ or $29.33 |
| 20 | $\frac{2}{15}(80) + \frac{1}{5}(60) + \frac{2}{5}(40) + \frac{1}{5}(20) + \frac{1}{15}(0) = \frac{128}{3}$ or $42.67 |

TABLE 4-17.

Using these figures and the figures for expected profit as calculated in Table 4-14, we can compare the expected profits and losses for the five given quantities of stock in our example. See Table 4-18. There the figures show

| Number of boxes stocked | Expected profit | Expected loss |
|:---:|:---:|:---:|
| 100 | $-$86.67 | $149.33 |
| 80 | $-$20.00 | 82.67 |
| 60 | 26.67 | 36.00 |
| 40 | 33.33 | 29.33 |
| 20 | 20.00 | 42.67 |

TABLE 4-18.

that the largest expected profit occurs for forty boxes of bread stocked. The lowest expected loss occurs for this quantity too.

*In general, the highest expected profit always accurs for the same quantity of stock as the lowest expected loss.*Thus, to obtain the highest expected profit, a business could choose to stock the quantity giving it the lowest expected loss.

*EXERCISES*

1.   For the example of this section compute the expected profits for 100, 80, 60, 40, and 20 boxes of bread stocked taking the salvage value into account.
2.   For the example of this section write out a table of possible losses for 100, 80, 60, 40, and 20 boxes of bread stocked taking the salvage value into account.
3.   For the example of this section compute the expected losses for 100, 80, 60, 40, and 20 boxes of bread stocked taking the salvage value into account.

*In the example of this section suppose in the last forty 6-day periods the following numbers of boxes of bread were sold the numbers of times given. Use this information for Exercises 4–11.*

| Number of boxes | Times sold |
|:---:|:---:|
| 100 | 10 |
| 80 | 6 |
| 60 | 15 |
| 40 | 4 |
| 20 | 5 |

Total: 40

4.   Compute for each of the five quantities of bread in the table above the probability that it was sold.

5. Assuming that selling conditions will remain constant, compute the expected number of boxes of bread that will be sold from the next shipment.
6. Write out the table of possible profits if Food King pays $5 for each box of bread and makes a profit of $2 for each box of bread sold.
7. Compute the expected profit for each of the five different quantities of bread stocked.
8. Suppose Food King can sell its old bread for $1 per box to a company that makes croutons. Write out the table of possible profits with this salvage value taken into account for the five given quantities of bread.
9. Compute the table of possible losses taking into account the salvage value given in Exercise 8 for the five given quantities of bread.
10. a. Compute the expected profits for each of the five quantities of bread given, taking salvage value into account.
    b. Compute the expected loss for each of the five quantities of bread given taking salvage value into account.
11. a. Write out a table comparing expected profits and losses for the five given quantities of bread.
    b. Which quantity of bread should Food King stock to obtain the highest expected profit? (Remember that the highest expected profit and the lowest expected loss should occur for the same quantity.)
    c. Verify that the difference between any two expected profits and the corresponding expected losses are the same. (For instance, in Table 4-18 the difference between the expected profits at 40 and 20 is $13.33; the difference between the corresponding expected losses is $13.34. The $.01 difference is due to rounding.)

*Charlie's Newsstand, which serves commuters during the week, is trying to decide how many evening newspapers to stock so that profits will be maximized. Last November Charlie found that for 200, 150, 100, and 50 papers stocked per day these quantities were sold completely with probabilities 0.10, 0.20, 0.25, and 0.45, respectively. Assume that he buys newspapers for $.08 and sells them for $.10. (His profit is therefore $.02 per newspaper.) Also assume that selling conditions are the same this November as last November.*

12. Compute the expected number of papers that Charlie's will sell per day.
13. Write out the table of possible profits for the four given quantities.
14. Compute the expected profit for each of the four different quantities of paper stocked.
15. Write out the table of possible losses for the four given quantities.
16. Compute the expected loss for each of the four different quantities of paper stocked.
17. a. Write out a table comparing expected profits and losses for the four given quantities of papers.

b. Which quantity gives the highest expected profit?
c. Which quantity gives the lowest expected loss?
d. Which quantity should Charlie's stock to obtain the highest average profit in the long run during the month of November?

*Mark's Bookstore must decide how many boxes of a certain type of Christmas card to stock this year. The store has been receiving shipments of 30 boxes daily. Those left at the end of the day are too shopworn for retail sale. The table below shows the number of sales per day for the 60-day period before Christmas last year.*

| Number of boxes sold daily | Times sold |
| --- | --- |
| 30 | 10 |
| 29 | 8 |
| 28 | 10 |
| 27 | 8 |
| 26 | 12 |
| 25 | 5 |
| 24 | 0 |
| 23 | 7 |

Total: 60

18. Compute for each of the eight quantities of Christmas cards in the table above the probability that it was sold.
19. Assuming selling conditions are the same this Christmas season as they were last Christmas season, compute the expected number of boxes of Christmas cards of the type in question which will be sold per day this season.
20. Write out the table of possible profits. Assume that the Christmas cards in question retail for $3.00, but cost Mark's $2.00 to buy.
21. Suppose Mark's can sell any shopworn boxes of Christmas cards at an after-Christmas sale at $1.00 per box. Write out the table of possible profits with this salvage value taken into account for the eight given quantities.
22. Compute for the eight given quantities the table of possible losses taking into account the salvage value in Exercise 21.
23. a. Compute the expected profit for each of the eight quantities of cards given taking salvage value into account.
    b. Compute the expected loss for each of the eight quantities of cards given taking salvage value into account.
24. a. Write out a table comparing expected profits and losses for the eight given quantities of cards.
    b. How many boxes of cards should Mark's stock daily to maximize expected profit and minimize expected loss?

###### —— 4-8   An Introduction to Finite Stochastic Processes

A. sequence of experiments in which the outcome of each depends on chance is called a *stochastic process*. A stochastic process in which there are a finite number of experiments, each with a finite number of possible outcomes having fixed probabilities of occurrence, is called a *finite stochastic process*.

Here is a very simple example of a finite stochastic process. Suppose the board of regents of a university decides to choose a student from the two coed dormitories to serve on its student housing committee. First, a dormitory is to be chosen at random; then a student is to be selected at random from that dormitory. Jordan Hall houses 25 conservatives $C$ and 5 radicals $R$; Starr Hall houses 20 conservatives $C$ and 10 radicals $R$. What is the probability $P(R)$ of a young radical's being chosen?

The above process of choosing a student member of the housing committee can be classified as a finite stochastic process made up of two experiments. The first consists of selecting a dormitory; the second consists of choosing a student, either a conservative or a radical. The probability of choosing either of the two coed dormitories, Jordan ($J$) or Starr ($S$), is

$$P(J) = P(S) = \frac{1}{2}.$$

The probability of choosing a radical $R$ if the student is from Jordan Hall, denoted $R \mid J$, is

$$P(R \mid J) = \frac{N(R \cap J)}{N(J)},$$

where $N(R \cap J)$ is the number of radicals in Jordan Hall and $N(J)$ is the total number of residents in the hall. Thus,

$$P(R \mid J) = \frac{5}{30} \quad \text{or} \quad \frac{1}{6}.$$

Similarly, the probability of choosing a conservative ($C$) if the student is from Jordan Hall is

$$P(C \mid J) = \frac{25}{30} \quad \text{or} \quad \frac{5}{6}.$$

Similarly, the probability of choosing a radical if the student is from Starr Hall is

$$R(R \mid S) = \frac{10}{30} \quad \text{or} \quad \frac{1}{3}.$$

and the probability of choosing a conservative if the student is from Starr Hall is

$$P(C \mid S) = \frac{20}{30} \quad \text{or} \quad \frac{2}{3}.$$

These probabilities can be summarized in the *tree diagram* shown in Figure 4-4, where the mutually exclusive possibilities and their corresponding

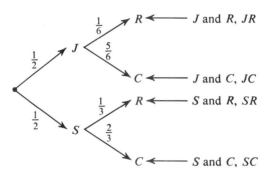

FIGURE 4-4.

probabilities are shown. Each branch of the tree represents an event. For instance, the top branch represents the event $J$ and $R$, $J \cap R$, shortened to $JR$, the event that a radical is chosen from Jordan Hall. On that branch are $P(J) = \frac{1}{2}$ and $P(R \mid J) = \frac{1}{6}$. (See Figure 4-5.) To find $P(J \cap R) = P(JR)$ we

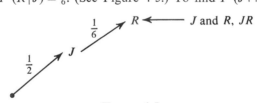

FIGURE 4-5.

can use the multiplication rule for probability from Section 4-3. We have

$$P(J \cap R) = P(JR) = P(J) \cdot P(R \mid J)$$

$$= \frac{1}{2} \cdot \frac{1}{6}$$

$$= \frac{1}{12}.$$

Similarly,

$$P(J \cap C) = P(JC) = P(J) \cdot P(C \mid J)$$

$$= \frac{1}{2} \cdot \frac{5}{6}$$

$$= \frac{5}{12},$$

$$P(S \cap R) = P(SR) = P(S) \cdot P(R \mid S)$$

$$= \frac{1}{2} \cdot \frac{1}{3}$$

$$= \frac{1}{6},$$

and

$$P(S \cap C) = P(SC) = P(S) \cdot P(C \mid S)$$

$$= \frac{1}{2} \cdot \frac{2}{3}$$

$$= \frac{1}{3}.$$

Note that the probability for each branch is the product of the probabilities along the path.

Since there are two mutually exclusive branches that lead to the event $R$ that a radical is chosen, namely $JR$ and $SR$, we find, since $R = JR \cup SR$, that

$$P(R) = P(JR \cup SR) = P(JR) + P(SR)$$

$$= \frac{1}{12} + \frac{1}{6}$$

$$= \frac{3}{12} \quad \text{or} \quad \frac{1}{4}.$$

Thus the probability of having a radical from a coed dormitory chosen to serve on the student housing committee is $\frac{1}{4}$.

Here is another example of a simple finite stochastic process. Suppose it is known that an important part was left out in two of the twelve cars produced one hour by a company. What is the probability of the event E, that the company will discover the two defective cars after examining only three of them?

To solve this problem, it is convenient to construct the corresponding tree diagram as shown in Figure 4-6. There $D$ stands for defective and $G$

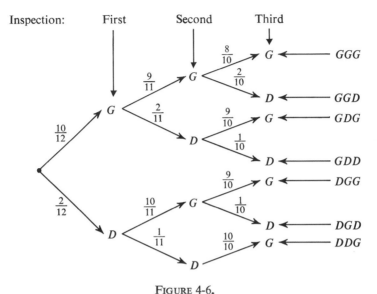

FIGURE 4-6.

stands for good (free of defects).

Each of the seven branches of the tree in Figure 4-6 represents the seven possible outcomes of examining three cars out of 12. For instance, the branch labeled $GGD$ represents $G \cap G \cap D$, the event of finding the first and second cars good, but the third car defective.

Figure 4-7 shows the branch corresponding to $GGD$. The first proba-

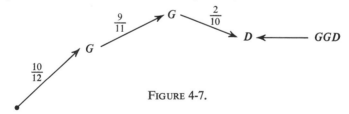

FIGURE 4-7.

bility $\frac{10}{12}$ along the branch corresponds to $P(G)$, the probability that a good car is discovered when the first car is chosen at random for inspection. That is,

$$P(G) = \frac{N(\text{good cars})}{N(\text{cars})} = \frac{10}{12}.$$

The second probability, $\frac{9}{11}$, along the branch corresponds to $P(G|G)$, the probability that a good car is examined when the second car is chosen at random for inspection, if a good car was found during the first inspection. For the second inspection there are 11 cars left to be examined. Of these only 9 are good, not 10 as before, since a good car has already been discovered and eliminated from further inspection. Thus,

$$P(G\,|\,G) = \frac{N(\text{good cars left})}{N(\text{cars left})} = \frac{9}{11}.$$

The third probability $\frac{2}{10}$ along the branch corresponds to $P(D\,|\,GG)$. For the third inspection there are only 10 cars left from which to pick the car to be examined. Of these 2 are defective, since no defective cars have been found so far. So,

$$P(D\,|\,GG) = \frac{N(\text{defective cars left})}{N(\text{cars left})} = \frac{2}{10}.$$

To find $P\,(GGD) = P\,(G \cap G \cap D)$ we can use an extension of the multiplication rule from Section 4-3. We have

$$P(GGD) = P(G \cap G \cap D) = P(G) \cdot P(G\,|\,G) \cdot P(D\,|\,GG)$$

$$= \frac{10}{12} \cdot \frac{9}{11} \cdot \frac{2}{10}$$

$$= \frac{3}{22}.$$

Thus $P\,(GGD)$, the probability of finding good cars when the first and second cars are inspected and a defective car when the third car is inspected is $\frac{3}{22}$. Note that the probability of this event is simply the product of the probabilities along the corresponding branch.

Similarly,

$$P(GGG) = \frac{10}{12} \cdot \frac{9}{11} \cdot \frac{8}{10} = \frac{6}{11},$$

$$P(GDG) = \frac{10}{12} \cdot \frac{2}{11} \cdot \frac{9}{10} = \frac{3}{22},$$

$$P(GDD) = \frac{10}{12} \cdot \frac{2}{11} \cdot \frac{1}{10} = \frac{1}{66},$$

$$P(DGG) = \frac{2}{12} \cdot \frac{10}{11} \cdot \frac{9}{10} = \frac{3}{22},$$

$$P(DGD) = \frac{2}{12} \cdot \frac{10}{11} \cdot \frac{1}{10} = \frac{1}{66},$$

and

$$P(DDG) = \frac{2}{12} \cdot \frac{1}{11} \cdot \frac{10}{10} = \frac{1}{66}.$$

Since there are three mutually exclusive branches of the three that lead to the event E that two defective cars are found on or before the third inspection, namely $GDD$, $DGD$, and $DDG$, we find, since $E = GDD \cup DGD \cup DDG$, that

$$P(E) = P(GDD) + P(DGD) + P(DDG)$$

$$= \frac{1}{66} + \frac{1}{66} + \frac{1}{66}$$

$$= \frac{3}{66} \quad \text{or} \quad \frac{1}{22}.$$

A final example of a finite stochastic process follows. Unified Airlines conducted a survey for Max's Coffee Company during a recent five-hour flight. Passengers were served at least one cup of three different types of Max's coffee during the flight. One cup was made from freshly ground coffee ($G$), one cup from freeze dried coffee ($F$), and the last from instant coffee ($I$). Passengers were asked to state which cup of coffee they preferred and whether they intended to purchase their stated preference at a later date. Table 4-19 summarizes the results.

| Type of coffee | % preferring | % intending to purchase |
|---|---|---|
| Ground ($G$) | 30% | 50% |
| Freeze dried ($F$) | 50% | 70% |
| Instant ($I$) | 20% | 40% |

TABLE 4-19.

The information in Table 4-19 can be put into the form of the diagram in Figure 4-8. There the percentages have been changed into convenient fractional probabilities. Included for each branch of the tree in Figure 4-8 is the probability for the event corresponding to it. We know from previous examples in this section that this probability is the product of the probabilities along the branch. For instance, the probability that a passenger preferred ground coffee and intended to purchase it is

$$P(G \cap \text{Yes}) = P(G) \cdot P(\text{Yes} \mid G)$$

$$= \frac{3}{10} \cdot \frac{1}{2}$$

$$= \frac{3}{20}.$$

From the calculations in Figure 4-8 we know that the probability of the event of a passenger's intending to purchase his preference of coffee is

$$P(\text{Yes}) = P(G \cap \text{Yes}) + P(F \cap \text{Yes}) + P(I \cap \text{Yes})$$

$$= \frac{3}{20} + \frac{35}{100} + \frac{4}{50}, \quad \text{or} \quad \frac{58}{100}.$$

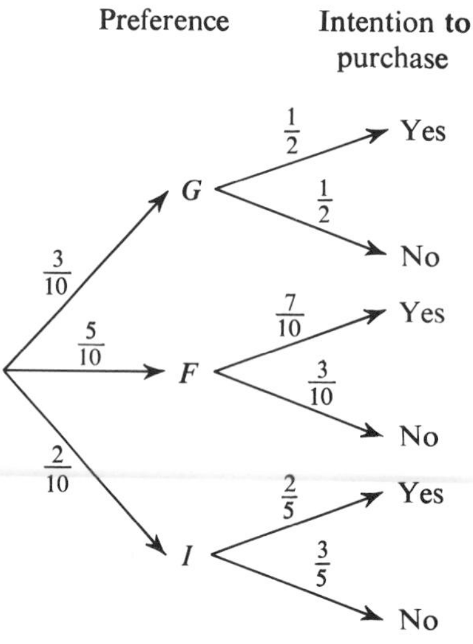

Preference        Intention to
                    purchase

$$P(G \cap \text{Yes}) = \frac{3}{10} \cdot \frac{1}{2} = \frac{3}{20}.$$

$$P(G \cap \text{No}) = \frac{3}{10} \cdot \frac{1}{2} = \frac{3}{20}.$$

$$P(F \cap \text{Yes}) = \frac{5}{10} \cdot \frac{7}{10} = \frac{35}{100}.$$

$$P(F \cap \text{No}) = \frac{5}{10} \cdot \frac{3}{10} = \frac{15}{100}.$$

$$P(I \cap \text{Yes}) = \frac{2}{10} \cdot \frac{2}{5} = \frac{4}{50}.$$

$$P(I \cap \text{No}) = \frac{2}{10} \cdot \frac{3}{5} = \frac{6}{50}.$$

Figure 4-8.

Thus, 58% of the passengers stated their intention to purchase the coffee they said they preferred in the survey.

We can also construct a tree diagram stating first whether or not the passengers intended to purchase the coffee he said he preferred in the survey. We found that $P(\text{Yes}) = \frac{58}{100}$. Thus $P(\text{No}) = 1 - \frac{58}{100} = \frac{42}{100}$. These two probabilities are shown in Figure 4-9 along with the probabilities corresponding to each branch as calculated in Figure 4-8. The branches in Figure 4-9 have the same probabilities as those in Figure 4-8, because only the order of the description has been altered. That is, $P(\text{Yes} \cap G) = P(G \cap \text{Yes})$.

Since we have seen that the probability corresponding to each branch is the product of the probabilities along the branch, we can fill in the missing probabilities in Figure 4-9. For the top branch corresponding to the event $P(G \cap \text{Yes})$, the probability that the passenger preferred ground coffee and will buy his preference, we have

$$P(G \cap \text{Yes}) = P(\text{Yes}) \cdot P(G \,|\, \text{Yes}),$$

$$\frac{3}{20} = \frac{58}{100} \cdot P(G \,|\, \text{Yes})$$

$$\frac{3}{20} \div \frac{58}{100} = P(G\,|\,\text{Yes})$$

$$\frac{15}{58} = P(G\,|\,\text{Yes}).$$

Thus we now know that the probability of a passenger's preferring ground coffee, if he says he will later buy it, is $\frac{15}{58}$.

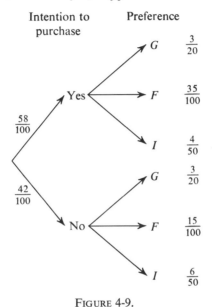

Intention to purchase          Preference

Yes

$G \qquad \frac{3}{20}$

$F \qquad \frac{35}{100}$

$I \qquad \frac{4}{50}$

$\frac{58}{100}$

$\frac{42}{100}$

No

$G \qquad \frac{3}{20}$

$F \qquad \frac{15}{100}$

$I \qquad \frac{6}{50}$

FIGURE 4-9.

Figure 4-10 gives the results of the calculations for the other branches of the tree in Figure 4-9. With these probabilities we can find, for instance, that the probability of a passenger's preferring instant coffee if he states that he does not intend to purchase it later, $P(I\,|\,\text{No})$, is $\frac{12}{42}$ or $\frac{6}{21}$, similarly,

$$P(F\,|\,\text{Yes}) = \frac{35}{58},$$

$$P(I\,|\,\text{Yes}) = \frac{8}{58},$$

$$P(G\,|\,\text{No}) = \frac{15}{42},$$

and

$$P(F\,|\,\text{No}) = \frac{15}{42}.$$

If a passenger stated he would later purchase the coffee he said he preferred, it is most likely that he preferred the freeze dried variety, and least likely that he preferred the instant variety.

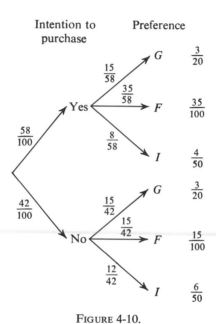

FIGURE 4-10.

*EXERCISES* ———————————————————————————————————————

*Reconsider the example of this section dealing with defective cars. Suppose that there are three defective cars instead of two.*

1.  Construct the corresponding tree diagram for the examination of three cars.
2.  What is the probability that the company will discover the three defective cars after examining only three cars?
3.  What is the probability that the company will discover none of the defective cars after examining only three cars?
4.  What is the probability that the company will discover exactly two defective cars after examining only three cars?
5.  What is the probability that the company will discover at least two defective cars after examining only three cars?

*Reconsider the example in this section dealing with coffee preferences. Suppose the results of the polling of passengers were as follows:*

| Type of coffee | % preferring | % intending to purchase |
|---|---|---|
| Ground (G) | 40% | 50% |
| Freeze dried (F) | 40% | 70% |
| Instant (I) | 20% | 40% |

6.  Construct the corresponding tree diagram starting off with the preferences stated by the passengers polled.
7.  Find the probability that a passenger did not intend to purchase his preference of coffee.
8.  Construct the tree diagram corresponding to the results given above, branching first according to whether the passenger intends to purchase his stated preference.
9.  If the passenger intends to purchase the coffee he preferred, what is the probability that he preferred
    a.  instant coffee?
    b.  freeze dried coffee?
    c.  ground coffee?
10. If the passenger does not intend to purchase the coffee he preferred, what is the probability that he preferred
    a.  instant coffee?
    b.  freeze dried coffee?
    c.  ground coffee?
11. Out of ten cartons of eggs, two cartons are known to contain spoiled eggs. What is the probability that these two cartons will be discovered
    a.  after two cartons are examined?
    b.  after at most three cartons are examined?
12. Out of 100 radio tubes it is known that five are defective. What is the probability that they will be discovered after five tubes are tested?

*On a true-false exam the probability that a student gives a correct answer is 1/2 if he guesses and 1 if he knows the correct answer. Suppose a good student knows 85% of the answers and a poor student knows 60% of the answers.*

13. If a poor student gets a correct answer, what is the probability that he guessed?

14. If a good student gets a correct answer, what is the probability that he guessed?

*The following table summarizes some facts about the population of the state of Hawaii.*

| Ethnic group | Per cent | Island or city | Percent living there |
|---|---|---|---|
| Japanese | 32% | Oahu | 79% |
| Caucasian | 32% | Honolulu | 46% |
| Filipino | 11% | Hilo | 24% |
| Hawaiian or part Hawaiian | 18% | | |
| Chinese | 6% | Note: Honolulu is on | |
| Other | 1% | the island of Oahu. | |

15. If a person from Hawaii is chosen at random, what is the probability that he is a Hawaiian or part Hawaiian resident of Honolulu?
16. If two people from Hawaii are chosen at random, what is the probability that at least one of them is a Hawaiian or part Hawaiian resident of Honolulu?
17. If three people from Hawaii are chosen at random, what is the probability that exactly one of them is a Caucasian living in Hilo?
18. If three people from Hawaii are chosen at random, what is the probability that none of them have Hawaiian blood or live on Oahu?

## —— 4-9  An Introduction to Markov Chains

In the last section we discussed experiments in which the outcomes were independent of any preceding outcomes. In this section we will discuss experiments (with a finite number of outcomes) in which the outcome of each trial depends at most on the outcome of the preceding trial. Such an experiment is called a *Markov chain*. The outcomes are often called *states*.

As a simple example of a Markov chain suppose Superb Soap Company and Supreme Manufacturing simultaneously introduce new enzyme detergents. During the year Superb Soap keeps 60% of its customers and loses 40% of its customers to Supreme Manufacturing. On the other hand Supreme keeps 50% of its customers and loses 50% of them to Superb Soap.

If we designate Superb Soap Company as $S_1$ and Supreme Manufacturing as $S_2$, the states of the Markov chain are $\{S_1, S_2\}$. If we interpret the percents given above as probabilities in fraction form we can arrange them in the matrix

$$\text{Now customer of} \begin{cases} S_1 \\ S_2 \end{cases} \overset{\overbrace{\begin{matrix} S_1 & S_2 \end{matrix}}}{\begin{pmatrix} \dfrac{3}{5} & \dfrac{2}{5} \\ \dfrac{1}{2} & \dfrac{1}{2} \end{pmatrix}} = T,$$

Next year
customer
of

which corresponds to a Markov chain.

The entry $\frac{3}{5}$, which is the entry in the $S_1$ row and $S_1$ column, gives the probability that a customer of $S_1$ now will also be a customer of $S_1$ next year. The entry $\frac{1}{2}$ in the $S_2$ row and $S_1$ column gives the probability that a customer of $S_2$ now will switch to $S_1$ next year. The other entries in the matrix can be interpreted similarly. Each entry of the matrix gives the probability of next year's states dependent on this year's states. For this reason the matrix $T$ is called a *transition matrix*. The two rows of $T$

$$\begin{pmatrix} \dfrac{3}{5} & \dfrac{2}{5} \end{pmatrix} \quad \text{and} \quad \begin{pmatrix} \dfrac{1}{2} & \dfrac{1}{2} \end{pmatrix}$$

are called *probability vectors*. Note that the sum of the elements of each vector is 1.

In general, if $S_1, S_2, \ldots S_n$ are the states of a Markov chain and $P_{ij}$ is the probability that an experiment will be in state $S_j$ if it is in $S_i$ now, the row vectors

$$(P_{11}, P_{12} \ldots P_{1n}),$$
$$(P_{21}, P_{22} \ldots P_{2n}),$$
$$\vdots$$
$$(P_{n1}, P_{n2} \ldots P_{nn})$$

are called probability vectors. The sum of the elements in each probability vector is 1. The matrix formed from these probability vectors

$$\begin{pmatrix} P_{11} & P_{12} & \cdots & P_{1n} \\ P_{21} & P_{22} & \cdots & P_{2n} \\ & & \vdots & \\ P_{n1} & P_{n2} & \cdots & P_{nn} \end{pmatrix}$$

is called the transition matrix.

Next suppose that conditions in our example will be the same after two years as they will be after one year. With this assumption in mind we can construct the tree diagram shown in Figure 4-11. Also shown in Figure 4-11

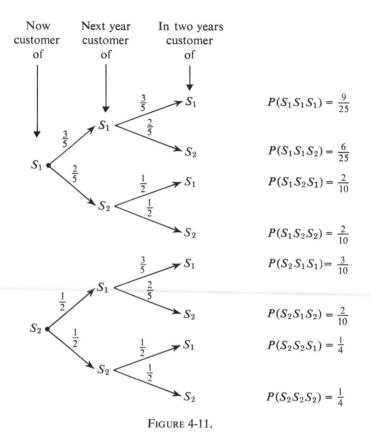

FIGURE 4-11.

are the probabilities found by multiplying the probabilities along each branch of the tree. For example,

$$P(S_1 S_2 S_1) = \frac{2}{5} \cdot \frac{1}{2} = \frac{2}{10}.$$

This means that the probability is 2/10 that a customer who patronizes $S_1$ now and who will patronize $S_2$ during the next year will patronize $S_1$ during the third year. We can use the probabilities found in Figure 4-11 to find the following probabilities:

$$P(S_1 \text{ in two years} \mid S_1 \text{ now}) = P(S_1 \, S_1 S_1) + P(S_1 \, S_2 \, S_1)$$

$$= \frac{9}{25} + \frac{2}{10} \quad \text{or} \quad \frac{14}{25},$$

$$P(S_2 \text{ in two years} \mid S_1 \text{ now}) = P(S_1 S_1 S_2) + P(S_1 S_2 S_2)$$

$$= \frac{6}{25} + \frac{2}{10} \quad \text{or} \quad \frac{11}{25},$$

$$P(S_1 \text{ in two years} \mid S_2 \text{ now}) = P(S_2 S_1 S_1) + P(S_2 S_2 S_1)$$

$$= \frac{3}{10} + \frac{1}{4} \quad \text{or} \quad \frac{11}{20},$$

$$P(S_2 \text{ in two years} \mid S_2 \text{ now}) = P(S_2 S_1 S_2) + P(S_2 S_2 S_2)$$

$$= \frac{2}{10} + \frac{1}{4} \quad \text{or} \quad \frac{9}{20}.$$

Now let us return to the transition matrix of our example and square it. We obtain

$$T^2 = \begin{pmatrix} \dfrac{3}{5} & \dfrac{2}{5} \\ \dfrac{1}{2} & \dfrac{1}{2} \end{pmatrix} \begin{pmatrix} \dfrac{3}{5} & \dfrac{2}{5} \\ \dfrac{1}{2} & \dfrac{1}{2} \end{pmatrix} = \begin{pmatrix} \dfrac{9}{25} + \dfrac{2}{10} & \dfrac{6}{25} + \dfrac{2}{10} \\ \dfrac{3}{10} + \dfrac{1}{4} & \dfrac{2}{10} + \dfrac{1}{4} \end{pmatrix}$$

$$= \begin{pmatrix} \dfrac{14}{25} & \dfrac{11}{25} \\ \dfrac{11}{20} & \dfrac{9}{20} \end{pmatrix}. \tag{1}$$

The entries in the resulting matrix should look familiar! They are in fact

$$\begin{pmatrix} P(S_1 \text{ in two years} \mid S_1 \text{ now}) & P(S_2 \text{ in two years} \mid S_1 \text{ now}) \\ P(S_1 \text{ in two years} \mid S_2 \text{ now}) & P(S_2 \text{ in two years} \mid S_2 \text{ now}) \end{pmatrix}.$$

This suggests that *squaring* the transition matrix $T$ gives us a matrix whose elements are the probabilities that an experiment now in state $S_i$ will be in state $S_j$ after the *second* trial.

In fact it is true in general that the elements $P_{ij}$ in the matrix formed by raising the transition matrix $T$ of a Markov chain to the nth power give the probabilities that an experiment in state $S_i$ will be in state $S_j$ after the nth trial.

For instance, the elements of the *fourth* power of the transition matrix of our example will give the probability that a customer who patronizes $S_i$ now will patronize $S_j$ *four* years from now.

$$T^4 = \begin{pmatrix} \dfrac{3}{5} & \dfrac{2}{5} \\ \dfrac{1}{2} & \dfrac{1}{2} \end{pmatrix}^4 = \begin{pmatrix} \dfrac{3}{5} & \dfrac{2}{5} \\ \dfrac{1}{2} & \dfrac{1}{2} \end{pmatrix}^2 \begin{pmatrix} \dfrac{3}{5} & \dfrac{2}{5} \\ \dfrac{1}{2} & \dfrac{1}{2} \end{pmatrix}^2$$

From (1) we know $T^2$, so

$$T^4 = \begin{pmatrix} \dfrac{14}{25} & \dfrac{11}{25} \\[2mm] \dfrac{11}{20} & \dfrac{9}{20} \end{pmatrix} \begin{pmatrix} \dfrac{14}{25} & \dfrac{11}{25} \\[2mm] \dfrac{11}{20} & \dfrac{9}{20} \end{pmatrix}$$

$$= \begin{pmatrix} \dfrac{196}{625} + \dfrac{121}{500} & \dfrac{154}{625} + \dfrac{99}{500} \\[3mm] \dfrac{154}{500} + \dfrac{99}{400} & \dfrac{121}{500} + \dfrac{81}{400} \end{pmatrix}$$

$$= \begin{pmatrix} 0.55560 & 0.44440 \\ 0.55550 & 0.44450 \end{pmatrix}.$$

In this matrix $P_{21} = 0.55550$. This indicates that the probability is $0.55550$ that a customer who now patronizes $S_2$, Supreme Manufacturing, will be patronizing $S_1$, Superb Soap Company, four years from now.

To obtain the probability that a customer who patronizes $S_i$ now will patronize $S_j$ *eight* years from now we examine the entries of the *eighth* power of the transition matrix:

$$T^8 = T^4 \cdot T^4 = \begin{pmatrix} 0.55560 & 0.44440 \\ 0.55550 & 0.44450 \end{pmatrix} \cdot \begin{pmatrix} 0.55560 & 0.44440 \\ 0.55550 & 0.44450 \end{pmatrix}$$

$$= \begin{pmatrix} 0.55555556 & 0.44444444 \\ 0.55555555 & 0.44444445 \end{pmatrix}.$$

As the transition matrix is raised to higher and higher powers the resulting matrix will get closer and closer to

$$\begin{pmatrix} 0.\overline{5} & 0.\overline{4} \\ 0.\overline{5} & 0.\overline{4} \end{pmatrix} = \begin{pmatrix} \dfrac{5}{9} & \dfrac{4}{9} \\[2mm] \dfrac{5}{9} & \dfrac{4}{9} \end{pmatrix}. \tag{2}$$

(Using the method in the exercises for Section 1-3 it can be shown that $0.\overline{4} = \frac{4}{9}$ and $0.\overline{5} = \frac{5}{9}$). Note that the vector $(\frac{5}{9}\ \frac{4}{9})$, which occurs in both rows of the matrix in (2) is a probability vector. If we multiply it by the original transition matrix

$$\begin{pmatrix} \dfrac{3}{5} & \dfrac{2}{5} \\[2mm] \dfrac{1}{2} & \dfrac{1}{2} \end{pmatrix},$$

we obtain

$$\begin{pmatrix} \dfrac{5}{9} & \dfrac{4}{9} \end{pmatrix} \begin{pmatrix} \dfrac{3}{5} & \dfrac{2}{5} \\ \dfrac{1}{2} & \dfrac{1}{2} \end{pmatrix} = \begin{pmatrix} \dfrac{15}{45} + \dfrac{4}{18} & \dfrac{10}{45} + \dfrac{4}{18} \end{pmatrix} = \begin{pmatrix} \dfrac{5}{9} & \dfrac{4}{9} \end{pmatrix}.$$

The product of the probability vector $(\frac{5}{9} \ \frac{4}{9})$ by the original transition matrix yields the vector $(\frac{5}{9} \ \frac{4}{9})$! For this reason we call $(\frac{5}{9} \ \frac{4}{9})$ a *fixed probability vector* for the given transition matrix.

In general, if $v$ is a probability vector such that

$$vA = v$$

for a matrix $A$, $v$ is called a *fixed probability vector for A*.

Instead of raising the transition matrix to higher and higher powers to find a corresponding fixed probability vector, it is possible to use the definition above. For the transition matrix of our example, where we call $(P_1 \ P_2)$ the fixed probability vector, we have by definition:

$$(P_1 \quad P_2) \begin{pmatrix} \dfrac{3}{5} & \dfrac{2}{5} \\ \dfrac{1}{2} & \dfrac{1}{2} \end{pmatrix} = (P_1 \quad P_2).$$

Multiplying gives us

$$\begin{pmatrix} \dfrac{3}{5}P_1 + \dfrac{1}{2}P_2 & \dfrac{2}{5}P_1 + \dfrac{1}{2}P_2 \end{pmatrix} = (P_1 \quad P_2). \tag{3}$$

Since the vectors in (3) are equal, we have

$$\frac{3}{5}P_1 + \frac{1}{2}P_2 = P_1 \quad \text{and} \quad \frac{2}{5}P_1 + \frac{1}{2}P_2 = P_2,$$

$$\frac{1}{2}P_2 = \frac{2}{5}P_1 \quad \text{and} \quad \frac{2}{5}P_1 = \frac{1}{2}P_2$$

both of which yield

$$\frac{4}{5}P_1 = P_2. \tag{4}$$

Since $(P_1 \quad P_2)$ is a probability vector, $P_1 + P_2 = 1$ or $P_1 = 1 - P_2$. Thus from (4)

$$\frac{4}{5}(1 - P_2) = P_2,$$

$$\frac{4}{5} - \frac{4}{5}P_2 = P_2$$

$$\frac{4}{5} = \frac{9}{5}P_2$$

$$\frac{4}{9} = P_2.$$

Therefore,

$$P_1 = \frac{5}{9}.$$

$(\frac{5}{9} \frac{4}{9})$ is the fixed probability vector we obtained previously.

If some power of a transition matrix contains only positive elements, it is said to be a *regular transition matrix*. The transition matrix $T$ of our example is certainly regular since the first power has only positive elements:

$$T = T^1 = \begin{pmatrix} \dfrac{3}{5} & \dfrac{2}{5} \\ \dfrac{1}{2} & \dfrac{1}{2} \end{pmatrix}.$$

When a transition matrix $T$ is regular it can be shown that

   i. $T$ has a unique fixed probability vector $v$, and $v$ has positive elements.
  ii. $T, T^2, T^3, \ldots, T^n$ approach the matrix all of whose rows are $v$.
 iii. If $v_1$ is any probability vector, then $v_1 T, v_1 T^2, v_1 T^3, \ldots, v_1 T^n$ approach the fixed probability vector $v$.

We have already seen that the first two results are true for our example. Suppose now that Superb Soap Company and Supreme Manufacturing had equal shares of the market before the introduction of their enzyme detergents. To find the share of the market for each company at the end of the year we can multiply the vector giving the original shares,

$$\begin{pmatrix} \dfrac{1}{2} & \dfrac{1}{2} \end{pmatrix},$$

$$\uparrow \qquad\qquad \uparrow$$
$$S_1\text{'s share} \quad S_2\text{'s share}$$

called the *original share vector*, by the transition matrix. (Note that the original share vector $(\frac{1}{2}\ \frac{1}{2})$ is a probability vector, since the sum of its elements is 1.) This gives us

$$\begin{pmatrix} \frac{1}{2} & \frac{1}{2} \end{pmatrix} \begin{pmatrix} \frac{3}{5} & \frac{2}{5} \\ \frac{1}{2} & \frac{1}{2} \end{pmatrix} = \begin{pmatrix} \frac{1}{2}\cdot\frac{3}{5}+\frac{1}{2}\cdot\frac{1}{2} & \frac{1}{2}\cdot\frac{2}{5}+\frac{1}{2}\cdot\frac{1}{2} \end{pmatrix}$$

$$= \begin{pmatrix} \frac{3}{10}+\frac{1}{4} & \frac{2}{10}+\frac{1}{4} \end{pmatrix}$$

$$= \begin{pmatrix} \frac{22}{40} & \frac{18}{40} \end{pmatrix}$$

$$= \begin{pmatrix} \frac{11}{20} & \frac{9}{20} \end{pmatrix}.$$

The vector $(\frac{11}{20}\ \frac{9}{20})$ tells us that at the end of the first year $S_1$, Superb Soap, will have $\frac{11}{20}$ of the market and $S_2$, Supreme Manufacturing, will have $\frac{9}{20}$ of the market.

To find each company's share at the end of the second year we can multiply the vector $(\frac{11}{20}\ \frac{9}{20})$, which gives the market share at the end of the first year (and, consequently the market share at the beginning of the second year) by the original transition matrix $T$. Equivalently, we could multiply the original share vector by $T^2$, which we already know.

$$\begin{pmatrix} \frac{1}{2} & \frac{1}{2} \end{pmatrix} T^2 = \begin{pmatrix} \frac{1}{2} & \frac{1}{2} \end{pmatrix} \begin{pmatrix} \frac{14}{25} & \frac{11}{25} \\ \frac{11}{20} & \frac{9}{20} \end{pmatrix}$$

$$= \begin{pmatrix} \frac{14}{50}+\frac{11}{40} & \frac{11}{50}+\frac{9}{40} \end{pmatrix}$$

$$= \begin{pmatrix} \frac{1110}{2000} & \frac{890}{2000} \end{pmatrix} \quad \text{or} \quad \begin{pmatrix} \frac{111}{200} & \frac{89}{200} \end{pmatrix}$$

Thus, at the end of the second year Superb Soap Company will have $\frac{111}{200}$ of the market, and Supreme Manufacturing will have $\frac{89}{200}$ of the market. Superb Soap appears to be gaining ground.

To find each company's share after $n$ years we need only to continue the process suggested above. Just multiply the original share vector by $T^n$, the

$n$th power of the transition matrix. As we have seen, $T^n$ approaches the matrix

$$\begin{pmatrix} \dfrac{5}{9} & \dfrac{4}{9} \\[2ex] \dfrac{5}{9} & \dfrac{4}{9} \end{pmatrix},$$

so $(\frac{5}{9}\ \frac{4}{9})$ is the fixed probability vector. Since $T$ is a regular transition matrix and $(\frac{1}{2}\ \frac{1}{2})$ is a probability vector (iii) tells us that the sequence

$$\begin{pmatrix} \dfrac{1}{2} & \dfrac{1}{2} \end{pmatrix}T, \begin{pmatrix} \dfrac{1}{2} & \dfrac{1}{2} \end{pmatrix}T^2, \begin{pmatrix} \dfrac{1}{2} & \dfrac{1}{2} \end{pmatrix}T^3, \ldots, \begin{pmatrix} \dfrac{1}{2} & \dfrac{1}{2} \end{pmatrix}T^n$$

will approach the fixed probability vector $(\frac{5}{9}\ \frac{4}{9})$. We can interpret this as indicating that in the long run Superb Soap will have $\frac{5}{9}$ of the market and Supreme Manufacturing will have $\frac{4}{9}$ of the market if trends continue.

As an illustration of how useful Markov chains and fixed probability vectors can be in decision making consider the following examples.

First suppose that Superb Soap Company and Supreme Manufacturing have competitive aerosol oven cleaners, Instantly Off ($I$) and Mr. Sparkle ($M$), respectively. A market test shows that the transition matrix is

$$\begin{array}{cc} & \begin{array}{cc} I & M \end{array} \\ \begin{array}{c} I \\ M \end{array} & \begin{pmatrix} 0.4 & 0.6 \\ 0.7 & 0.3 \end{pmatrix}. \end{array}$$

The fixed probability vector is found by using the definition above to be $(\frac{7}{13}\ \frac{6}{13})$. This indicates that Superb Soap will have $\frac{7}{13}$ of the market and Supreme Manufacturing will have $\frac{6}{13}$ of the market in the long run, if the trend continues. Since Superb Soap would like to increase its share of the market, it decides to field test two new oven cleaners called Poof ($P$) and Whiz ($W$). Field tests indicate that the transition matrices are

$$\begin{array}{c} \begin{array}{ccc} I & M & P \end{array} \\ \begin{array}{c} I \\ M \\ P \end{array} \begin{pmatrix} 0.5 & 0.2 & 0.3 \\ 0.3 & 0.4 & 0.3 \\ 0.2 & 0.4 & 0.4 \end{pmatrix} \end{array} \quad \text{and} \quad \begin{array}{c} \begin{array}{ccc} I & M & W \end{array} \\ \begin{array}{c} I \\ M \\ W \end{array} \begin{pmatrix} 0.4 & 0.1 & 0.5 \\ 0.3 & 0.5 & 0.2 \\ 0.3 & 0.3 & 0.4 \end{pmatrix}. \end{array}$$

The fixed probability vector for Instantly Off, Mr. Sparkle, and Poof is found to be $(\frac{1}{3}\ \frac{1}{3}\ \frac{1}{3})$ and the fixed probability vector for Instantly Off, Mr. Sparkle, and Whiz is found to be $(\frac{8}{24}\ \frac{7}{24}\ \frac{9}{24})$. If Superb Soap introduces Poof, the fixed probability vector $(\frac{1}{3}\ \frac{1}{3}\ \frac{1}{3})$ indicates that it can expect $\frac{1}{3} + \frac{1}{3} = \frac{2}{3}$ of the market in the long run if trends continue. On the other hand, if Superb Soap introduces Whiz, the fixed probability vector $(\frac{8}{24}\ \frac{7}{24}\ \frac{9}{24})$ indicates that it can expect

$$\frac{8}{24} + \frac{9}{24} = \frac{17}{24}$$

of the market over a period of time. Since

$$\frac{2}{3} < \frac{17}{24},$$

Superb Soap should introduce Whiz.

Next, suppose an investor is trying to decide whether to buy stock in Superb Soap Company ($S_1$) or Supreme Manufacturing ($S_2$). From company reports he discovers that Superb Soap has 900,000 out of a total of 1,500,000 customers and Supreme Manufacturing has 600,000 customers. In addition, the reports predict that 10% of Superb Soap's customers are expected to switch to Supreme Manufacturing per month, while 5% of Supreme Manufacturing's customers are expected to switch to Superb Soap products during the same period. In other words, Superb Soap will retain 90% of its customers per month and lose 10% of them to Supreme Manufacturing. Meanwhile, Supreme Manufacturing will keep 95% of its customers and lose 5% of them to Superb Soap. The transition matrix $T$ for this Markov chain can be formed from this information. It is

$$\begin{array}{cc} & \begin{array}{cc} S_1 & S_2 \end{array} \\ \begin{array}{c} S_1 \\ S_2 \end{array} & \begin{pmatrix} 0.90 & 0.10 \\ 0.05 & 0.95 \end{pmatrix} \end{array} = T.$$

The fixed probability vector for this transition matrix is found by the short cut above to be ($\frac{1}{3}$ $\frac{2}{3}$). This indicates that Superb Soap will have $33\frac{1}{3}$% of the market and Supreme Manufacturing will have $66\frac{2}{3}$% of the market in the long run, if selling conditions remain unchanged. The investor should buy stock in Supreme Manufacturing.

Suppose next that the investor does not want to hold his stock for a long period. Should he still invest in Supreme Manufacturing? To decide he could take into account the number of months it will take Supreme Manufacturing to win $\frac{2}{3}$ of the market. At the end of the first month the market share vector will be

$$(900{,}000 \quad 600{,}000) \begin{pmatrix} 0.90 & 0.10 \\ 0.05 & 0.95 \end{pmatrix} = (840{,}000 \quad 660{,}000),$$

the product of the original share vector and the transition matrix $T$. At the end of the first month Superb Soap will have 840,000 customers out of 1,500,000 and Supreme Manufacturing will have 660,000 customers. At the end of the second month the market share vector will be

$$(840{,}000 \quad 660{,}000) \begin{pmatrix} 0.90 & 0.10 \\ 0.05 & 0.95 \end{pmatrix} = (789{,}000 \quad 711{,}000).$$

Thus after two months, Superb Soap will have 789,000 customers and Supreme Manufacturing will have 711,000 customers. Supreme Manufacturing is gaining ground! At the end of the third month the market share vector will be

$$(789{,}000 \quad 711{,}000)\begin{pmatrix} 0.90 & 0.10 \\ 0.05 & 0.95 \end{pmatrix} = (745{,}650 \quad 754{,}350).$$

After only three months Supreme Manufacturing has overtaken Superb Soap. So even if the investor wants to hold his stock a short time, he should invest in Supreme Manufacturing.

### EXERCISES

*In the first example of this section involving enzyme detergents, assume that Superb Soap Company $(S_1)$ keeps 70% of its customers and loses 30% of them to Supreme Manufacturing $(S_2)$. Also assume that Supreme Manufacturing keeps 80% of its customers and loses 20% of them to Superb Soap.*

1. What are the states of the Markov chain?
2. What is the transition matrix $T$?
3. a. Find $T^2$.
   b. What is the probability that a customer who patronizes Superb Soap now will patronize Supreme Manufacturing after two years if trends continue.
   c. What is the probability that a customer who patronizes Supreme Manufacturing now will patronize Superb Soap after two years if trends continue?
   d. What is the probability that a customer of Superb Soap now will still be a customer after two years if trends continue?
   e. What is the probability that a customer of Supreme Manufacturing now will still be a customer after two years if trends continue?
4. a. Find $T^4$.
   b. What is the probability that a customer who patronizes Superb Soap now will patronize Supreme Manufacturing after four years if trends continue?
   c. What is the probability that a customer who patronizes Supreme Manufacturing now will patronize Superb Soap after four years if trends continue?
   d. What is the probability that a customer of Superb Soap now will still be a customer after four years if trends continue?
   e. What is the probability that a customer of Supreme Manufacturing now will still be a customer after four years if trends continue?
5. Find the fixed probability vector using its definition.
6. Before the introduction of their enzyme detergents suppose Superb Soap had 45% of the market and Surpeme Manufacturing had 55% of the market. What is the original share vector?

7. Find the market share of each company after each of the following periods of time. Assume trends continue.
   a.  one year.
   b.  two years.
   c.  four years.
8. If trends continue, what portion of the market will each company have in the long run?

*Foods of the Future, Inc. and Foods from the Sea are competing for the market of imitation bacon with Fubac (F) and Seabac (S), respectively. A market test shows that the transition matrix is*

$$
\begin{array}{c}
 \\
F \\
 \\
S
\end{array}
\begin{array}{cc}
F & S \\
\left(\begin{array}{cc}
\dfrac{2}{3} & \dfrac{1}{3} \\[2ex]
\dfrac{1}{2} & \dfrac{1}{2}
\end{array}\right).
\end{array}
$$

9. a.  Find the fixed probability vector.
   b.  In the long run what will be the market share of each company if trends continue?

*To increase its market share Foods from the Sea decides to field test two other imitation products, imitation turkey, Seaturk ($S_1$), and imitation beef, Seabeef ($S_2$). Surveys indicate the following transition matrices:*

$$
\begin{array}{c}
F \\
S \\
S_1
\end{array}
\begin{array}{ccc}
F & S & S_1 \\
\left(\begin{array}{ccc}
\dfrac{1}{2} & \dfrac{1}{3} & \dfrac{1}{6} \\[2ex]
\dfrac{1}{4} & \dfrac{1}{2} & \dfrac{1}{4} \\[2ex]
\dfrac{1}{3} & \dfrac{1}{3} & \dfrac{1}{3}
\end{array}\right)
\end{array}
\text{ and }
\begin{array}{c}
F \\
S \\
S_2
\end{array}
\begin{array}{ccc}
F & S & S_2 \\
\left(\begin{array}{ccc}
\dfrac{2}{3} & \dfrac{1}{6} & \dfrac{1}{6} \\[2ex]
\dfrac{1}{3} & \dfrac{1}{3} & \dfrac{1}{3} \\[2ex]
\dfrac{1}{3} & \dfrac{1}{2} & \dfrac{1}{6}
\end{array}\right).
\end{array}
$$

10. a.  Find the fixed probability vector for Fubac, Seabac, and Seaturk.
    b.  In the long run what share of the market could Foods from the Sea expect with this combination of products if trends continue?
11. a.  Find the fixed probability vector for Fubac, Seabac, and Seabeef.
    b.  In the long run what share of the market could Foods from the Sea expect with this combination of products if trends continue?

*An investor in growth stocks is trying to decide whether to buy stock in Foods of the Future, Inc. ($F_1$) or Foods from the Sea ($F_2$), the only two com-*

*panies engaged in production of simulated protein products. He learns from company reports that currently $F_1$ has 500,000 customers and $F_2$ has 400,000 customers. Interviews with company officials reveal that $F_1$ expects to lose 20% of its business to $F_2$ this year and keep 80% of its customers. On the other hand, $F_2$ officials expect to keep all but 10% of its customers, whom they expect to switch to $F_1$ during the year.*

12.  What is the transition matrix?
13.  a.  What is the fixed probability vector?
     b.  How many customers will $F_1$ have in the long run if trends continue?
     c.  How many customers will $F_2$ have in the long run if trends continue?
     d.  From which company should the investor purchase stock?

*Use the assumptions in the following table for Exercises 14–17, supposing that the trends indicated continue.*

*Maximum educational level*
*children will achieve*

|  |  | College | High School | Elementary School |
|---|---|---|---|---|
| Highest educational level of parents | College | 80% | 18% | 2% |
| | High School | 40% | 50% | 10% |
| | Elementary School | 20% | 60% | 20% |

14.  What is the transition matrix?
15.  What is the probability that the grandchild of a college graduate is a college graduate?
16.  What is the probability that the grandchild of a high school graduate is a college graduate?
17.  What is the probability that the grandchild of an elementary school graduate is a college graduate?

*There were several months between the government ban on artificial sweetener A and the date the ban went into effect. During the first month after the ban it was found that 20% of the users of A continued using A as long as they could buy it. Fifty per cent of the users of A changed to artificial sweetener B, 20% to artificial sweetener C, and 10% went back to sugar. On the other hand, 10% of the users of B switched to sweetener C, and 20% of the users of B switched back to sugar. Further, 10% of the users of C changed to sweetener B and 10% to sugar. No users of B and C switched to A and the sugar users remained sugar users.*

18.  a.  What is the transition matrix?
     b.  Is it regular?

19.  Suppose that before the government ban 20% of the people used $A$, 10% used $B$, 2% used $C$, and 68% used sugar.
  a.  One month after the ban what share did each of the sweeteners have?
  b.  Two months after the ban what share did each of the sweeteners have assuming the trend of the first month continued?
20.  Assume that right before the government ban, there were 40 million consumers of sweetener $A$, 20 million consumers of sweetener $B$, 4 million consumers of sweetener $C$, and 136 million consumers of sugar. One month after the government ban, how many consumers were there of each of the four different sweeteners?

*Campaign aides to Washington's Senator Jack Adams have informed him that he has to carry Seattle, Tacoma, and Spokane, the three major cities in his state, to be reelected. During the final week of his campaign he decides to concentrate on these cities. Senator Adams decides to follow this procedure: He will campaign in only one city each day. If he speaks in Tacoma one day, he will speak in Seattle the next day. If he speaks in Seattle one day, chances are even that he will speak in Tacoma or Spokane the next day. If he speaks in Spokane one day, chances are even that he will speak in Spokane, Tacoma or Seattle the next day.*

21.  a.  What is the transition matrix $T$?
  b.  Is $T$ regular?
22.  What is the probability that Senator Adams will speak in Spokane on Thursday if he spoke in Spokane on Tuesday?
23..  What is the probability that Senator Adams will speak in Tacoma on Friday if he campaigned in Seattle on Tuesday?

# An Introduction to Statistics     **5**

## ——5-1 Samples and Populations

"How long will I live?" "Who will be the next President?" "When is the best time to buy a new car?" "How many students will be in college next year?" "How will high school honor roll students do in college?" "What will be the voter turnout for the primary elections?" None of these questions can be answered without collecting facts about them.

Statistics is the science of collecting, organizing, and interpreting facts. By making observations, statisticians obtain these facts, called *data*, in the form of measurements or counts. For instance, in studying public opinion on a controversial issue such as the location of a new stadium, a small percentage of the residents of the county could be selected and asked which site they favor. Or, in studying the quality of products from a certain bakery, a number of baked goods could be selected and tested.

In every statistical investigation it is necessary to define clearly the group to which the findings apply. The group being investigated is called the *population*. In statistics the word population may in its ordinary sense refer to people, but it may also refer to tires, beetles, bacteria, bottles of a certain soft drink, etc. In the examples above, the populations are the collection of all inhabitants of the county in which the stadium is to be built and the collection of all products of the bakery, respectively.

For practical reasons such as limited accessibility, time, and money, it is not always possible to study the entire population. In such instances one can collect information about a *sample* or portion of the population. In testing the taste of a lemon meringue pie in a baking contest, for example, it is not necessary to eat the whole pie to determine how the pie tastes. However, tasting just the filling or the meringue or the crust would not give enough information about the pie's taste. Instead, the most representative sample would be a small wedge of the pie. Unfortunately, the problem of how to select a representative sample from a population so that conclusions valid for the entire population can be drawn is usually more complex than this pie-testing situation.

Consider the following example. Suppose a pollster wishes to predict the outcome of a Presidential election. Surely, it would be nearly impossible for him to poll the entire population of registered voters. Instead he will choose a sample of the voting population, but how should he choose this sample so that it will be representative? Should he take a large sample of voters living in the country's large cities? No! This would be a *biased* sample since residents of large cities usually have different voting patterns from those of residents of rural and suburban areas. Should he poll all government employees or all registered voters listed in the country's phone books? No! Again, these groups might have voting patterns that would automatically make the sample biased.

Instead, the pollster should arrange his sample so that all members of the population of the country's registered voters have an *equal* chance of being selected. Samples of this nature, called *random samples*, are advocated by statisticians as the samples that most accurately represent the population from which they are taken. By averaging the results of more than one random sample from a given population, an even more accurate representation of the entire population is obtained; and this accuracy continues to improve as sampling continues.

Statisticians have worked out procedures for selecting random samples. One common, if cumbersome, procedure for selecting samples that are a fair representation of the population involves writing the name of each member of the population on a slip of paper. Then these names are placed in a container from which a predetermined number of slips are drawn. Those people whose names are drawn make up the sample.

Thus, the election pollster in our example might use voter registration rolls, from which he could select a random sample in this manner. Since it would not be practical to use all the voter registration rolls in the country our pollster might select several urban, rural, and suburban communities and use their rolls. Although they include some people who will not vote, they reflect the actual voting population more than any other list that could be devised.

There is a simple, effective procedure for selecting a random sample from a large population through the use of a *table of random numbers* such as the one shown in Table 5-1 on pages 232 and 233. We illustrate the procedure by applying it to our election poll example.

Suppose our pollster wished to choose a sample of 10,000 people from a population of 40,000. Each member of the population might be given a code number from 1 to 40,000. Then the pollster could pick 10,000 numbers from a table of 5-digit random numbers. Of course, he would discard all numbers he picked that were greater than 40,000 since there would be no member of his population assigned any of those numbers. The 10,000 people corresponding to the 10,000 numbers picked from the table would make up the pollster's random sample.

This example of a political poll is a problem in *descriptive statistics*, the field that is concerned with estimating some property of the population from samples. Other problems in descriptive statistics might involve a study of the attitude of the student body of a university towards the administration or a study by a television sponsor of the popularity of his program. On the other hand, the field of statistics called *statistical inference* is concerned with using samples to make predictions about the population or to test a hypothesis. Thus, studying a sample of light bulbs to estimate how long we can expect the light bulbs to last is a problem in statistical inference. Another problem in statistical inference is a test of the hypothesis that more automobile accidents occur during hours of darkness than during hours of daylight. Still another problem in statistical inference is the prediction of the weather. Before a weatherman makes his forecast, he has studied weather data collected over a large region—and despite studying masses of data he is sometimes wrong! In the next section we will study the nature of data and some ways to organize it.

*EXERCISES* ───────────────────────────────────────────

1. List some possible ways to choose representative samples that might be used in a study of each of the following:
   a. The IQ of sixth graders in a school.
   b. The incidence of heart disease in a tribe in Nigeria.
   c. The quality of the ice cream marketed by the Dairyfresh Company.
   d. The attitude of a senator's constituents concerning a bill he is trying to have passed in Congress.
   e. The attitude of airline passengers towards the service of a certain airline.

2. List some possible populations that each of the following samples might represent.
   a. One hundred army privates.
   b. Fifty pounds of California grapes.
   c. Ten former Miss Americas.
   d. The members of the audience at the opening performance of the symphony.

| | | | | | | | | | |
|---|---|---|---|---|---|---|---|---|---|
| 03991 | 10461 | 93716 | 16894 | 98953 | 73231 | 39528 | 72484 | 82474 | 25593 |
| 38555 | 95554 | 32886 | 59780 | 09958 | 18065 | 81616 | 18711 | 53342 | 44276 |
| 17546 | 73704 | 92052 | 46215 | 15917 | 06253 | 07586 | 16120 | 82641 | 22820 |
| 32643 | 52861 | 95819 | 06831 | 18640 | 99413 | 90767 | 04235 | 13574 | 17200 |
| 69572 | 68777 | 39510 | 35905 | 85244 | 35159 | 40188 | 28193 | 29593 | 88627 |
| 24122 | 66591 | 27699 | 06494 | 03152 | 19121 | 34414 | 82157 | 86887 | 55087 |
| 61196 | 30231 | 92962 | 61773 | 22109 | 78508 | 63439 | 75363 | 44989 | 16822 |
| 30532 | 21704 | 10274 | 12202 | 94205 | 20380 | 67049 | 09070 | 93399 | 45547 |
| 03788 | 97599 | 75867 | 20717 | 82037 | 10268 | 79495 | 04146 | 52162 | 90286 |
| 48228 | 63379 | 85783 | 47619 | 87481 | 37220 | 91704 | 30552 | 04737 | 21031 |
| 88618 | 19161 | 41290 | 67312 | 71857 | 15957 | 48545 | 35247 | 18619 | 13674 |
| 71299 | 23853 | 05870 | 01119 | 92784 | 26340 | 75122 | 11724 | 74627 | 73707 |
| 27954 | 58909 | 82444 | 99005 | 04921 | 73701 | 92904 | 13141 | 32392 | 19763 |
| 80863 | 00514 | 20247 | 81759 | 45197 | 25332 | 69902 | 63742 | 78464 | 22501 |
| 33564 | 60780 | 48460 | 85558 | 15191 | 18782 | 94972 | 11598 | 62095 | 36787 |
| 90899 | 75754 | 60833 | 25983 | 01291 | 41349 | 19152 | 00023 | 12302 | 80783 |
| 78038 | 70267 | 43529 | 06318 | 38384 | 74761 | 36024 | 00867 | 76378 | 41605 |
| 55986 | 66485 | 88722 | 56736 | 66164 | 49431 | 94458 | 74284 | 05041 | 48907 |
| 87539 | 08823 | 94813 | 31900 | 54155 | 83436 | 54158 | 34243 | 46978 | 35482 |
| 16818 | 60311 | 74457 | 90561 | 72848 | 11834 | 75051 | 93029 | 47665 | 64382 |
| 34677 | 58300 | 74910 | 64345 | 19325 | 81549 | 60365 | 94653 | 35075 | 33949 |
| 45305 | 07521 | 61318 | 31855 | 14413 | 70951 | 83977 | 42402 | 56623 | 34442 |
| 59747 | 67277 | 76503 | 34513 | 39663 | 77544 | 32960 | 07405 | 36409 | 83232 |
| 16520 | 69676 | 11654 | 99893 | 02181 | 68161 | 19322 | 53845 | 57620 | 52606 |
| 68652 | 27376 | 92852 | 55866 | 88448 | 03584 | 11220 | 94747 | 07399 | 37408 |
| 79375 | 95220 | 01159 | 63267 | 10622 | 48391 | 31751 | 57260 | 68980 | 05339 |
| 33521 | 26665 | 55823 | 47641 | 86225 | 31704 | 88492 | 99382 | 14454 | 04504 |
| 59589 | 49067 | 66821 | 41575 | 49767 | 04037 | 30934 | 47744 | 07481 | 83828 |
| 20554 | 91409 | 96277 | 48257 | 50816 | 97616 | 22888 | 48893 | 27499 | 98748 |
| 59404 | 72059 | 43947 | 51680 | 43852 | 59693 | 78212 | 16993 | 35902 | 91386 |
| 42614 | 29297 | 01918 | 28316 | 25163 | 01889 | 70014 | 15021 | 68971 | 11403 |
| 34994 | 41374 | 70071 | 14736 | 65251 | 07629 | 37239 | 33295 | 18477 | 65622 |
| 99385 | 41600 | 11133 | 07586 | 36815 | 43625 | 18637 | 37509 | 14707 | 93997 |
| 66497 | 64646 | 78138 | 66559 | 64397 | 11692 | 05327 | 82162 | 83745 | 22567 |
| 48509 | 23929 | 27482 | 45476 | 04515 | 25624 | 95096 | 67946 | 16930 | 33361 |
| 15470 | 48355 | 88651 | 22596 | 83761 | 60873 | 43253 | 84145 | 20368 | 07126 |
| 20094 | 98977 | 74843 | 93413 | 14387 | 06345 | 80854 | 09279 | 41196 | 37480 |
| 73788 | 06533 | 28597 | 20405 | 51321 | 92246 | 80088 | 77074 | 66919 | 31678 |
| 60530 | 45128 | 74022 | 84617 | 72472 | 00008 | 80890 | 18002 | 35352 | 54131 |
| 44372 | 15486 | 65741 | 14014 | 05466 | 55306 | 93128 | 18464 | 79982 | 68416 |
| 18611 | 19241 | 66083 | 24653 | 84609 | 58232 | 41849 | 84547 | 46850 | 52326 |
| 58319 | 15997 | 08355 | 60860 | 29735 | 47762 | 46352 | 33049 | 69248 | 93460 |
| 61199 | 67940 | 55121 | 29281 | 59076 | 07936 | 11087 | 96294 | 14013 | 31792 |
| 18627 | 90872 | 00911 | 98936 | 76355 | 93779 | 52701 | 08337 | 56303 | 87315 |
| 00441 | 58997 | 14060 | 40619 | 29549 | 69616 | 57275 | 36898 | 81304 | 48585 |
| 32624 | 68691 | 14945 | 46672 | 61958 | 77100 | 20857 | 73156 | 70284 | 24326 |
| 65961 | 73488 | 41839 | 55382 | 17267 | 70943 | 15633 | 84924 | 90415 | 93614 |
| 20288 | 34060 | 39685 | 23309 | 10061 | 68829 | 92694 | 48297 | 39904 | 02115 |
| 59362 | 95938 | 74416 | 53166 | 35208 | 33374 | 77613 | 19019 | 88152 | 00080 |
| 99782 | 93478 | 53152 | 67433 | 35663 | 52972 | 38688 | 32486 | 45134 | 63545 |

TABLE 5-1.    Random numbers.

| | | | | | | | | | |
|---|---|---|---|---|---|---|---|---|---|
| 27767 | 43584 | 85301 | 88977 | 29490 | 69714 | 94015 | 64874 | 32444 | 48277 |
| 13025 | 14338 | 54066 | 15243 | 47724 | 66733 | 74108 | 88222 | 88570 | 74015 |
| 80217 | 36292 | 98525 | 24335 | 24432 | 24896 | 62880 | 87873 | 95160 | 59221 |
| 10875 | 62004 | 90391 | 61105 | 57411 | 06368 | 11748 | 12102 | 80580 | 41867 |
| 54127 | 57326 | 26629 | 19087 | 24472 | 88779 | 17944 | 05600 | 60478 | 03343 |
| 60311 | 42824 | 37301 | 42678 | 45990 | 43242 | 66067 | 42792 | 95043 | 52680 |
| 49739 | 71484 | 92003 | 98086 | 76668 | 73209 | 54244 | 91030 | 45547 | 70818 |
| 78626 | 51594 | 16453 | 94614 | 39014 | 97066 | 30945 | 57589 | 31732 | 57260 |
| 66692 | 13986 | 99837 | 00582 | 81232 | 44987 | 69170 | 37403 | 86995 | 90307 |
| 44071 | 28091 | 07362 | 97703 | 76447 | 42537 | 08345 | 88975 | 35841 | 85771 |
| 59820 | 96163 | 78851 | 16499 | 87064 | 13075 | 73035 | 41207 | 74699 | 09310 |
| 25704 | 91035 | 26313 | 77463 | 55387 | 72681 | 47431 | 43905 | 31048 | 56699 |
| 22304 | 90314 | 78438 | 66276 | 18396 | 73538 | 43277 | 58874 | 11466 | 16082 |
| 17710 | 59621 | 15292 | 76139 | 59526 | 52113 | 53856 | 30743 | 08670 | 84741 |
| 25852 | 58905 | 55018 | 56374 | 35824 | 71708 | 30540 | 27886 | 61732 | 75454 |
| 46780 | 56487 | 75211 | 10271 | 36633 | 68424 | 17374 | 52003 | 70707 | 70214 |
| 59849 | 96169 | 87195 | 46092 | 26787 | 60939 | 59202 | 11973 | 02902 | 33250 |
| 47670 | 07654 | 30342 | 40277 | 11049 | 72049 | 83012 | 09832 | 25571 | 77628 |
| 94304 | 71803 | 73465 | 09819 | 58869 | 35220 | 09504 | 96412 | 90193 | 79568 |
| 08105 | 59987 | 21437 | 36786 | 49226 | 77837 | 98524 | 97831 | 65704 | 09514 |
| 64281 | 61826 | 18555 | 64937 | 64654 | 25843 | 41145 | 42820 | 14924 | 39650 |
| 66847 | 70495 | 32350 | 02985 | 01755 | 14750 | 48968 | 38603 | 70312 | 05682 |
| 72461 | 33230 | 21529 | 53424 | 72877 | 17334 | 39283 | 04149 | 90850 | 64618 |
| 21032 | 91050 | 13058 | 16218 | 06554 | 07850 | 73950 | 79552 | 23781 | 89683 |
| 95362 | 67011 | 06651 | 16136 | 57216 | 39618 | 49856 | 99326 | 40902 | 05069 |
| 49712 | 97380 | 10404 | 55452 | 09971 | 59481 | 37006 | 22186 | 72682 | 07385 |
| 58275 | 61764 | 97586 | 54716 | 61459 | 21647 | 87417 | 17198 | 21443 | 41808 |
| 89514 | 11788 | 68224 | 23417 | 46376 | 25366 | 94746 | 49580 | 01176 | 28838 |
| 15472 | 50669 | 48139 | 36732 | 26825 | 05511 | 12459 | 91314 | 80582 | 71944 |
| 12120 | 86124 | 51247 | 44302 | 87112 | 21476 | 14713 | 71181 | 13177 | 55292 |
| 95294 | 00556 | 70481 | 06905 | 21785 | 41101 | 49386 | 54480 | 23604 | 23554 |
| 66986 | 34099 | 74474 | 20740 | 47458 | 64809 | 06312 | 88940 | 15995 | 69321 |
| 86020 | 51790 | 11436 | 38072 | 40405 | 68032 | 60942 | 00307 | 11897 | 92674 |
| 55411 | 85667 | 77535 | 99892 | 71209 | 92061 | 92329 | 98932 | 78284 | 46347 |
| 95083 | 06783 | 28102 | 57816 | 85561 | 29671 | 77936 | 63574 | 31384 | 51924 |
| 90726 | 57166 | 98884 | 08583 | 95889 | 57067 | 38101 | 77756 | 11657 | 13897 |
| 68984 | 83620 | 89747 | 98882 | 92613 | 89719 | 39641 | 69457 | 91339 | 22502 |
| 36421 | 16489 | 18059 | 51061 | 67667 | 60631 | 84054 | 40455 | 99396 | 63680 |
| 92638 | 40333 | 67054 | 16067 | 24700 | 71594 | 47468 | 03577 | 57649 | 63266 |
| 21036 | 82808 | 77501 | 97427 | 76479 | 68562 | 43321 | 31370 | 28977 | 23896 |
| 13173 | 33365 | 41468 | 85149 | 49554 | 17994 | 91178 | 10174 | 29420 | 90438 |
| 86716 | 38746 | 94559 | 37559 | 49678 | 53119 | 98189 | 81851 | 29651 | 84215 |
| 92581 | 02262 | 41615 | 70360 | 64114 | 58660 | 96717 | 54244 | 10701 | 41393 |
| 12470 | 56500 | 50273 | 93113 | 41794 | 86861 | 39448 | 93136 | 25722 | 08564 |
| 01016 | 00857 | 41396 | 80504 | 90670 | 08289 | 58137 | 17820 | 22751 | 36518 |
| 34030 | 60726 | 25807 | 24260 | 71529 | 78920 | 47648 | 13885 | 70669 | 93406 |
| 50259 | 46345 | 06107 | 97965 | 88302 | 98041 | 11947 | 56203 | 19324 | 20504 |
| 73959 | 76145 | 60808 | 54444 | 74412 | 81105 | 69181 | 96845 | 38525 | 11600 |
| 46874 | 37088 | 80940 | 44893 | 10408 | 36222 | 14004 | 23153 | 69249 | 05747 |
| 60883 | 52109 | 19516 | 90120 | 46759 | 71643 | 62342 | 07589 | 08899 | 05985 |

TABLE 5-1.    (continued).

3.  A manufacturer of laundry soap wishes to evaluate public reaction to his products. He encloses questionnaires in sample boxes of soap that are sent free of charge to 5,000 addresses from the Chicago phone book. His evaluation of the public's attitude towards his product is based on the information in the questionnaires returned. Criticize the manufacturer's procedure of evaluating public reaction.

4.  A report on the eating habits of American teenagers is based on a large number of interviews with teenagers who volunteered to be questioned. Can the results be generalized to all American teenagers? If not, define the population which the data obtained can be used to describe.

5.  In 1936 the *Literary Digest* conducted a poll to predict the outcome of the presidential election that year. It sent out ten million ballots to Americans who were either telephone owners or subscribers to the magazine. Two million answers were received. On the basis of these answers the magazine predicted that Landon would be elected. In actuality, however, Roosevelt received 60% of the votes cast in the election. Where did the magazine go wrong in choosing a sampling procedure?

6.  The Popcorn Poll conducted by an organization in Nashville, Tennessee, has not been wrong in predicting the outcome of a presidential election since 1948. In this poll data is collected by inserting questionnaires in boxes of popcorn sold in theaters throughout the United States. Despite the excellent record of the poll criticize the procedure used to predict the outcome of presidential elections.

7.  To choose a random sample using a table of random numbers, how many digits should be in each number in the table if the population consists of
    a. 12,438?
    b. 2,945?
    c. 253?

## ——5-2  Classification of Data

As mentioned previously, the facts that statisticians collect are called *data*. Data consist of *variables*, characteristics of a group that can assume different values. There are two main types of variables, *ordered* and *unordered*. IQ score, weight, age, and attitude towards the president are examples of ordered variables. On the other hand, marital status, sex, and make of car are unordered variables. Ordered variables that have a numerical value are called *scaled* variables. For instance, a person's income is a scaled variable since it is measured in terms of numbers. Scaled variables may either be *continuous* or *discrete*. Continuous variables are those, such as weight, height, length, and

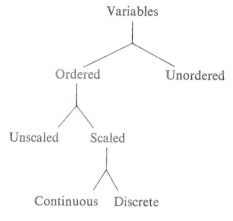

FIGURE 5-1.

time , which can assume any value in some interval of values. Discrete variables, however, can only assume integer values. Therefore, the number of votes received by a candidate, the number of cases of influenza in a year, and the number of marriages in June are all examples of discrete variables.

The diagram in Figure 5-1 summarizes the relationships among the different kinds of variables.

Now that we have discussed the different types of data, we need some methods of organizing and interpreting this information once it has been collected. Suppose, for instance, that the following are the scores on the written test required for a driver's license that were obtained during one day at a driver licensing bureau.

|    |    |    |     |    |    |    |    |
|----|----|----|-----|----|----|----|----|
| 77 | 89 | 75 | 95  | 93 | 81 | 84 | 83 |
| 82 | 89 | 97 | 100 | 73 | 79 | 87 | 86 |
| 93 | 87 | 92 | 77  | 83 | 90 | 98 | 85 |
| 78 | 84 | 83 | 87  | 91 | 85 | 76 | 89 |
| 83 | 89 | 95 | 79  | 83 | 91 | 79 | 80 |

These forty scores do not tell much of a story. However, if they are arranged in order from highest to lowest and if tally marks are used to record the occurrences of the respective scores, then the *frequency f* with which each score occurred can be determined, and the occurrence pattern of the test scores emerges. (See Table 5-2.) From this kind of summary of data, called a *frequency distribution*, we have a better idea of the results of the test. Notice that the sum of the frequencies for all the scores must equal the total number of measurements.

Frequency distributions are easier to visualize if they are represented graphically. For a discrete type of variable such as that of test scores in our

| Score | Tally Marks | Frequency f |
|-------|-------------|-------------|
| 100 | \| | 1 |
| 99 | | |
| 98 | \| | 1 |
| 97 | \| | 1 |
| 96 | | |
| 95 | \|\| | 2 |
| 94 | | |
| 93 | \|\| | 2 |
| 92 | \| | 1 |
| 91 | \|\| | 2 |
| 90 | \| | 1 |
| 89 | \|\|\|\| | 4 |
| 88 | | |
| 87 | \|\|\| | 3 |
| 86 | \| | 1 |
| 85 | \|\| | 2 |
| 84 | \|\| | 2 |
| 83 | ⧵⧵⧵⧵⧵ | 5 |
| 82 | \| | 1 |
| 81 | \| | 1 |
| 80 | \| | 1 |
| 79 | \|\|\| | 3 |
| 78 | \| | 1 |
| 77 | \|\| | 2 |
| 76 | \| | 1 |
| 75 | \| | 1 |
| 74 | | |
| 73 | \| | 1 |

TABLE 5-2.

example we may represent the frequency distribution by a *line chart* such as the one shown in Figure 5-2.

It is easy to see from this line chart that the grade received by the most people was 83 and that no one received grades of 74, 88, 94, 96, and 99.

Let us now consider a problem in statistics in which the variable is continuous rather than discrete. Suppose a study is being made of the weights of college freshman girls in a certain university. The weights obtained for a sample of forty girls are:

| | | | | | | | |
|---|---|---|---|---|---|---|---|
| 142 | 97 | 112 | 105 | 127 | 124 | 126 | 132 |
| 141 | 135 | 101 | 113 | 139 | 128 | 150 | 140 |
| 114 | 120 | 121 | 131 | 162 | 108 | 132 | 145 |
| 133 | 130 | 107 | 118 | 150 | 115 | 161 | 146 |
| 152 | 125 | 137 | 120 | 130 | 125 | 170 | 140 |

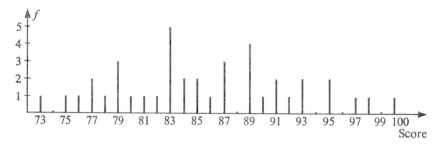

FIGURE 5-2.

First let us arrange this data in a frequency table as before. This time, however, we will break the weights into *intervals*. Since the least weight in the sample is 97 and the greatest is 170, we can conveniently divide the range of weights into ten-pound intervals starting with the interval 89.5–99.5 pounds. (Note: *To avoid having measurements fall on the boundary of two adjacent intervals, boundaries are usually chosen to one-half unit beyond the accuracy of the measurements.*) Resulting frequency table is shown in Table 5-3.

Just as with our examples of test scores this frequency distribution would be even clearer if we represented it graphically. Because we are dealing with a continuous variable, a graph called a *histogram* is more useful than a line drawing. The histogram for our frequency distribution of weights is shown in Figure 5-3. The width of each rectangle corresponds to the ten-pound weight intervals and the height of each rectangle corresponds to the frequency of occurrence of weights in the interval. Note that measurements falling in the interval 89.5–99.5 are represented by a rectangle between 89.5 and 99.5 on the horizontal axis of the histogram.

From the histogram it is clear that more freshman girls had weights in the 119.5–129.5 and 129.5–139.5 intervals than in any others. The distribution of weights here is roughly bell-shaped. It is very similar to frequency distributions that are obtained in nature and in industry. See Section 5-5 for a discussion of distributions of this sort.

| Weight in lbs. | Tally marks | Frequency f |
|---|---|---|
| 89.5 — 99.45 | \| | 1 |
| 99.5 — 109.45 | \|\|\|\| | 4 |
| 109.5 — 119.45 | ++++ | 5 |
| 119.5 — 129.45 | ++++ \|\|\|\| | 9 |
| 129.5 — 139.45 | ++++ \|\|\|\| | 9 |
| 139.5 — 149.45 | ++++ \| | 6 |
| 149.5 — 159.45 | \|\|\| | 3 |
| 159.5 — 169.45 | \|\| | 2 |
| 169.5 — 179.45 | \| | 1 |

TABLE 5-3.

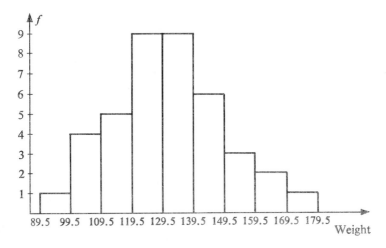

FIGURE 5-3.

*EXERCISES* ——————————————————————————————

1. Classify each of the following variables as (i) ordered or unordered. If the variable is ordered, classify it as (ii) scaled or unscaled, (iii) continuous or discrete.
   a. Marital status.
   b. Number of teachers in each state.
   c. Weight at birth.
   d. Age at marriage.
   e. Time needed to fly between two cities.
   f. Hair color.
   g. Number of cigarette smokers classified by age.
   h. Occupation.

2. The following list gives for each state the minimum legal marriageable age for men with parental consent.

| 17 | 18 | 18 | 18 | 18 | 16 | 16 | 18 | 18 | 18 |
| 17 | 18 | 15 | 18 | 18 | 18 | 18 | 18 | 16 | 18 |
| 18 | 18 | 18 | 17 | 15 | 18 | 18 | 18 | 14 | 18 |
| 18 | 16 | 16 | 18 | 18 | 18 | 18 | 16 | 18 | 16 |
| 18 | 16 | 16 | 16 | 18 | 18 | 17 | 18 | 18 | 18 |

Organize this data by making a frequency distribution and line drawing for the ages.

3. Toss three coins forty-eight times and record the number of heads and tails on each throw. Make a frequency distribution organizing the data you obtain by completing the table below. Then make a line drawing corresponding to the resulting frequency distribution. About what fraction of the time did you get zero heads? One head? Two heads? Three heads?

| Numbers of heads | Frequency |
|---|---|
| 0 | |
| 1 | |
| 2 | |
| 3 | |

4. The weights of boys reporting for tryouts on the varsity football team were:

| | | | | | |
|---|---|---|---|---|---|
| 191 | 206 | 170 | 165 | 220 | 204 |
| 178 | 155 | 200 | 195 | 190 | 188 |
| 175 | 182 | 197 | 188 | 169 | 207 |
| 168 | 177 | 189 | 203 | 200 | 193 |
| 188 | 167 | 201 | 193 | 198 | 215 |

Using intervals of 10 (149.5–159.5, 159.5–169.5, . . .), make a frequency distribution and histogram for the weights.

5. The usual rainfall in each month for San Francisco and Honolulu is given below in inches. Compare the rainfall in the two cities by organizing each set of data into a frequency distribution and a histogram with intervals of 0.005–0.505, 0.505–1.005, and so on.

   San Francisco: 4.0, 3.5, 2.7, 1.3, 0.5, 0.1, 0.05, 0.05, 0.2, 0.7, 1.6, 4.1;
   Honolulu: 3.8, 3.3, 2.9, 1.3, 1.0, 0.3, 0.4, 0.9, 1.0, 1.8, 2.2, 3.0.

6. The following table gives the hourly earnings in manufacturing industries in the United States from 1958–1966.

| Year | 1958 | 1959 | 1960 | 1961 | 1962 | 1963 | 1964 | 1965 | 1966 |
|---|---|---|---|---|---|---|---|---|---|
| Hourly earnings | 2.11 | 2.19 | 2.26 | 2.32 | 2.39 | 2.46 | 2.53 | 2.61 | 2.71 |

Using intervals of 0.25 (2.005–2.255, 2.255–2.505, . . .), make a frequency distribution and histogram for the earnings.

7. The following table gives the number (in millions) of radio and television sets in use in the United States from 1960-1966.

| Year | 1960 | 1961 | 1962 | 1963 | 1964 | 1965 | 1966 |
|---|---|---|---|---|---|---|---|
| Radios | 156 | 168 | 183 | 196 | 208 | 227 | 262 |
| Televisions | 55.7 | 58 | 61.6 | 66.6 | 73.0 | 80.0 | 88.2 |

Using intervals of 10 million (149.5–159.5, 159.5–169.5, . . . and 55.55–65.55, 65.55-75.55, . . . respectively), make a frequency distribution and histogram for each set of data.

8.  The following list gives the number of births in each state and the District of Columbia in 1966. Organize the information in the list into a frequency distribution and corresponding histogram using intervals of .5–25, 000.5, 25, 000.5–50, 000.5, and so on.

| | | | |
|---|---|---|---|
| 65,808 | 90,504 | 63,756 | 116,873 |
| 6,515 | 14,977 | 101,827 | 22,022 |
| 32,176 | 12,600 | 164,210 | 322,765 |
| 34,461 | 200,290 | 65,960 | 92,863 |
| 350,091 | 94,596 | 48,276 | 12,411 |
| 36,107 | 49,598 | 80,989 | 190,160 |
| 51,289 | 34,925 | 12,526 | 39,439 |
| 10,203 | 59,222 | 25,450 | 32,860 |
| 29,103 | 77,609 | 8,655 | 196,927 |
| 101,643 | 18,105 | 12,039 | 16,837 |
| 50,609 | 12,525 | 71,011 | 212,271 |
| 23,067 | 7,870 | 79,703 | 50,116 |
| 30,797 | 79,869 | 5,792 | |

## ——5-3  Measures of Central Tendency

In the last section we showed how data can be classified and how line drawings and histograms can be used to display the distribution of the data. Although these graphic representations of data yield a lot of useful information concerning the distribution of data, even more valuable information can be obtained by describing the distribution arithmetically.

One way to describe the distribution of a set of data is to speak of the *mode*, or most common measurement, of the distribution. In other words, the mode is the measurement with the maximum frequency. For instance, for the set of measurements or scores

    3  4  4  2
    3  4  4  1
    3  2  1  4

a frequency table is shown in Table 5-4.

| Measurement | Tally | Frequency |
|:-----------:|:-----:|:---------:|
| 1 | \|\| | 2 |
| 2 | \|\| | 2 |
| 3 | \|\|\| | 3 |
| 4 | ++++ | 5 |

TABLE 5-4.

The mode of these measurements is 4, since 4 has the highest frequency, 5. Thus, the measurements tend to cluster at the mode. In the first example of the previous section the mode for the group of scores on the test given by the driver licensing bureau is 83. More people had a score of 83 than any other. However, for the second example involving weights of freshman girls there are two modes: one mode is contained in the weight interval 119.5–129.5, the other is in the weight interval 129.5–139.5. We call a distribution such as this *bimodal*, because it has two modes. It is possible for distributions with many modes, called *multimodal distributions*, to occur.

In some instances it is useful to find the *median* or middle member (if there is one) of a set of measurements, after the set is arranged in order according to size. (Each measurement is listed as many times as it occurs.) An odd number of measurements is listed below. The median is the middle score, 9, since there are equally many scores, namely two, above 9 and below 9.

14
10
9 ← median
7
4

When the distribution involves an even number of measurements, as does the one below, then the median is half-way between the two middle scores. In this case the two middle scores are 10 and 7, so the median is $(10 + 7)/2$, or 8.5.

14
11
10
7 ← median
6
3

For data that has been *classified*, as in the histogram of Figure 5-3 of the weights of freshman girls, the median is the point on the horizontal scale at which a vertical line cuts the histogram into two parts of equal area. Since there is an even number of measurements, forty, in the sample of freshman girls, we need to find the point on the horizontal axis so that twenty measurements will be to the left of it and twenty to the right of it. So, ideally the median is located between the twentieth and twenty-first measurement of the set. If the frequencies in the first four intervals are summed up we find that we have accounted for nineteen measurements. We thus know that the median lies in the interval 129.5–139.5. Since there are nine measurements in this interval, and we need only one of them to have a total of twenty measurements to the left of the median, the median is located 1/9 of the way along the interval. The interval is ten units long (that is, it extends over ten pounds) and it starts at 129.5, so the value of the median is

$$129.5 + \frac{1}{9}(10) \approx 130.6.$$

(Many of our calculations are carried out to only a few decimal places, yielding answers that are approximately correct.)

Besides finding the value on the horizontal axis of the histogram that divides the area in the histogram into a left and a right half, we often find two other values, one that divides the histogram at a point such that one-fourth of the area of the histogram lies to the left of it and the other such that one-fourth of the area lies to the right of it. These two values together with the median are the three *quartiles* of the distribution. The smallest quartile is the first quartile, the median is the second quartile, and the largest quartile is the third quartile.

Thus for the example dealing with the weights of freshman girls, the first quartile is the point on the horizontal axis of the histogram so that $(\frac{1}{4})40$ or ten measurements are to the left of it. That point is 119.5, since there are ten measurements in the first three intervals of the histogram in Figure 5-3. The second quartile is the median of the distribution, about 130.6, as determined above. The third quartile is

$$149.5 - \frac{4}{6}(10) \approx 142.8,$$

since there is a total of six measurements in the last three intervals and $\frac{4}{6}$ of the ten units in the fourth from the last interval are needed in order to have ten measurements to the right of the third quartile.

One can also describe distributions using *deciles* instead of quartiles or medians. Deciles are values of the data that divide the histogram of the distribution into tenths rather than fourths or halves. These descriptions of distributions may even be extended to percentiles, which are those values of the data that divide the histogram into one hundred equal parts. Percentiles are frequently used in psychological and educational testing.

Another way to describe a distribution is by finding the *average* or *mean* of the sample values. For example, if five sample values were found to be

8    7    11    4    8,

the mean could be obtained by adding all the values and dividing the total by the number of values. Thus, in this case, the mean would be

$$\frac{8 + 7 + 11 + 4 + 8}{5} = 7.6.$$

Let us call the $n$ values in a set of data

$$x_1, x_2, x_3, \ldots, x_n.$$

Then the mean, which we shall denote $\overline{X}$, is

$$\overline{X} = \frac{x_1 + x_2 + x_3 + \cdots + x_n}{n}.$$

Mathematicians write this formula using the summation symbol $\Sigma$, the capital Greek letter sigma. They write, for instance, the sum of $x_1$, $x_2$, and $x_3$ as

$$x_1 + x_2 + x_3 = \sum_{i=1}^{3} x_i.$$

The right member of the above equation might be read as "the sum, for integer values of $i$ ranging from 1 to 3, of numbers $x_i$." (See Appendix I.) Using this notation, then, we could write our formula for the mean of $n$ values as

$$\overline{X} = \frac{\sum_{i=1}^{n} x_i}{n} = \frac{1}{n} \sum_{i=1}^{n} x_i.$$

If the data in a given sample has been classified, say, by means of a frequency distribution, we may modify the above formula to take advantage of the classification. Instead of adding each data value as often as it occurs, we may multiply each *distinct* value $x_i$ by the frequency $f_i$ with which it occurs and sum the products $x_i f_i$ in calculating the numerator of the above fraction. For example, in our sample of five measurements,

$$8 \quad 7 \quad 11 \quad 4 \quad 8,$$

we could let

$$x_1 = 8, \quad \text{and} \quad f_1 = 2,$$

since $x_1 = 8$ occurs two times in the sample. Similarly,

$$x_2 = 7 \quad \text{and} \quad f_2 = 1,$$
$$x_3 = 11 \quad \text{and} \quad f_3 = 1,$$
$$x_4 = 4 \quad \text{and} \quad f_4 = 1.$$

The mean is the sum of the products $x_i f_i$, divided by the total number of measurements. Therefore we have for the mean of the above five values

$$\bar{X} = \frac{x_1 f_1 + x_2 f_2 + x_3 f_3 + x_4 f_4}{n}$$

$$= \frac{8 \cdot 2 + 7 \cdot 1 + 11 \cdot 1 + 4 \cdot 1}{5}$$

$$= \frac{16 + 7 + 11 + 4}{5}$$

$$= \frac{38}{5} = 7.6.$$

That is, $\bar{X} = 7.6$, in agreement with the value computed earlier.

We may also use the summation symbol in describing this method of finding the mean, as follows:

$$\bar{X} = \frac{1}{n} \sum_{i=1}^{r} x_i f_i,$$

where the $x_i$ are the different values that appear in the sample data, the $f_i$ are the corresponding frequencies, $r$ is the number of different values in the sample, and $n$ is the total number of values in the sample.

We can use this formula to find the mean of the scores made on the test taken by people obtaining their driver's license in the example of the last section. From Table 5-2 we obtain the information which is summarized here in Table 5-5. Notice that $n = \sum_{i=1}^{r} f_i$. That is, the number of values in the sample of data is equal to the sum of the frequencies for the $r$ different values in the sample. We find

$$\bar{X} = \frac{1}{n} \sum_{i=1}^{r} x_i f_i$$

$$= \frac{1}{40} (3427)$$

$$= 85.675.$$

Thus, the mean score on the test was 85.675.

In the preceding calculation of the mean we were dealing with discrete variables that were not classified into intervals. However, if the data are classified into intervals we assume for convenience that each member of the sample in an interval occurs at the middle value in the interval. Using this technique to obtain the mean of the weights of the freshman girls from the histogram of Figure 5-3, our result is slightly different from the one we would obtain if we used the actual weights. However, the difference is small. The members of the sample in the interval 89.5–99.5 will each be assumed to have

| $i$ | $x_i$ | $f_i$ | $x_i f_i$ |
|---|---|---|---|
| 1 | 100 | 1 | 100 |
| 2 | 98 | 1 | 98 |
| 3 | 97 | 1 | 97 |
| 4 | 95 | 2 | 190 |
| 5 | 93 | 2 | 186 |
| 6 | 92 | 1 | 92 |
| 7 | 91 | 2 | 182 |
| 8 | 90 | 1 | 90 |
| 9 | 89 | 4 | 356 |
| 10 | 87 | 3 | 261 |
| 11 | 86 | 1 | 86 |
| 12 | 85 | 2 | 170 |
| 13 | 84 | 2 | 168 |
| 14 | 83 | 5 | 415 |
| 15 | 82 | 1 | 82 |
| 16 | 81 | 1 | 81 |
| 17 | 80 | 1 | 80 |
| 18 | 79 | 3 | 237 |
| 19 | 78 | 1 | 78 |
| 20 | 77 | 2 | 154 |
| 21 | 76 | 1 | 76 |
| 22 | 75 | 1 | 75 |
| $r = 23$ | 73 | 1 | 73 |
|  |  | $n = \sum\limits_{i=1}^{r} f_i = \overline{40}$ | $\sum\limits_{i=1}^{r} x_i f_i = \overline{3427}$ |

TABLE 5-5.

a weight of 94.5, those in the interval 99.5–109.5 a weight of 104.5, etc. We summarize in Table 5-6 the information from Table 5-3 needed to find the

| $i$ | $x_i$ | $f_i$ | $x_i f_i$ |
|---|---|---|---|
| 1 | 94.5 | 1 | 94.5 |
| 2 | 104.5 | 4 | 418.0 |
| 3 | 114.5 | 5 | 572.5 |
| 4 | 124.5 | 9 | 1,120.5 |
| 5 | 134.5 | 9 | 1,210.5 |
| 6 | 144.5 | 6 | 867.0 |
| 7 | 154.5 | 3 | 463.5 |
| 8 | 164.5 | 2 | 329.0 |
| $r = 9$ | 174.5 | 1 | 174.5 |
|  |  | $n = \sum\limits_{i=1}^{r} f_i = \overline{40}$ | $\sum\limits_{i=1}^{r} x_i f_i = \overline{5{,}250.0}$ |

TABLE 5-6.

mean of the weights. From this information we have

$$\overline{X} = \frac{1}{n} \sum_{i=1}^{r} x_i f_i$$

$$= \frac{1}{40}(5250) = 131.25.$$

Thus, the average or mean weight of the girls in the sample as computed from the histogram is 131.25 pounds. Notice that this mean is near the middle of the base of the histogram of the distribution of weights in Figure 5-3. In fact, the mean of any distribution usually gives a fairly good idea of where the corresponding histogram is centered along the horizontal axis.

In this section we have shown how the mode, median, and mean can be used to describe arithmetically distributions of both discrete and continuous variables. Let us summarize by finding the mode, median, and mean for the distribution of the age of each of the first thirty-six* presidents of the United States on his day of inauguration. The distribution is described by the histogram in Figure 5-4 and its corresponding frequency table in Table 5-7.

In computing the entries in Table 5-7 remember that each member of the set of data in a histogram is represented by the middle value of the interval. Thus, for example, the two members of the set of data in the 39.5–43.5 interval are given the value 41.5.

From the histogram we see that the distribution of the ages of the presidents on inauguration day is *bimodal*. The two modes are the intervals 47.5–51.5 and 51.5–55.5.

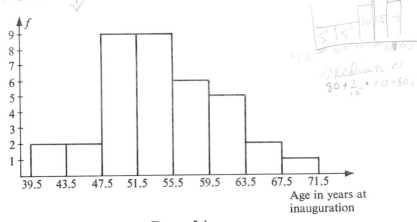

FIGURE 5-4.

To find the median age of the thirty-six presidents when they took office we need to find the point on the horizontal axis so that eighteen measurements are to the left of it and eighteen measurements are to the right of it. Ideally, the median lies between the eighteenth and nineteenth measurement of the set. The frequencies in the first three intervals add up to thirteen.

---

* Grover Cleveland is counted twice here.

| $i$ | Age at inauguration in four-year intervals $x_i$ | Frequency $f_i$ | $x_i f_i$ |
|---|---|---|---|
| 1 | 39.5 — 43.5 | 2 | 83.0 |
| 2 | 43.5 — 47.5 | 2 | 91.0 |
| 3 | 47.5 — 51.5 | 9 | 445.5 |
| 4 | 51.5 — 55.5 | 9 | 481.5 |
| 5 | 55.5 — 59.5 | 6 | 345.0 |
| 6 | 59.5 — 63.5 | 5 | 307.5 |
| 7 | 63.5 — 67.5 | 2 | 131.0 |
| $r = 8$ | 67.5 — 71.5 | 1 | 69.5 |
| | | $n = \sum_{i=1}^{r} f_i = 36$ | $\sum_{i=1}^{r} x_i f_i = 1{,}954.0$ |

TABLE 5-7.

Therefore, we need five more measurements from the fourth interval to have a total of eighteen measurements. We can see that the median is located in the interval 51.5–55.5. Since we need only five of the nine measurements in that interval to have eighteen measurements, and since the interval starts at 51.5 and is four units long, the median is

$$51.5 + \frac{5}{9}(4) \approx 53.7 \text{ years.}$$

Thus, we know that half of the presidents were younger than 53.7 years old and half were older than 53.7 years old on inauguration day.

Next we compute the mean age of each president on his inauguration day. From the values of $n$ and $\sum_{i=1}^{r} x_i f_i$ in Table 5-7, we find that the mean is

$$\bar{X} = \frac{1}{n}\sum_{i=1}^{r} x_i f_i = \frac{1}{36} \cdot 1954.0,$$

$$\bar{X} \approx 54.28.$$

Notice how close the median and the mean are in this case.

In this section we have seen how the histogram of a distribution, together with the mode, median, and mean of a distribution, give a good idea about the *central tendencies* of the distribution. In the next section we will show how to describe not only the central tendencies, but also the distribution of the data up and down the scale.

*EXERCISES* ——————————————————————————

1.  Consider industries where there are more laborers working at the lowest wage scale than at any of the others.
    a.  Which measure—mode, median, or mean—of central tendency do you think labor leaders prefer to quote? Why?
    b.  Which measure of central tendency do you think management leaders prefer to quote? Why?

 c. What is the most realistic measure of central tendency? Why?

2. The heights of the members of two basketball teams are given below in inches. Compare the means of the two sets of heights. Is either of the teams at an advantage?

  Team $X$: 72″, 75″, 70″, 71″, 76″,
  Team $Y$: 75″, 71″, 76″, 77″, 74″.

3. Compute the mode, median, and mean for the distribution in the data in Exercise 2, Section 5-2.

4–8. Compute the mode, median, and mean for the distributions given in the data in Exercises 4–8, Section 5-2.

9. The IQ's of twenty students in the sophomore political science honors section are listed below:

| | | | | |
|---|---|---|---|---|
| 115 | 125 | 121 | 132 | 118 |
| 142 | 119 | 126 | 134 | 128 |
| 123 | 147 | 118 | 138 | 151 |
| 131 | 123 | 129 | 131 | 142 |

 a. Organize the scores into a frequency distribution and histogram using intervals of 113.5–117.5, 117.5–121.5 and so on.

 b. Calculate the mode of the distribution.

 c. Calculate the mean of the distribution.

 d. Calculate the first and third quartiles of the distribution.

 e. Calculate the ninetieth percentile of the distribution.

 f. Calculate the ninety-fifth percentile.

## ——5-4  Measures of Dispersion

 The mode, median, and mean that were discussed in the last section are measures of central tendency. In this section we will discuss ways of describing the *dispersion* or spread of data values in a distribution.

 The difference between the lowest and highest values in a set of sample data gives the *range* of the distribution. In our example of the last section, which dealt with the age of each President of the United States on his inauguration day, the range is 68 − 42 or 26, since at 68 William Henry Harrison was the oldest man to become President of the United States and 42-year-old Theodore Roosevelt was the youngest.

 The usefulness of the range as a measure of dispersion is limited. To see this consider the two different sets of data with their corresponding frequencies shown in Table 5-8.

 The distributions are very different, yet each has a range of 4 and a mean of 9.6. If the frequency of any score in either distribution were changed the mean would be affected. However, the only change in the distributions

| Value | Frequency | Value | Frequency |
|-------|-----------|-------|-----------|
| 10 | 9 | 12 | 4 |
| 9 | 0 | 11 | 0 |
| 8 | 0 | 10 | 0 |
| 7 | 0 | 9 | 8 |
| 6 | 1 | 8 | 3 |
| Distribution (a) | | Distribution (b) | |

TABLE 5-8.

that would change the ranges would be a change in either the highest or lowest scores of each. Thus, the range as a measure of dispersion of a distribution is sensitive only to the extreme scores of the distribution. It is completely insensitive to all other features of the distribution. We need a more sensitive measure of dispersion.

Suppose Students A and B go to a school where they are graded on a 100-point system. Their semester grades are shown in Table 5-9 . Student A's grades show no variation while Student B's grades vary quite a bit.

| Student A | Student B |
|-----------|-----------|
| 75 | 100 |
| 75 | 80 |
| 75 | 60 |
| 75 | 50 |
| 75 | 10 |

TABLE 5-9.

In statistics the variability of data values is measured by the deviations of the values from the mean. We can find the *average deviation from the mean* for values of a data set by finding the sum of their deviations from the mean value and then dividing by the total number of items in the set of data. The calculations in Table 5-10 show the computation of the average deviation from $\overline{X}$, the mean, for the grades of Student A and the grades of Student B.

For Student A, there is no variation at all. For Student B, however, the sum of deviations below $\overline{X}$ is $^-60$ and the sum of deviations above $\overline{X}$ is 60. Thus, the sum of deviations above and below $\overline{X}$ is zero, causing the average deviation from the mean to be 0. In fact for unclassified data, the sum of the negative and positive deviations from the mean score is zero. (For the case of data classified into intervals the sum of the deviations above and below the mean may not be zero, since it is assumed that each member of the sample in an interval occurs at the middle point when the mean is calculated.)

Now let us do the following to Student B's grades:
1. Square each deviation from the mean.
2. Sum the squares.
3. Divide by the number of members in the set of sample data (here, grades).

STUDENT A

| $i$ | Grade $x_i$ | Deviation from $\overline{X}$ $x_i - \overline{X}$ |
|---|---|---|
| 1 | 75 | $75 - 75 = 0$ |
| 2 | 75 | $75 - 75 = 0$ |
| 3 | 75 | $75 - 75 = 0$ |
| 4 | 75 | $75 - 75 = 0$ |
| $n = r = 5$ | 75 | $75 - 75 = 0$ |

$$\overline{X} = \frac{\sum\limits_{i=1}^{n} x_i}{n} = \frac{375}{5} = 75 \qquad \frac{\sum\limits_{i=1}^{n}(x_i - \overline{X})}{n} = \frac{0}{5} = 0$$

STUDENT B

| $i$ | Grade $x_i$ | Deviation from $\overline{X}$ $x_i - \overline{X}$ |
|---|---|---|
| 1 | 100 | $100 - 60 = \phantom{-}40.0$ |
| 2 | 80 | $80 - 60 = \phantom{-}20.0$ |
| 3 | 60 | $60 - 60 = \phantom{-}0.0$ |
| 4 | 50 | $50 - 60 = {}^-10.0$ |
| $n = r = 5$ | 10 | $10 - 60 = {}^-50.0$ |

$$\overline{X} = \frac{\sum\limits_{i=1}^{n} x_i}{n} = \frac{300}{5} = 60 \qquad \frac{\sum\limits_{i=1}^{n}(x_i - \overline{X})}{n} = \frac{0}{5} = 0$$

TABLE 5-10.

These computations are shown in Table 5-11.
    The number

$$\sum_{i=1}^{n} \frac{(x_i - \overline{X})^2}{n}$$

is the average of the sum of the squares of the deviations of the scores from their mean. It is called the *variance* of the distribution. The variance is a measure of average dispersion from the mean. We may write the formula for variance of a set of data as

$$\text{variance} = \frac{1}{n} \sum_{i=1}^{n} (x_i - \overline{X})^2$$

if each of the $n$ distinct values $x_i$ has a frequency of 1, as in our example. More generally, we may write

$$\text{variance} = \frac{1}{n} \sum_{i=1}^{r} (x_i - \overline{X})^2 f_i,$$

when there are $r$ distinct values of data, value $x_i$ occurs with frequency $f_i$, and there are $n$ values (not necessarily all distinct) in the sample.

STUDENT B

| $i$ | Grade $x_i$ | Deviation from $\overline{X}$ $x_i - \overline{X}$ | (Deviation from $\overline{X}$ )² $(x_i - \overline{X})^2$ |
|---|---|---|---|
| 1 | 100 | $100 - 60 = \phantom{-}40.0$ | $(40)^2 = 1{,}600$ |
| 2 | 80 | $80 - 60 = \phantom{-}20.0$ | $(20)^2 = \phantom{0}400$ |
| 3 | 60 | $60 - 60 = \phantom{-}0.0$ | $(0)^2 = \phantom{000}0$ |
| 4 | 50 | $50 - 60 = {}^-10.0$ | $(^-10)^2 = \phantom{00}100$ |
| $n = 5$ | 10 | $10 - 60 = {}^-50.0$ | $(^-50)^2 = 2{,}500$ |

$$\overline{X} = \frac{\sum\limits_{i=1}^{n} x_i}{n} = \frac{300}{5} = 60 \qquad\qquad \frac{\sum\limits_{i=1}^{n}(x_i - \overline{X})^2}{n} = \frac{4{,}600}{5} = 920$$

TABLE 5-11.

Another measure of dispersion, which is determined directly from the variance, is the *standard deviation*, commonly denoted by $\sigma$ (the small Greek letter sigma) or by s.d. The standard deviation is defined to be the square root of the variance. Thus,

$$\sigma = \sqrt{\frac{\sum\limits_{i=1}^{r}(x_i - \overline{X})^2 f_i}{n}}.$$

For Student B, then, the standard deviation is

$$\sigma = \sqrt{920} \approx 30.33.$$

Applying the above formulas for variance and standard deviation requires much computation. Before computing these measures of dispersion for any more distributions, let us derive a way to shorten the calculations.

We shall need the following properties of summation notation. Their verification is easy and is left as an exercise. (See Appendix I.)

PROPERTY 1.   For any constant $c$, $\sum_{i=1}^{n} cx_i = c \sum_{i=1}^{n} x_i$.

PROPERTY 2.   $\sum_{i=1}^{n} (x_i \pm y_i) = \sum_{i=1}^{n} x_i \pm \sum_{i=1}^{n} y_i$.

In the derivation that follows, we will refer to the above properties by number. We begin with our present formula for the variance of a set of data, and carry out a sequence of steps that will result in a much simpler formula.

$$\text{variance} = \frac{1}{n} \sum_{i=1}^{r} (x_i - \overline{X})^2 f_i$$

$$= \frac{1}{n} \sum_{i=1}^{r} (x_i^2 - 2x_i \overline{X} + \overline{X}^2) f_i \qquad\qquad \begin{array}{l}(\text{since } (a - b)^2 \\ \quad = a^2 - 2ab + b^2)\end{array}$$

$$= \frac{1}{n} \sum_{i=1}^{r} (x_i^2 f_i - 2x_i \overline{X} f_i + \overline{X}^2 f_i)$$

$$= \frac{1}{n} \left[ \sum_{i=1}^{r} x_i^2 f_i - \sum_{i=1}^{r} 2x_i \overline{X} f_i + \sum_{i=1}^{r} \overline{X}^2 f_i \right] \qquad \text{(by Property 2)}$$

$$= \frac{1}{n} \left[ \sum_{i=1}^{r} x_i^2 f_i - 2\overline{X} \sum_{i=1}^{r} x_i f_i + \overline{X}^2 \sum_{i=1}^{r} f_i \right] \qquad \text{(by Property 1)}$$

$$= \frac{1}{n} \sum_{i=1}^{r} x_i^2 f_i - 2\overline{X} \left( \frac{1}{n} \sum_{i=1}^{r} x_i f_i \right) + \overline{X}^2 \cdot \frac{1}{n} \sum_{i=1}^{r} f_i$$

Now recall that

$$\sum_{i=1}^{r} f_i = n \qquad \text{and} \qquad \overline{X} = \frac{1}{n} \sum_{i=1}^{r} x_i f_i \, .$$

Thus,

$$\text{variance} = \frac{1}{n} \sum_{i=1}^{r} x_i^2 f_i - 2\overline{X}\,\overline{X} + \overline{X}^2 \cdot \frac{1}{n} \cdot n$$

$$= \frac{1}{n} \sum_{i=1}^{r} x_i^2 f_i - \overline{X}^2.$$

Thus we have the new formula

$$\boxed{\text{variance} = \frac{1}{n} \sum_{i=1}^{r} x_i^2 f_i - \overline{X}^2.}$$

While this last formula seems as complicated as the original formula for variance, its evaluation is much less tedious. It says that to find the variance of a distribution all we have to do is find the sum of the squares of each of the $r$ data values, multiplied by its corresponding frequency, divide by $n$, and then subtract the square of the mean. For Student B, then, the variance using this shorter method is

$$\text{variance} = \frac{(100)^2 + (80)^2 + (60)^2 + (50)^2 + (10)^2}{5} - (60)^2$$

$$= \frac{10{,}000 + 6{,}400 + 3{,}600 + 2{,}500 + 100}{5} - 3{,}600$$

$$= \frac{22{,}600}{5} - 3{,}600$$

$$= 4{,}520 - 3{,}600$$

$$= 920.$$

This is the same result as before.

Using this shortened formula for variance it follows that the standard deviation can be written

$$\sigma = \sqrt{\frac{1}{n} \sum_{i=1}^{r} x_i^2 f_i - \overline{X}^2}.$$

Now let us return to our example of computing the variances and standard deviations for semester grades. For Student B's grades of

$$100 \quad 80 \quad 60 \quad 50 \quad 10$$

we found that

$$\text{variance} = 920 \quad \text{and} \quad \sigma \approx 30.33.$$

Suppose his classmate, Student C, had semester grades of

$$90 \quad 85 \quad 80 \quad 75 \quad 75.$$

Were his grades more or less variable than Student B's? Just by inspection it looks as if they showed less variation. Let us see what variance and standard deviation indicate. We find that the mean is

$$\overline{X} = \frac{90 + 85 + 80 + 2(75)}{5} = 81.$$

Using our simplified formula we have

$$\text{variance} = \frac{(90)^2 + (85)^2 + (80)^2 + 2(75)^2}{5} - 81^2$$

$$= \frac{8{,}100 + 7{,}225 + 6{,}400 + 11{,}250}{5} - 6{,}561$$

$$= \frac{32{,}975}{5} - 6{,}561$$

$$= 6{,}595 - 6{,}561$$

$$= 34.$$

Thus, the variance is 34 and the standard deviation is

$$\sigma = \sqrt{34} \approx 5.8.$$

Our hunch is verified! The variance and standard deviation for Student C's grades, 34 and 5.8, are much less than 920 and 30.33, the variance and standard deviation for Student B's grades.

For the last example in this section let us compute the variance and standard deviation for the distribution of normal monthly temperatures in

| Month | Normal temperature in °F |
|-------|--------------------------|
| Jan. | 38° |
| Feb. | 41° |
| March | 44° |
| April | 49° |
| May | 56° |
| June | 60° |
| July | 65° |
| Aug. | 64° |
| Sept. | 60° |
| Oct. | 52° |
| Nov. | 44° |
| Dec. | 41° |

TABLE 5-12.

Seattle, Washington. The information is given in Table 5-12.

It is evident from the table that the range is 27 since the highest normal temperature is 65 and the lowest normal temperature is 38. Let us organize the information in Table 5-12 into a frequency table with intervals of 4°. (See Table 5-13.)

In order to compute the variance and standard deviation we need to find the mean. Remember that each entry that lies in a certain interval is represented by the midpoint of the interval. Therefore, we have

$$\bar{X} = \frac{(39.5)3 + (43.5)2 + (47.5)1 + (51.5)1 + (55.5)1 + (59.5)2 + (63.5)2}{12},$$

| $i$ | Temperature in ° $x_i$ | $f_i$ | $x_i - \bar{X}$ | $(x_i - \bar{X})^2$ | $(x_i - \bar{X})^2 f_i$ |
|-----|------------------------|-------|-----------------|---------------------|--------------------------|
| 1 | 37.5 − 41.5 | 3 | ⁻11 | 121 | 363 |
| 2 | 41.5 − 45.5 | 2 | ⁻7 | 49 | 98 |
| 3 | 45.5 − 49.5 | 1 | ⁻3 | 9 | 9 |
| 4 | 49.5 − 53.5 | 1 | 1 | 1 | 1 |
| 5 | 53.5 − 57.5 | 1 | 5 | 25 | 25 |
| 6 | 57.5 − 61.5 | 2 | 9 | 81 | 162 |
| $r = 7$ | 61.5 − 65.5 | 2 | 13 | 169 | 338 |
| | | $n = \sum_{i=1}^{r} f_i = 12$ | | | |

$$\frac{\sum_{i=1}^{r} (x_i - \bar{X})^2 f_i}{n} = \frac{996}{12} = 83$$

TABLE 5-13.

$$X = \frac{606}{12},$$

$$X = 50.5.$$

The average temperature in Seattle is 50.5°. From the calculations in Table 5-13 we see that

$$\text{variance} = 83.$$

Thus, the standard deviation is

$$\sigma = \sqrt{83} \approx 9.1.$$

## EXERCISES

1. Calculate and compare the mean and the standard deviation for each of the two sets of data below. Are your comparisons as you expected? Why?

    6, 7, 8, 9, 10    and    4, 6, 8, 10, 12.

2. The mean $X$ was 37 and the standard deviation about 3.9 on a test in the sociology seminar. Copy and complete the following table.

| Student | Test Score $x_i$ | $x_i - \bar{X}$ | Distance of score from mean (Measured in standard deviation) |
|---------|------------------|-----------------|--------------------------------------------------------------|
| A | 42 | $42 - 37 = 5$ | $5/3.9 = 1.3$ |
| B | 30 | $30 - 37 = {}^-7$ | ${}^-7/3.9 = {}^-1.8$ |
| C | 35 | | |
| D | 36 | | |
| E | 40 | | |
| F | 39 | | |

3. The daily high tides at the Golden Gate Bridge, San Francisco Bay, are given below (in feet) for June and November of 1968. Compare the tides during the two months by calculating the range, variance, and standard deviation for the tides in each month. During which month do the tides vary more?

   June: 4.4, 4.8, 4.9, 5.2, 5.9, 6.0, 6.4, 6.6, 6.8, 6.8, 6.7, 4.6, 6.4, 6.0, 5.1, 5.2, 5.4, 5.5, 5.6, 5.7, 5.8, 5.8, 5.8, 5.8, 5.8, 5.8, 5.8, 4.5, 5.6, 5.3;

   November: 5.7, 5.8, 5.8, 5.8, 5.8, 5.7, 5.5, 5.4, 5.2, 5.0, 4.8, 4.5, 4.7, 4.2, 5.3, 5.6, 6.0, 6.3, 6.6, 6.8, 6.8, 6.6, 6.3, 5.9, 5.4, 5.1, 5.3, 5.5, 5.7, 5.9.

4–8.  Calculate the range, variance, and standard deviation for each set of data in Exercises 4–8, Section 5-2.

9.  If the data values in Exercise 1 were changed by adding 10 points to each value, how would the range, mean, and standard deviation be affected?

## ——5-5  The Normal Distribution

It has been found that many distributions of data found in nature and industry closely follow the pattern of a *normal distribution*. A normal distribution has a histogram somewhat like the one shown in Figure 5-5. In all normal distributions the measurements are clustered near the middle of the histogram as shown.

If the midpoints of the tops of the rectangles in each of the intervals in the histogram are connected, a roughly bell-shaped curve results. Such a curve is shown in Figure 5-5 superimposed over the corresponding histogram. A perfect bell-shaped curve called a *normal* curve can be represented by the equation $f(x) = e^{-x^2}$. (See Figure 5-6.) Note its symmetrical shape. Also notice how quickly it approaches zero at each end.

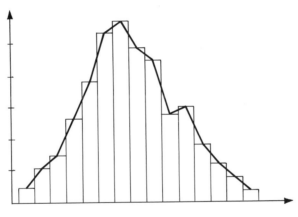

FIGURE 5-5.

If one were to collect data on the heights of thousands of twelve-year-old children, on the weights of thousands of oranges of a certain species, or on the thicknesses of thousands of metal parts made by a manufacturing company, one would probably obtain a distribution that would look approximately like the normal curve in Figure 5-6. Figure 5-7, for instance, shows the distribution of the weights of ninety-seven seventh graders. If more than ninety-seven weights had been graphed, the shape of the distribution would have been more bell-shaped.

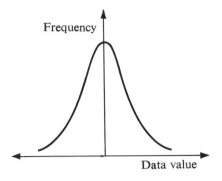

FIGURE 5-6.

Because of the geometrical significance of the mean and because a normal distribution is symmetrical, we know that the mean $\overline{X}$ of a normal distribution lies at the symmetry point on the horizontal axis as shown in Figure 5-8. The points $\overline{X} + \sigma$, $\overline{X} - \sigma$, $\overline{X} + 2\sigma$, $\overline{X} - 2\sigma$, $\overline{X} + 3\sigma$, and $\overline{X} - 3\sigma$, where $\sigma$ stands for the standard deviation of the distribution, are also marked.

It can be shown by advanced statistical methods that the standard deviation $\sigma$ for a normal distribution can be interpreted as follows:

1. The area under the normal curve between $\overline{X} - \sigma$ and $\overline{X} + \sigma$ is 68% of the total area under the curve, to the nearest 1 per cent.
2. The area under the normal curve between $\overline{X} - 2\sigma$ and $\overline{X} + 2\sigma$ is 95% of the total area to the nearest 1 per cent.

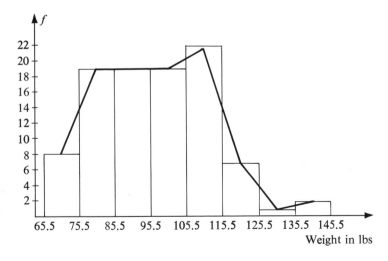

FIGURE 5-7.

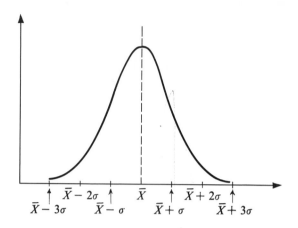

FIGURE 5-8.

3. The area under the normal curve between $\overline{X} - 3\sigma$ and $\overline{X} + 3\sigma$ is 99.7 per cent of the total area, to the nearest .1 per cent.

Thus, for a distribution that is normal the interval from $\overline{X} - \sigma$ to $\overline{X} + \sigma$ includes approximately 68 per cent of the measurements, the interval from $\overline{X} - 2\sigma$ to $\overline{X} + 2\sigma$ includes about 95 per cent of the measurements, and the interval from $\overline{X} - 3\sigma$ to $\overline{X} + 3\sigma$ includes about 99.7 per cent of the measurements.

The location and shape of a normal curve are completely determined by its mean $\overline{X}$ and standard deviation $\sigma$. For instance, Figures 5-9 and 5-10 both show normal curves, centered for convenience at 0 on the horizontal axis. However, the normal curve in Figure 5-9 has a mean of 0 and a standard deviation of 3, while the normal curve in Figure 5-10 has a mean of 0 and a standard deviation of 1. Since the latter normal curve, with its standard deviation of 1, is easier to work with, it is called the *standard normal curve*. All other normal curves, even those not centered at 0, may be easily changed to the standard normal curve. If, for instance, we wished to change the normal curve of Figure 5-9 to the standard normal curve of Figure 5-10 we would change the scale on its horizontal axis so that three units on the axis of the curve in Figure 5-9 would correspond to one unit on the horizontal axis of

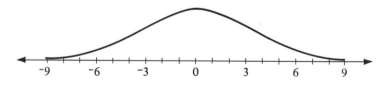

FIGURE 5-9.

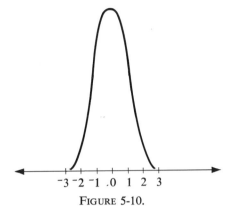

FIGURE 5-10.

the standard normal curve. The point 3 on the horizontal axis of the curve in Figure 5-9 would then correspond to the point 1 on the axis of the standard normal curve and the point ⁻6 on the horizontal axis of the normal curve in Figure 5-9 would correspond to the point ⁻2 on the axis of the standard normal curve. If we let $x$ stand for a point on the axis of any nonstandard normal curve with mean $\overline{X}$ and standard deviation $\sigma$, the corresponding point $Z$ on a standard normal curve is

$$Z = \frac{x - \overline{X}}{\sigma}$$

Using this result with the normal curve with $\sigma = 3$ and $\overline{X} = 0$ in Figure 5-9, we see that the point 3.3 of Figure 5-9 corresponds to the point 1.1 on the standard normal curve, since

$$\frac{3.3 - 0}{3} = 1.1.$$

The total area under a standard normal curve is 1. Appendix V gives the area under certain parts of a standard normal curve, to four decimal places. As an example, let us find the area under the standard normal curve from $Z = 1$ to $Z = 2$, the shaded area in Figure 5-11. We must subtract the area between $Z = 0$ and $Z = 1$ from the area between $Z = 0$ and $Z = 2$.

To find the area from $Z = 0$ to $Z = 2$ we read down the column for $Z$ values in Appendix V until we reach the value 2.0, then across to the entry in the column labeled 00. The area we are looking for is 0.4772. We find the area from $Z = 0$ to $Z = 1$ similarly. It is 0.3413. Thus, the area from $Z = 1$ to $Z = 2$ is

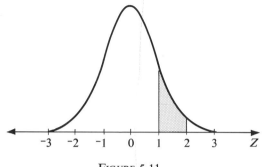

FIGURE 5-11.

$$0.4772 - 0.3413 = 0.1359.$$

Suppose now we wish to find the area from $Z = {}^-2$ to $Z = 2$. We need, simply, to add the area from $Z = 0$ to $Z = 2$ to the area from $Z = 0$ to $Z = {}^-2$. Because of the symmetry of the normal curve, these two areas are the same. From the example above we know already that the area from $Z = 0$ to $Z = 2$ is 0.4772. So, the area from $Z = {}^-2$ to $Z = 2$ is

$$0.4772 + 0.4772 = 0.9544.$$

Since the total area under the normal curve is 1, we conclude that about 95.44% of the total area lies between $Z = {}^-2$ and $Z = 2$. This corresponds to the second property listed before Figure 5-8.

We may also find areas under normal curves that are not standard if we first convert all points in question on the horizontal axis to the corresponding $Z$-values. Suppose that the minimum daily temperatures for June in Mountain View are distributed normally, that the mean minimum temperature is $\overline{X} = 76°$, and that $\sigma = 5°$. About what percentage of the time will the temperature be 80° or less? First we must convert 80° to its equivalent $Z$-value. We have

$$Z = \frac{80 - 76}{5} = \frac{4}{5} = 0.8.$$

Therefore, we can find the desired percentage by adding the area under the normal curve between $Z = 0$ and $Z = 0.8$ to 0.50, the entire area under the normal curve left of $Z = 0$. We thus have

$$0.2881 + 0.5 = 0.7881.$$

In view of this result, residents in Mountain View should expect temperature minimums of 80° or less about 79% of the time in June. This result might be given the interpretation that there is a probability of 0.7881 that minimum temperatures will be 80° or less in Mountain View during June.

## EXERCISES

1. Assume that women's shoe sizes are normally distributed. Suppose that about 95% of the women have shoe sizes between size $4\frac{1}{2}$ and size $8\frac{1}{2}$. Approximately what are the mean and standard deviation of the distribution?

2. Assume that the lengths of Bluefield bananas are normally distributed. If about 85% of all Bluefield bananas are between 7 and 10 inches long, approximately what are the mean and standard deviation of the distribution?

3. Given that a continuous variable $x$ is normally distributed with a mean of 10 and standard deviation of 2, calculate the probability that:
   a.  $x < 7$.
   b.  $x > 12$.
   c.  $7 < x < 9$.
   d.  $9 < x < 11$.

4. Given that a continuous variable $x$ is normally distributed with a mean of 14 and a standard deviation of 4, calculate the percentage of values of $x$ such that
   a.  $x > 16$.
   b.  $x < 15$.
   c.  $4 < x < 6$.
   d.  $12 < x < 17$.

5. Assume that the height of college men is normally distributed with a mean of 69 inches and a standard deviation of 3 inches. Calculate the probability that the height of a college man is:
   a.  Between 69 inches and 72 inches.
   b.  66 inches or lower.
   c.  Between 66 inches and 70 inches.
   d.  72 inches or higher.

6. Assume that the weight of Washington Delicious apples is normally distributed, that the mean is 6 ounces, and that the standard deviation is 2 ounces. What is the probability that a Delicious apple weighs
   a.  More than 11 ounces?
   b.  Less than 5 ounces?
   c.  Between 3 and 5 ounces?
   d.  Between 5 and 8 ounces?

7. Assume that the diameters in inches of a type of steel rod produced by a certain manufacturing company are normally distributed with a mean of 0.463 and a standard deviation of 0.012. About what percentage of the steel rods will have diameters that are
   a.  More than 0.495 inches?
   b.  Less than 0.450 inches?
   c.  Between 0.455 and 0.475 inches?

## ——5-6  Correlation

So far in our discussion of statistics we have been concerned with ways of describing the distributions of sets of data. In this section we will take up the problem of finding relationships between sets of data.

In mathematics we say that there is a definite relationship between the diameter $d$ and radius $r$ of a circle. In fact, we can even express this relationship with the simple formula

$$d = 2r.$$

Further, we can display the relationship between the radius and the diameter of any circle by graphing the points $(r, d)$ for nonnegative values of $r$. (We ignore negative values of $r$, since a circle does not have a negative radius.) Figure 5-12 shows this graph. Points such as $(2, 4)$, $(3, 6)$, and $(8, 16)$ lie on

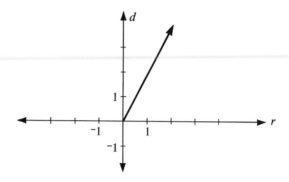

Figure 5-12.

the graph. We see that when $r = 2$, $d = 2 \cdot 2$ or 4 and so on. Since the graph of this relationship is a line, we say that the relationship is _linear_.

Is there a relationship between the heights of nine college boys and the amounts of money in their checking accounts, which is as definite as the one between the radius and the circumference of a circle? Table 5-14 shows the height of each boy and the amount in his checking account.

The _scatter diagram_ formed by graphing the pair of values $(h, c)$ obtained for each boy from the information in Table 5-14 is shown in Figure 5-13. Neither the diagram nor the table indicates any apparent relationship between the two sets of data. If a relationship exists, it does not appear to be linear.

Now consider the information given in Table 5-15. The first column gives the average daily temperature $t$ in degrees Fahrenheit for one week during September and the second column gives the number $c$ of ice cream cones sold by the Plaza Ice Creamery each day that week.

The points $(t, c)$ are plotted in the scatter diagram in Figure 5-14.

| Height in inches<br>h | Checking account to<br>the nearest dollar<br>c |
|---|---|
| 69″ | 120 |
| 72″ | 80 |
| 68″ | 200 |
| 71″ | 75 |
| 73″ | 240 |
| 70″ | 50 |
| 72″ | 60 |
| 74″ | 20 |
| 67″ | 95 |

TABLE 5-14.

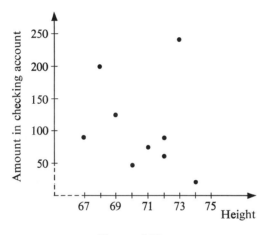

FIGURE 5-13.

It appears from the data in Table 5-15 and from Figure 5-14 that there is a relationship between the temperature on each day and the number of ice cream cones sold. The relationship appears to be almost linear.

| Temperature in °F<br>t | Number of cones<br>c |
|---|---|
| 65° | 110 |
| 70° | 150 |
| 62° | 100 |
| 71° | 155 |
| 72° | 165 |
| 64° | 105 |
| 60° | 90 |

TABLE 5-15.

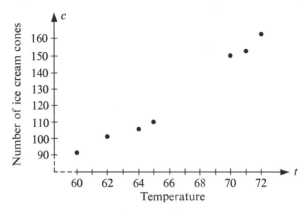

FIGURE 5-14.

To get an idea of how linear this relationship is, we need to devise a measure of linearity that will tell us how well a line can fit the data. There are two properties we would like this measure to have.

First, it would be convenient if such a measure were independent of the origin chosen for the corresponding scatter diagram. (For instance, we might want to choose the origin in Figure 5-14 as (60, 90) for convenience.) We can do this by choosing the variables $t_i - \overline{T}$ and $c_i - \overline{C}$, where $t_i$ and $c_i$ are the values of $t$ and $c$ shown in Table 5-15 and $\overline{T}$ and $\overline{C}$ are the means of the $t_i$ and $c_i$, respectively.

Second, it would be handy if the measure of the relationship were independent of the scales used for $t$ and $c$. (Suppose, for example, that we wanted to measure $t$ in degrees Centigrade, instead of Fahrenheit, and $c$ in dozens of cones sold.) We can accomplish this by dividing the $t_i$ and $c_i$ by quantities of the same respective units. The quantities that are most handy are $\sigma_t$ and $\sigma_c$, the standard deviations of the $t_i$ and $c_i$, respectively.

To obtain the two properties above we can examine

$$u_i = \frac{(t_i - \overline{T})}{\sigma_t} \quad \text{and} \quad v_i = \frac{(c_i - \overline{C})}{\sigma_c}.$$

The values of $u_i$ and $v_i$ are the values of $t_i$ and $c_i$ converted to *standard units*.

In this way we can convert the values of $t_i$ and $c_i$ in Table 5-15 to standard units, where $\overline{T}$ is calculated to be $66\frac{2}{7}$, $\overline{C}$ is calculated to be 125, $\sigma_t \approx 4.36$, and $\sigma_c \approx 28.28$. See Table 5-16.

The pairs $(u_i, v_i)$ in Table 5-16 are graphed in Figure 5-15. Note that all of the points are in the first and third quadrants. In the first quadrant all of the $u_i$ and $v_i$ are positive, so the products $u_i \cdot v_i$ are all positive. In the third quadrant all of the $u_i$ and $v_i$ are negative, so the products $u_i \cdot v_i$ are all positive

| Temperature in °F $t_i$ | Number of cones $c_i$ | $t_i - \bar{T}$ | $c_i - \bar{C}$ | $u_i = \dfrac{t_i - \bar{T}}{\sigma_t}$ | $v_i = \dfrac{c_i - \bar{C}}{\sigma_c}$ |
|---|---|---|---|---|---|
| 65 | 110 | $-1\frac{2}{7}$ | $-15$ | $-0.29$ | $-0.53$ |
| 70 | 150 | $3\frac{5}{7}$ | $25$ | $0.85$ | $0.88$ |
| 62 | 100 | $-4\frac{2}{7}$ | $-25$ | $-0.98$ | $-0.88$ |
| 71 | 155 | $4\frac{5}{7}$ | $30$ | $1.08$ | $1.06$ |
| 72 | 165 | $5\frac{5}{7}$ | $40$ | $1.31$ | $1.42$ |
| 64 | 105 | $-2\frac{2}{7}$ | $-20$ | $-0.52$ | $-0.71$ |
| 60 | 90 | $-6\frac{2}{7}$ | $-35$ | $-1.44$ | $-1.24$ |

TABLE 5-16.

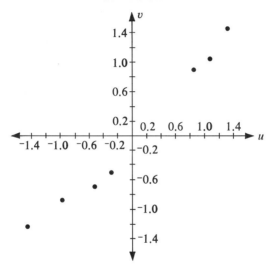

FIGURE 5-15.

as well. (If there had been points of the scatter diagram in the second and fourth quadrants, the corresponding products $u_i \cdot v_i$ would have been negative.) Thus the sum of the seven products $u_i \cdot v_i$,

$$\sum_{i=1}^{7} u_i \cdot v_i,$$

is positive. If some of the $u_i \cdot v_i$ terms had been negative, the trend in the scatter diagram in Figure 5-14 would have been less linear and the sum

$$\sum_{i=1}^{7} u_i \cdot v_i$$

would have been less positive. For this reason the value of

$$\sum_{i=1}^{n} u_i \cdot v_i,$$

where $n$ is the number of points in the scatter diagram, is a good measure of the scatter diagram's linearity. So that the size of this sum can be used to measure linearity,

$$\sum_{i=1}^{n} u_i \cdot v_i$$

is divided by $n$. Unless this is done, a change in the number of points, such as tripling the number of points, might approximately triple the size of the sum without really changing the basically linear pattern of the scatter diagram. The resulting sum

$$\sum_{i=1}^{n} \frac{u_i v_i}{n}$$

is a measure of the linear relationship in the scatter diagram. It is called the *correlation coefficient* and is commonly denoted by $r$. For our example,

$$r = \sum_{i=1}^{n} \frac{u_i v_i}{n} = \sum_{i=1}^{n} \frac{\dfrac{(t_i - \bar{T})(c_i - \bar{C})}{\sigma_t \quad \sigma_c}}{n}$$

$$= \sum_{i=1}^{n} \frac{(t_i - \bar{T})(c_i - \bar{C})}{n\sigma_t \sigma_c}$$

$$= \frac{1}{n\sigma_t \sigma_c} \sum_{i=1}^{n} (t_i - \bar{T})(c_i - \bar{C})$$

$$= \frac{1}{7(4.36)(28.28)} \cdot \frac{4005}{7}$$

$$= \frac{4005}{6041.7392} \approx 0.66.$$

There is therefore a correlation coefficient of about 0.66 between the temperatures in our set of data and the number of ice cream cones sold by the Plaza Ice Creamery. A correlation coefficient of 1.0 would indicate a perfectly linear relationship. This value of 0.66 for $r$ thus indicates a strong trend toward linearity, as is verified by the scatter diagrams in Figure 5-15. (Note that in the computation above we found

$$\sum_{i=1}^{n} (t_i - \bar{T})(c_i - \bar{C})$$

and multiplied by $1/n\sigma_t \sigma_c$. This is much easier than dividing each of the $(t_i - \bar{T})$ by $\sigma_t$ and each of the $(c_i - \bar{C})$ by $\sigma_c$ as shown in Table 5-16 before finding the sum and dividing by $n$.)

For comparison compare the value of $r \approx 0.66$ found for our example with the scatter diagrams in Figure 5-16. For each diagram the approximate value of $r$ is given. Figures 5-16 (a) and (b) show relationships which are almost linear. The value of $|r|$ is therefore about 1. (The value of $r$ in Figure 5-16 (b) is about $^-1$, since all of the products $u_i \cdot v_i$ contribute negative terms to the sum $\sum_{i=1}^{n} u_i v_i/n$.) There is a slight linear relationship in the scatter diagrams shown in Figures 5-16 (c) and (d), where $|r| = 0.5$. There is apparently no linear relationship in Figure 5-15(e) and $r = 0$. In Figure 5-16(f) there appears to be a relationship. However, it is not linear, and $r$ is again 0.

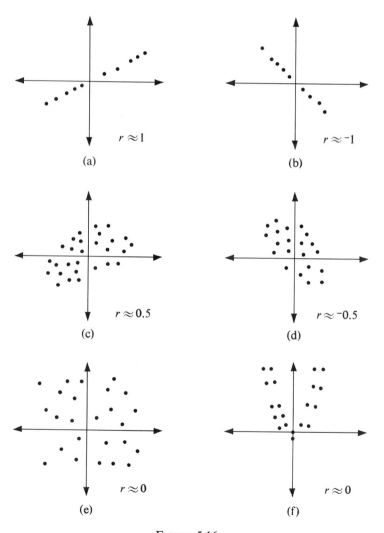

FIGURE 5-16.

As hinted by the scatter diagrams in Figure 5-16 and their corresponding values of *r*, it can be shown that the correlation coefficient for two sets of data always satisfies the compound inequality

$$^{-}1 \leq r \leq 1.$$

Furthermore $r = 1$ or $r = {}^{-}1$ if and only if all points of the scatter diagram lie on a straight line.

As an example of how correlation coefficients may be used, consider the values of *r* in Table 5-17. To obtain these, 110 seventh-graders were asked

| Student's self-concept and perception of | *r* |
|---|---|
| Mother's image of him | 0.50 |
| Father's image of him | 0.52 |
| Teacher's image of him | 0.55 |
| Peer's image of him | 0.47 |

TABLE 5-17.

the questions "How talented are you academically?," "How talented academically does your mother think you are?," and so forth. Table 5-17 shows the correlations between the students' self-concepts and their perceptions of what four others think of their ability.

The correlations in Table 5-17 indicate that there is some linear relation between a student's concept of his academic ability and his perception of the concept he believes others hold of this ability. Note that the correlations between a student's self-concept and the concept of him he believes held by his teacher is slightly higher than for any of the other three persons. Although these correlations indicate a slight mathematical relationship they should not be interpreted as implying a cause or effect. A student's concept of his academic ability and his concept of others' attitudes toward his ability may be influenced by other variables that cause the slightly linear relationship.

An often quoted example is the correlation of more than 0.90 between teachers' salaries and television sales over a period of time. It cannot be concluded that one caused the other! During this time there was a steady rise in all salaries. Times were prosperous. Naturally, there was more money around for everyone to spend on luxury items such as television sets.

Beware of reading too much into correlation coefficients!

### EXERCISES

In Exercises 1–11, *guess whether the correlation coefficient between the two sets of data pairs is closer to* $^{-}1, 0,$ *or* $1$.

1. Amount of education and highest yearly salary attained.

2. Beauty and brains.
3. Years of smoking and incidence of lung cancer.
4. Amount of rain and attendance at football games.
5. Amount of alcohol consumed and incidence of automobile accidents.
6. Grade point average and IQ.
7. Consumption of sugar and the price of sugar.
8. Height of a twenty-one-year-old male and his weight.
9. Amount of rain and the number of swimsuits sold.
10. Age of U.S. president at time of inauguration and length of his term.
11. Weight and test scores.
12. In the example of this section suppose the temperature in °F and number of cones sold each day of a week in October were as follows:

| Temperature in °F $t$ | Number of cones $c$ |
|---|---|
| 51° | 70 |
| 45° | 51 |
| 40° | 50 |
| 42° | 60 |
| 50° | 74 |
| 52° | 80 |
| 49° | 70 |

Compute $r$.

13. The following table shows the number of cups of hot coffee in hundreds sold during one season at the football stadium, along with the temperature at game time.

| Temperature in °F $t$ | Number of cups of coffee in hundreds $c$ |
|---|---|
| 80° | 10 |
| 75° | 15 |
| 65° | 20 |
| 62° | 30 |
| 60° | 40 |
| 60° | 50 |
| 54° | 45 |
| 40° | 70 |

Compute $r$.

14.  The following table gives the overall high school and college grade point averages (GPA) for 10 pupils.

| GPA<br>High School | GPA<br>College |
|:---:|:---:|
| 0.5 | 1.0 |
| 1.8 | 2.5 |
| 3.5 | 3.0 |
| 2.5 | 3.2 |
| 3.9 | 3.8 |
| 2.0 | 1.5 |
| 2.2 | 4.0 |
| 2.8 | 3.0 |
| 3.0 | 3.6 |
| 1.8 | 2.4 |

Find $r$ for this group of students.

## ——— 5-7   An Introduction to Curve Fitting

Let us now return to Figure 5-14 and the question of the relationship between the number of ice cream cones sold on a certain day and the temperature that day. It appears that a relationship exists since when the temperature was relatively high, the number of ice cream cones sold was relatively high, but when the temperature was relatively low, the number of ice cream cones sold was relatively low. Although we cannot state the correlation between the two sets of data with mathematical exactness we can find an *approximate* mathematical statement to describe the relationship.

First, notice that the points in the scatter diagram in Figure 5-14 form a very close approximation to a straight line. In fact, the approximation is so close that we would have a good mathematical description of the relationship between the two sets of data if we could find the equation of the line that is closest (by some standard of "closeness") to the points. This line is called the *line of best fit*.

Every line in the $(x, y)$ coordinate system has an equation of form $y = ax + b$, where $a$ and $b$ are constants depending upon the particular line being considered. For the time being, let $y = ax + b$ represent the line of best fit. We must obtain values for $a$ and $b$ so that the resulting equation does indeed describe the line of best fit.

We will use the *method of least squares* to determine this line. The reason for the name of the method will soon be apparent. Suppose that

$$(x_1, y_1), (x_2, y_2), (x_3, y_3), \ldots, (x_n, y_n)$$

represent the points for which we are seeking the line of best fit. Some of the points $(x_i, y_i)$ may be on the line of best fit. Suppose, though, that $(x_1, y_1)$ is not on the line as shown in Figure 5-17.

Using Figure 5-17 as a guide, we see that $(x_1, y_1)$ and $(h_1, k_1)$ are on the same vertical line, and therefore the *square* of the distance between $(x_1, y_1)$ and $(h_1, k_1)$ is $(y_1 - k_1)^2$. This squared distance gives some indication of how close the line $y = ax + b$ comes to the point $(x_1, y_1)$. This closeness might be improved by changing the line $y = ax + b$, but the new line, while closer

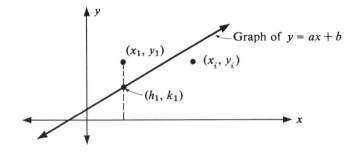

FIGURE 5-17.

to $(x_1, y_1)$, might do a much poorer job of coming close to other points $(x_i, y_i)$ in the set of points $(x_1, y_1), (x_2, y_2), \ldots, (x_n, y_n)$. How can we obtain a line which does a "best possible job" of coming close to *all* of the points in the set? One reasonable approach is to try to minimize the sum of all of the squared distances $(y_i - k_i)^2$ corresponding to points $(x_i, y_i)$ in the set— that is, to make the sum

$$(y_1 - k_1)^2 + \cdots + (y_n - k_n)^2 = \sum_{i=1}^{n} (y_i - k_i)^2$$

as small as possible. For convenience, let

$$S = \sum_{i=1}^{n} (y_i - k_i)^2$$

We saw that $h_1 = x_1$. (See Figure 5-17.) Similarly, $h_2 = x_2, \ldots, h_n = x_n$. Since each point $(h_i, k_i)$ is on the graph of $y = ax + b$, we have $k_1 = ah_1 + b = ax_1 + b$, $k_2 = ax_2 + b, \ldots, k_n = ax_n + b$. The quantity $S$, which we wish to minimize, takes on a new appearance:

$$S = \sum_{i=1}^{n} (y_i - k_i)^2 = \sum_{i=1}^{n} (y_i - ax_i - b)^2.$$

The minimization of $S$ depends on choosing $a$ and $b$ wisely, since $x_i$ and $y_i$ are constants for all values of $i$ from 1 to $n$ inclusive. That is, $S$ is a function of the two variables $a$ and $b$.

Suppose that $S$ is a minimum when $a = a_0$ and $b = b_0$. If we let $a = a_0$

and do not fix $b$, we have an equation in one variable $b$:

$$S = \sum_{i=1}^{n} (y_i - a_0 x_i - b)^2.$$

Using calculus it can be shown that for the fixed value $a_0$, the value of $b$ which minimizes $S$ is

$$\frac{1}{n} \left[ \sum_{i=1}^{n} y_i - a_0 \sum_{i=1}^{n} x_i \right] = b = b_0.$$

Now let $b = b_0$ and substitute it into the expression

$$S = \sum_{i=1}^{n} (y_i - a x_i - b)^2.$$

We again have an equation in one variable $a$,

$$S = \sum_{i=1}^{n} (y_i - a x_i - b_0)^2.$$

Now we seek a value $a_0$ which will produce the minimum value of $S$ as a function of $a$.

Again, using calculus, it can be shown that the value of $a$ which minimizes $S$ when $b = b_0$ is

$$\frac{\sum_{i=1}^{n} x_i y_i - b_0 \sum_{i=1}^{n} x_i}{\sum_{i=1}^{n} x_i^2} = a = a_0.$$

The two boxed equations form a system of two simultaneous equations which can now be solved for $a_0$ and $b_0$ in terms of the known quantities $x_i$ and $y_i$.

Let us now examine the above expressions for $a_0$ and $b_0$ to find the line of best fit for our example involving the relationship between the average daily temperature and the number of ice cream cones sold each day. It is easiest to arrange our calculations in a table as shown in Table 5-18.

We use the results in the table to find expressions for $a_0$ and $b_0$. We have

$$a_0 = \frac{58{,}855 - 464 b_0}{30{,}890} \tag{1}$$

and

$$b_0 = \frac{1}{7}(875 - 464 a_0). \tag{2}$$

Rewriting Equation (1), we have

$$30{,}890 a_0 + 464 b_0 = 58{,}855. \tag{3}$$

| $x_i$ | $y_i$ | $x_i y_i$ | $x_i^2$ |
|---|---|---|---|
| 65 | 110 | 7,150 | 4,225 |
| 70 | 150 | 10,500 | 4,900 |
| 62 | 100 | 6,200 | 3,844 |
| 71 | 155 | 11,005 | 5,041 |
| 72 | 165 | 11,880 | 5,184 |
| 64 | 105 | 6,720 | 4,096 |
| 60 | 90 | 5,400 | 3,600 |
| $\sum_{i=1}^{n} x_i = 464$ | $\sum_{i=1}^{n} y_i = 875$ | $\sum_{i=1}^{n} x_i y_i = 58,855$ | $\sum_{i=1}^{n} x_i^2 = 30,890$ |

TABLE 5-18.

If we substitute the expression for $b_0$ from Equation (2) into Equation (3), we have

$$30,890a_0 + 464 \frac{(875 - 464a_0)}{7} = 58,855$$

$$216,230a_0 + 406,000 - 215,296a_0 = 411,985$$

$$934a_0 = 5,985$$

$$a_0 \approx 6.4.$$

Substituting $a_0 \approx 6.4$ into Equation (2) yields

$$b_0 \approx \frac{1}{7}(875 - 464(6.4)),$$

$$b_0 \approx \frac{875 - 2,969.6}{7},$$

$$b_0 \approx \frac{^-2094.6}{7},$$

$$b_0 \approx {}^-299.2.$$

Therefore, the approximate line of best fit ("approximate" because we only obtain approximate values for $a_0$ and $b_0$) for the points in Figure 5-14 is

$$y = 6.4x - 299.2.$$

If a given set of data points does not appear to have a linear trend, a better fit may be found by using the method of least squares to fit the points with a parabola or a curve involving logarithms or powers. We will not discuss these techniques here, but the interested reader may consult texts such as *Introduction to Mathematical Analysis with Applications to Problems of Economics*, by Daus and Whyburn [Addison-Wesley: Reading, Mass.].

*EXERCISES* ───────────────────────────────

*Find the line of best fit for each of the sets of values in Exercises 1 and 2.*

1.
| $x$ | $y$ |
|-----|-----|
| 0 | 2 |
| 1 | 2 |
| 2 | 3 |
| 3 | 4 |
| 4 | 4 |
| 5 | 6 |

2.
| $x$ | $y$ |
|-----|-----|
| 0 | -3 |
| 1 | -2 |
| 2 | -1 |
| 3 | -1 |
| 4 | 2 |
| 5 | 1 |

3. The table gives the average weights of 20- to 24-year-old American men for heights 69″ to 75″. Find the line of best fit.

| Men | | Women | |
|-----|-----|-----|-----|
| Height in inches | Weight in pounds | Height in inches | Weight in pounds |
| 69 | 153 | 62 | 115 |
| 70 | 157 | 63 | 118 |
| 71 | 161 | 64 | 121 |
| 72 | 166 | 65 | 125 |
| 73 | 170 | 66 | 129 |
| 74 | 174 | 67 | 132 |
| 75 | 178 | 68 | 136 |

4. The table gives the average weights of 20- to 24-year-old American women for heights of 62″ to 68″. Find the line of best fit.

5. The following table shows, rounded to the nearest thousand, the number of teachers in American public schools every tenth year from 1900 to 1960. Find the line of best fit.
   (*Hint*: To ease the work of computation let the year 1900 be represented by $x = 0$, the year 1910 by $x = 1$, and so on.)

| Year | Number of teachers in thousands |
|------|---------------------------------|
| 1900 | 423 |
| 1910 | 523 |
| 1920 | 679 |
| 1930 | 854 |
| 1940 | 875 |
| 1950 | 914 |
| 1960 | 1,355 |

6. The following table shows the years of life expected at birth for every tenth year from 1900 to 1960. Find the line of best fit. (See hint in Exercise 5.)

| Year | Life expectancy in years |
|------|--------------------------|
| 1900 | 47.3 |
| 1910 | 50.0 |
| 1920 | 54.1 |
| 1930 | 59.7 |
| 1940 | 62.9 |
| 1950 | 68.2 |
| 1960 | 69.7 |

7. The following graph shows the monthly medical care costs from January 1966 through September 1969. (These costs are components of the government consumer price index.)| Pick eight evenly spaced values from the graph and compute the line of best fit. (See hint in Exercise 5.)

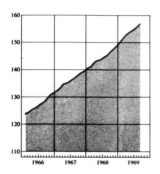

8. The following graph shows the percent of jobless married men from January 1967 through October 1969. Pick six evenly spaced values from the graph and compute the line of best fit. (See hint in Exercise 5.)

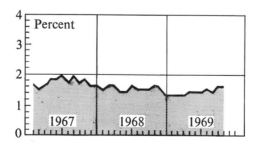

## ——— 5-8   An Introduction to the Chi-Square Distribution

In the preceding sections we looked at ways to describe sets of data which have already been obtained, concluding with a way to obtain the line of best fit for points that seem to have a linear pattern. There are cases where one wishes to make a guess (hypothesis) as to how data for a given problem will be distributed, and then to accumulate and examine data to see how well the hypothesis predicted the actual pattern of data. This is called *hypothesis testing*.

As an example, consider the experiment of tossing a die $n = 36$ times. For this experiment there are $k = 6$ possible outcomes, namely 1, 2, 3, 4, 5, 6. We expect each of these outcomes to occur $\frac{1}{6}$ of 36 or 6 times. That is, we hypothesize that the die is fair, so that each face will turn up $\frac{1}{6}$ of the time. In Table 5-19 are shown the results of one such experiment. The values in the $o$

*Outcomes*

|   | 1 | 2 | 3 | 4 | 5 | 6 |
|---|---|---|---|---|---|---|
| $o$ | 9 | 2 | 3 | 12 | 9 | 1 |
| $e$ | 6 | 6 | 6 | 6 | 6 | 6 |

TABLE 5-19.

row are the frequencies observed when tossing the die; the values in the $e$ row are the expected frequencies. (Note that the sum of each row is $n = 36$.) Each pair of values $(o, e)$ in a given column is a *cell* of Table 5-19, which thus has 6 cells.

To test our hypothesis we can use the measure $\chi^2$, called *chi-square*, which is defined as

$$\chi^2 = \sum_{i=1}^{k} \frac{(o_i - e_i)^2}{e_i},$$

where $o_i$ is the observed frequency for the $i$th cell, $e_i$ is the expected frequency for that cell, and $k$ is the number of possible outcomes. Each difference $o_i - e_i$ in the formula gives the amount by which the observed frequency differs from the expected frequency in the $i$th outcome. (The squares of these differences are used in obtaining our measure of the over-all difference between the observed frequencies and the expected frequencies; otherwise, negative and positive values of the various $o_i - e_i$ might offset one another to give us a falsely optimistic picture of the accuracy of our hypothesis.)

For our example,

$$\chi^2 = \frac{(9-6)^2}{6} + \frac{(2-6)^2}{6} + \frac{(3-6)^2}{6} + \frac{(12-6)^2}{6} + \frac{(9-6)^2}{6} + \frac{(1-6)^2}{6}$$

$$= \frac{9}{6} + \frac{16}{6} + \frac{9}{6} + \frac{36}{6} + \frac{9}{6} + \frac{25}{6} = \frac{104}{6} \approx 17.3.$$

Thus for this experiment, $\chi^2 \approx 17.3$.

Does this indicate that the die is fair? If the die conformed perfectly to theoretical expectations, each observed value $o_i$ would be 6, making each difference $o_i - e_i$ equal to $6 - 6$ or 0. Consequently, $\chi^2$ would be the sum of $k$ zeros or 0 in the case of perfect agreement with expectation. Larger and larger values of $\chi^2$ would indicate, on the other hand, increasing disagreement with theoretical expectations. Suppose we took a die that we knew to be fair, repeated the above experiment a number of times, computed $\chi^2$ for each experiment, and formed a histogram of the values of $\chi^2$ thus obtained. Then we would have a way of judging whether $\chi^2 \approx 17.3$ is a value we could expect to obtain when tossing a fair die.

Since there are only a finite number of distributions of observed frequencies for our example, there are only a finite number of values of $\chi^2$ possible. Thus the frequency distribution of $\chi^2$ is discrete. However, this discrete distribution can be approximated by the continuous distribution shown in Figure 5-18. Shown there is the point corresponding to $\chi^2 = 11.07$.

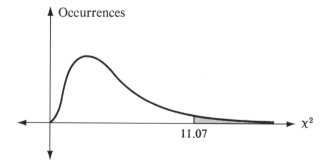

FIGURE 5-18.

To the right of this point lie only 5% of the possible occurrences of $\chi^2$ for our die problem. This region, which is shaded in the figure, is called the 5% *critical region*. A result that lies in this critical region is said to be *significant*. A result that does not lie in this critical region is called *not significant*. Five per cent is said to be the *significance level*. It is a commonly used, but some-what subjectively chosen, quantity. Since only 5 % of the possible occurrences of $\chi^2$ lie to the right of the point corresponding to $\chi^2 = 11.07$, we sometimes write $\chi^2 0.050 = 11.07$.

Because our result for $\chi^2$ is greater than 11.07, it is said to be significant. Since large values of $\chi^2$ indicate poor experimental agreement, we should reject the hypothesis that our die is fair.

A handy feature of a $\chi^2$ distribution is that its form depends only upon $k$, the number of cells. Customarily, a $\chi^2$ distribution is labeled by its number of *degrees of freedom*, $v = k - 1$. Note that the degree of freedom is $k - 1$, rather than $k$, for once $k - 1$ cells are filled, the entry in the last cell is deter-mined. This is because the sum of the rows of observed and expected fre-quencies must add up to $n$. In our example in Table 5-19 the first *five* observed frequencies added up to 35, so the value of $o$ for an outcome of 6 had to be $36 - 35$ or 1. Thus $v = 5$. In general, the number of degrees of freedom is the number of cells which must be filled in order to completely determine the contents of the remaining cells.

Figure 5-19 shows the distribution of $\chi^2$ for $v = 1, 3$, and 5. Since these

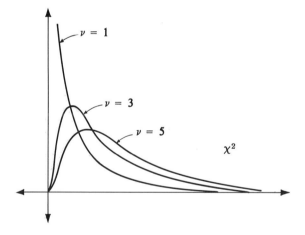

FIGURE 5-19

curves are approximations to the discrete distributions of $\chi^2$ for the cor-responding numbers of degrees of freedom, it is important that they be used only when the approximations are good. Experience has shown that the approximation is good if the expected frequencies in all cells are 5 or more. If the expected frequency in a cell is not at least 5, then it can be combined with one or more other cells.

The values of $\chi^2$ that determine critical regions such as the 5 % critical region decided upon in our example concerning the fairness of the die can be found for degrees of freedom from 1 through 100 in Appendix VI. Each row corresponds to a degree of freedom $v$. Each column corresponds to a critical region whose size is indicated at the top of the column. For our example, $v = 6 - 1$ or 5. The value, 11.0705, in the $v = 5$ row and $\chi^2$ 0.050 column indicates that only 5% of the possible occurrences of $\chi^2$ exceed 11.0705 when the number of degrees of freedom is 5. We interpret this to mean that in only 5% of a large number of repeated experiments will we obtain a value of $\chi^2$ greater than 11.0705. When our first experiment yields $\chi^2 \approx 17.3$, we have good reason to doubt the fairness of the die.

Now consider another application of $\chi^2$.

The value of $\chi^2$ can be used to test a hypothesis concerning the relationship between two variables such as college students' ratings of professors' teaching abilities and the professors' highest educational levels. Let us hypothesize that these two variables are independent.

A *contingency table* is used to study the relationship between two such variables. See Table 5-20. Shown there are the results of classifying 500

*Student rating of teaching ability*

| Highest level of education | Very high | High | Average | Low | Very low | Totals |
|---|---|---|---|---|---|---|
| Postdoctorate study | 10 | 10 | 10 | 10 | 10 | 50 |
| Ph.D. | 70 | 60 | 90 | 30 | 50 | 300 |
| M.A. | 26 | 19 | 30 | 10 | 15 | 100 |
| B.A. | 19 | 11 | 15 | 0 | 5 | 50 |
| Totals | 125 | 100 | 145 | 50 | 80 | 500 |

TABLE 5-20.

professors in the proper categories. For a study such as this it is not possible to decide upon the expected frequencies for each cell as it was in the experiment of tossing a die, so we can choose the sample so that there is a fixed proportion of professors at each level of education. For the study of our example the sample was chosen so that $\frac{50}{500}$ or 10% of the professors had been engaged in post doctorate study, $\frac{300}{500}$ or 60% had Ph.D's, $\frac{100}{500}$ or 20% had M.A.'s, and $\frac{50}{500}$ or 10% had B.A.'s. Since those professors with postdoctorate training made up 10% of the sample, they should account for 10% of the professors in each column, if there is no relationship between level of a professor's education and student ratings of his teaching ability. Thus, there should be, for those professors with postdoctorate training, an expected frequency of 10% of 125 or about 12 in the very high category, 10% of 100 or 10 in the high category, 10% of 145 or about 15 in the average category, 10% of 50 or 5 in the low category, and 10% of 80 or about 8 in the very low category. These expected frequencies are shown in parentheses in the revised contingency table in Table 5-21. The expected frequencies for professors with Ph.D.'s are obtained for each cell in the second row by multiplying each corresponding column total by $60\% = 0.60$, since this was the highest educational level of $60\%$ of the professors in the sample. The other expected frequencies are obtained in the same way.

*Student rating of teaching ability*

| Highest level education | Very high | High | Average | Low | Very low | Totals |
|---|---|---|---|---|---|---|
| Postdoctorate study | 10(12) | 10(10) | 10(15) | 10(5) | 10(8) | 50 |
| Ph.D. | 70(75) | 60(60) | 90(87) | 30(30) | 50(48) | 300 |
| M.A. | 26(25) | 19(20) | 30(29) | 10(10) | 15(16) | 100 |
| B.A. | 19(13) | 11(10) | 15(14) | 0(5) | 5(8) | 50 |
| Totals | 125 | 100 | 145 | 50 | 80 | 500 |

TABLE 5-21.

Using the numbers in parentheses as expected frequencies, and the original contingency table entries as observed frequencies, the value of $\chi^2$ for Table 5-21 is about 17.3.

As in our previous example, each pair $(o, e)$ consisting of an observed frequency and the corresponding expected frequency is a cell. However, the number of degrees of freedom for the table is not chosen to be $k - 1 = 20 - 1$ or 19. Instead it is chosen to be 12, the number of cells in the table *excluding* the cells in the last row and column. This is why: The row and column totals are known. Thus the observed and expected frequencies in the last row and column are determined once the frequencies for these other cells are determined; and, as in our first example, the number of degrees of freedom is the number of cells which must be filled in order to specify the contents of the remaining cells. In general it can be said that the number of degrees of freedom of a contingency table having $r$ rows and $c$ columns is

$$v = (r - 1)(c - 1).$$

For our example $r = 4$ and $c = 5$. Thus

$$v = (4 - 1)(5 - 1) = 3 \cdot 4 \text{ or } 12.$$

Now that we have determined that the number of degrees of freedom of Table 5-21 is 12, we can look up the $5\%$ critical value of $\chi^2$ in Appendix VI.

It is 21.0261. Our computed value of $\chi^2$ is about 17.3. Since it does not fall in the 5% critical region it is considered *not significant*. This means that on the basis of this experiment we have no reason to reject our hypothesis concerning the independence of a professor's education level and student ratings of his teaching ability.

One last comment should be made concerning this example. Because there is no reason to believe that our choice of distribution of professors at the various educational levels affected our results, it can be assumed that the results would hold true if the sampling for the experiment were unrestricted.

## EXERCISES

1. A die is tossed 60 times. The following frequencies are observed.

   |   | 1 | 2 | 3 | 4 | 5 | 6 |
   |---|---|---|---|---|---|---|
   | $O$ | 12 | 13 | 8 | 7 | 11 | 9 |

   a. What is the expected frequency for each outcome?
   b. Compute $\chi^2$.
   c. How many degrees of freedom are there?
   d. Using the table in Appendix VI tell whether the result for $\chi^2$ computed in b is significant (i.e., falls in the 5% critical region).

2. The numbers of weddings performed during each week of a two-month period in a certain community were as follows: 5, 8, 7, 8, 5, 6, 7, 10. Suppose it is believed that the same number of weddings is likely to be performed during each week of the same two-month period.
   a. Compute $\chi^2$.
   b. Using the result for $\chi^2$ computed in a is there reason for this belief?

3. The following table gives the number of daughters in a study of 64 families with 4 children each. Also given is the expected frequency for each outcome (number of daughters). These expected values can be easily obtained by techniques developed in Chapter 4.

   | Number of daughters | 0 | 1 | 2 | 3 | 4 |
   |---|---|---|---|---|---|
   | Number of families | 5 | 14 | 25 | 15 | 5 |
   | Expected number of families | 4 | 16 | 24 | 16 | 4 |

   a. Compute $\chi^2$.
   b. Using the value for $\chi^2$ computed in a and the table in Appendix VI state whether the hypothesis yielding the expected number of families for each outcome is satisfactory or should be rejected.

4.  Consider the contingency table below and the hypothesis that the two variables are independent.

| Variable I \ Variable II | | | | Totals |
|---|---|---|---|---|
| | 5 | 10 | 5 | 20 |
| | 10 | 5 | 15 | 30 |
| Totals | 15 | 15 | 20 | 50 |

a.  Compute the expected frequency for each cell.
b.  Compute $\chi^2$.
c.  Find the number of degrees of freedom $v$.
d.  Using the value of $\chi^2$ computed in b and the value of $v$ decided upon in c state whether or not $\chi^2$ falls within the 5% critical region as given in the table in Appendix VI.
e.  On the basis of these results, should the hypothesis of independence be rejected?

5.  In the example of the section concerning a professor's level of education and student ratings of his teaching ability suppose 400 professors were studied.

The contingency table below shows the results obtained.

Student rating of teaching ability

| Highest level of education | Very high | High | Average | Low | Very low | Totals |
|---|---|---|---|---|---|---|
| Postdoctorate study | 20 | 20 | 32 | 10 | 18 | 100 |
| Ph.D | 12 | 28 | 40 | 12 | 8 | 100 |
| M.A. | 16 | 24 | 36 | 8 | 16 | 100 |
| B.A. | 12 | 24 | 52 | 10 | 2 | 100 |
| Totals | 60 | 96 | 160 | 40 | 44 | 400 |

a.  Find the expected frequency for each cell.
b.  Compute $\chi^2$.
c.  On the basis of the result in b should the hypothesis concerning the independence of the two variables be rejected?

# An Introduction to Linear Programming

# 6

## —— 6-1 Introduction

Linear programming is one of the youngest branches of mathematics. It was first developed to help some of the military strategists during the 1940s. Today, however, linear programming can be used to solve an astounding number of different problems. A list of these problems includes the following:

1. *The diet problem.* How can one meet certain nutritional requirements while minimizing cost?

2. *The product-mix problem.* Given quantities of raw materials for certain products, how can a manufacturer decide on the mix that will maximize profits or minimize costs?

3. *The transportation problem.* How can a company minimize the cost or time of shipping products from a set of origins to a set of destinations?

4. *The personnel assignment problem.* How can a company assign personnel so that they will be of maximum value?

5. *The trim problem.* How can a forest products company trim paper to specified dimensions from huge rolls with a minimum of waste?

6. *Traveling salesman problem.* How can a salesman, starting at a given city, find the shortest round trip route through a group of cities?

Unfortunately, a thorough treatment of the problems listed above and other applications of linear programming is beyond the scope of this text.

However, it is hoped that the simple examples discussed in this chapter will give you a taste for the many possible ways in which linear programming can be used.

As an example of a rather simple linear programming problem, consider the following:

Mr. Paul has a very bad cold. His doctor has ordered him to supplement his daily diet with 25,000 units of vitamin A and 1300 units of vitamin C. Unfortunately, Mr. Paul's druggist has run out of these vitamins in pure form. However, Mr. Paul can buy for 0.8 cents apiece Once-A-Day vitamin pills, which supply 5,000 units of vitamin A and 300 units of vitamin C. He can also buy Vitality vitamin capsules for 3 cents apiece. They each contain 10,000 units of vitamin A and 400 units of vitamin C. Mr. Paul absolutely refuses to swallow more than 6 pills and capsules per day. Keeping this in mind, how many pills and capsules should Mr. Paul purchase per day in order to follow his doctor's orders at minimum cost?

Here is an analysis of the problem. Let $x$ be the number of Once-A-Day vitamin pills Mr. Paul should take per day to minimize the cost, and $y$ be the number of Vitality vitamin capsules Mr. Paul should take per day to minimize the cost.

The problem imposes restrictions called *constraints*, upon the values of $x$ and $y$. First, $x$ and $y$ must be nonnegative, since it is nonsense to talk of a negative number of pills or capsules. That is,

$$x \geq 0 \quad \text{and} \quad y \geq 0.$$

In addition, $x$ Once-A-Day vitamin pills will each provide 5,000 units of vitamin A and $y$ Vitality vitamin capsules will each provide 10,000 units of vitamin A. Together these two dosages will provide

$$5{,}000x + 10{,}000y$$

units of vitamin A. Since Mr. Paul must have *at least* 25,000 units of vitamin A each day, we have the constraint

$$5{,}000x + 10{,}000y \geq 25{,}000.$$

Similarly, the total amount of vitamin C obtained daily must amount to *at least* 1,300 units. Thus we have still another constraint:

$$300x + 400y \geq 1{,}300.$$

Finally, since Mr. Paul refuses to take more than 6 pills and capsules per day,

$$x + y \leq 6.$$

We shall see that there are many possible values of $x$ and $y$ which will meet the five constraints listed above. However, our object is to select the pair of values of $x$ and $y$ that will cost Mr. Paul the least, and simultaneously fulfill his doctor's orders. The cost is given by the equation

$$\text{cost} = 0.8x + 3y.$$

Thus we want to minimize the cost and also meet the five constraints. Stated mathematically this means that our problem is to find

$$x \geq 0 \quad \text{and} \quad y \geq 0 \tag{1}$$

so that

$$5{,}000x + 10{,}000y \geq 25{,}000, \tag{2}$$

$$300x + \phantom{0}400y \geq \phantom{0}1{,}300, \tag{3}$$

$$x + \phantom{00}y \leq 6, \tag{4}$$

and

$$\text{cost} = 0.8x + 3y \tag{5}$$

is minimum.

The above formulation is typical of linear programming problems, and will be used to introduce some of the basic vocabulary. The fundamental notion is that of a linear form. If $x$, $y$, $z$, $w$, $\ldots$ are variables and $a$, $b$, $c$, $d$, $\ldots$ are fixed real numbers, then the expression $ax + by + cz + dw + \cdots$ is a *linear form* in the variables $x$, $y$, $z$, $w$, $\ldots$. A linear form may involve any finite number of variables.

Looking at statements (1)–(5) above, we thus see that each statement contains a linear form. Statement (5), expressing cost as a function in terms of the linear form $0.8x + 3y$, is called the *objective function*. (It is our *objective* to *minimize* this function.) Statements (1), (2), (3), and (4) place certain *limitations* on $x$ and $y$, using linear forms in $x$ and/or $y$; for example, (1) insists that $x$ and $y$ be nonnegative, while (3) requires $x$ and $y$ to be chosen so that

$$300x + 400y \geq 1{,}300.$$

Such statements limiting the selection of $x$ and $y$ are called *linear constraints*.

In (5) the linear form $0.8x + 3y$ was used to define a *linear function*,

$$\text{cost} = f(x, y) = 0.8x + 3y.$$

That is, if $x$ and $y$ are given particular values, then $\text{cost} = f(x, y)$ also has a particular value. In general, if $f(x, y) = ax + by$, the value of the function $f$ at the point $(r, s)$ is the real number $ar + bs$. Thus, for our objective function (5), the value assumed by the cost function at the point $(1, {}^{-}2)$ is

$$\text{cost} = f(1, {}^{-}2) = 0.8(1) + 3({}^{-}2)$$

$$= 0.8 + ({}^{-}6) = {}^{-}5.2.$$

The following properties of linear functions will be useful:
If $f(x, y)$ is a linear function then

1. $f(mx, my) = mf(x, y)$ for all real numbers $m$.
2. $f(x_1 + x_2, y_1 + y_2) = f(x_1, y_1) + f(x_2, y_2)$ for all real numbers $x_1, x_2, y_1, y_2$.

Using our example

$$f(x, y) = 0.8x + 3y$$

with $m = 2$, Property 1 above asserts that

$$f(2x, 2y) = 2f(x, y).$$

We can verify this as follows:

$$f(2x, 2y) = 0.8(2x) + 3(2y) = 1.6x + 6y$$

and

$$2f(x, y) = 2(0.8x + 3y) = 1.6x + 6y.$$

We can also verify Property 2 using our example

$$f(x, y) = 0.8x + 3y.$$

We have

$$f(x_1 + x_2, y_1 + y_2) = 0.8(x_1 + x_2) + 3(y_1 + y_2)$$
$$= 0.8x_1 + 0.8x_2 + 3y_1 + 3y_2$$
$$= (0.8x_1 + 3y_1) + (0.8x_2 + 3y_2)$$
$$= f(x_1, y_1) + f(x_2, y_2).$$

The properties above connected with the concept of linearity will prove invaluable in our development of a technique for solving linear programming problems.

*EXERCISES* ————————————————————————

*State whether or not each of the following is a linear form:*

1. $f(x, y) = 3x + 2y$.    2. $f(x, y) = x + y$.
3. $f(x, y) = 2x^2 - y$.    4. $f(x, y) = 3x(x + y)$.
5. $f(x, y) = y$.    6. $f(x, y) = x$.

*For each of the following linear functions find the value at the given point:*

7. $f(x, y) = 2x - 2y$ at $(2, {}^-2)$.    8. $f(x, y) = 3x + y$ at $(1, {}^-2)$.
9. $f(x, y) = 4x - 2y$ at $(0, 1)$.    10. $f(x, y) = 5x + 4y$ at $({}^-3, 2)$.

*Give the constraints and objective function for each of the following linear programming problems. State whether the objective function is to be maximized or minimized.*

11. A company manufactures two products $X$ and $Y$, each of which must be assembled and packed. The amount of time required by one unit of each product in each phase is shown in the table below.

Time required in hours per unit

| Product | Assembly | Packing |
|---------|----------|---------|
| $X$ | 0.20 | 0.04 |
| $Y$ | 0.30 | 0.02 |

Each week there are 240 hours of assembly time available and 96 hours of packing time. The manufacturer can get a profit of $0.55 for each unit of $X$ sold and $0.40 for each unit of $Y$ sold. What quantity of each product should he produce in order to maximize his profit?

12. Sally Straight is on a crash diet. She may eat only cottage cheese and eggs. In addition she must be certain that she gets at least 15 mg of iron, 800 mg of calcium, and 5,000 units of vitamin A daily. How many cups of cottage cheese and how many eggs must she eat to simultaneously satisfy these three requirements and minimize her daily caloric intake? (Use the information in the table below.)

| Food | Calories | Iron (mg) | Calcium (mg) | Vitamin A (units) |
|------|----------|-----------|--------------|-------------------|
| 1 cup cottage cheese | 240 | 0.9 | 207 | 430 |
| 1 egg | 75 | 1.2 | 54 | 590 |

13. Grandma's Candy Company makes two kinds of candy bars, Chock-Full-of-Health Bars for health food nuts and Yummies for those who aren't concerned about nutrients. The candy is manufactured in three stages: mixing, cooking, and boxing. For the next production run the mixing equipment will be available for up to $26\frac{2}{3}$ hours of machine time, the cooking equipment for 50 hours, and the boxing equipment for $16\frac{2}{3}$ hours. The table below gives the average time in minutes needed to manufacture a box of each type of candy bar at each stage of production. If the profit per box of Chock-Full-of-Health Bars is $.60 and the profit per box of Yummies is $.50, how many boxes of each type of candy bar should Grandma's make during this production run for maximum profits?

Average Processing Time (min)

| Candy | Mixing | Cooking | Boxing |
|-------|--------|---------|--------|
| Chock-Full-of-Health | 2 | 4 | 1 |
| Yummies | 3 | 5 | 2 |

## —— 6-2   Constraints

In this section we will examine more carefully each of the constraints of the sample linear programming problem introduced in Section 6-1. Recall that those constraints were

$$x \geq 0 \text{ and } y \geq 0,$$
$$5,000x + 10,000y \geq 25,000,$$
$$300x + 400y \geq 1,300,$$
$$x + y \leq 6,$$

and that we are interested only in points $(x, y)$ satisfying all of the constraints.
    Now consider the first constraint

$$x \geq 0.$$

It actually means that either $x = 0$ or $x > 0$. Graphically, the solution set of $x = 0$ is the set shown in Figure 6-1(a), namely, the $y$-axis. This axis is formed by all of the points whose coordinates have the form

$$(0, y)$$
$$\uparrow$$
$$x \text{ is } 0.$$

The requirement that

$$x > 0$$

corresponds graphically to the set of all points whose coordinates have the form

$$(a, y).$$
$$\uparrow$$
$$a \text{ is greater than } 0.$$

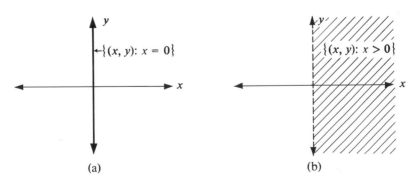

(a)                    (b)

FIGURE 6-1.

All such points are located to the right of the $y$-axis as shown in Figure 6-1(b). The dotted $y$-axis shows that there are no points on the $y$-axis in the set

$$\{(x, y): x > 0\}.$$

The union of the sets graphed in Figures 6-1(a) and (b)

$$\{(x, y): x = 0\} \cup \{(x, y): x > 0\}$$

gives us the graph of

$$\{(x, y): x \geq 0\}$$

as shown in Figure 6-2. This graph is called a *closed half-plane*.

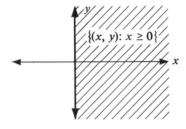

FIGURE 6-2.

Similarly, the graph of the constraint

$$y \geq 0$$

is pictured in Figure 6-3(c). It is the union

$$\{(x, y): y = 0\} \cup \{(x, y): y > 0\}.$$

The two sets in this union are pictured in Figures 6-3(a) and (b), respectively.

Since the solution of our problem requires that both $x \geq 0$ and $y \geq 0$, we need the set of points which are in both of the sets pictured in Figure 6-2 and Figure 6-3(c). In other words, we need the intersection

$$\{(x, y): x \geq 0\} \cap \{(x, y): y \geq 0\}.$$

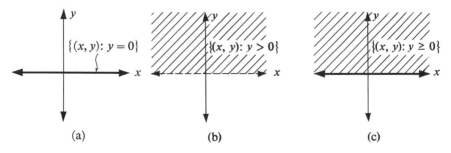

(a)                    (b)                    (c)

FIGURE 6-3.

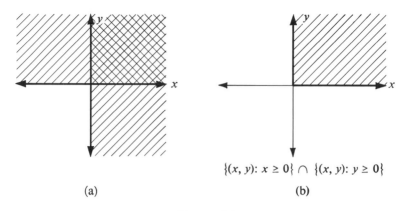

$$\{(x, y): x \geq 0\} \cap \{(x, y): y \geq 0\}$$

(a)                                        (b)

FIGURE 6-4.

This intersection is shown in Figure 6-4.

Our next task is to select from the infinite set in Figure 6-4(b) those points that meet the requirements of the other three constraints

$$5000x + 10,000y \geq 25,000,$$

$$300x + 400y \geq 1,300,$$

and

$$x + y \leq 6.$$

First consider the constraint

$$5000x + 10,000y \geq 25,000.$$

We may rewrite it as

$$10,000y \geq 25,000 - 5,000x \tag{1}$$

by subtracting $5,000x$ from both sides. Next, multiplying both sides by $\frac{1}{10000}$ and rearranging terms, we obtain

$$y \geq \frac{-1}{2}x + \frac{5}{2}.$$

This inequality is equivalent to (1). It requires that either

$$y = \frac{-1}{2}x + \frac{5}{2} \quad \text{or} \quad y > \frac{-1}{2}x + \frac{5}{2}.$$

We know from Chapter 1 that the graph of $y = {}^{-}\frac{1}{2}x + \frac{5}{2}$ is a line. Its graph is shown in Figure 6-5.

Now let $P$ denote the set of points

$$\left\{(x, y) : y > \frac{-1}{2}x + \frac{5}{2}\right\}.$$

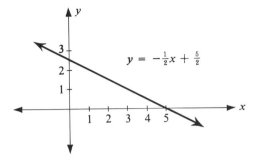

FIGURE 6-5.

$P$ will consist of all the points *above* the line $y = {}^-\frac{1}{2}x + \frac{5}{2}$; for, suppose $(x_1, y_1)$ is an arbitrary point of $P$ as in Figure 6-6. Then

$$y_1 > \frac{{}^-1}{2}x_1 + \frac{5}{2}. \tag{2}$$

Further suppose that $(x_1, y_2)$ is a point on the line $y = {}^-\frac{1}{2}x + \frac{5}{2}$. (This is also shown in Figure 6-6.) Then

$$y_2 = \frac{{}^-1}{2}x_1 + \frac{5}{2}. \tag{3}$$

Substituting (3) into (2) we have

$$y_1 > y_2.$$

Since the $x$-coordinates of the two points are the same, $(x_1, y_1)$ lies above $(x_1, y_2)$. We can conclude that the graph of the set $\{(x, y): y > {}^-\frac{1}{2}x + \frac{5}{2}\}$ is the set of all points *above* (and not on) the line $y = {}^-\frac{1}{2}x + \frac{5}{2}$! (See Figure 6-7.) This region forms an *open half-plane*.

The graph of the set of points $\{(x, y): y \geq {}^-\frac{1}{2}x + \frac{5}{2}\}$ is the union of the line shown in Figure 6-5 and the region shown in Figure 6-7. See Figure 6-8 for the closed half-plane thus formed.

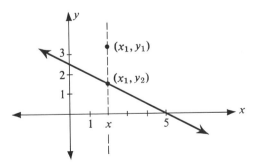

FIGURE 6-6.

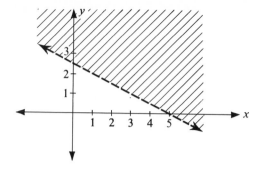

FIGURE 6-7.

Using similar reasoning we can obtain the graph of the set of points corresponding to the fourth constraint

$$300x + 400y \geq 1{,}300. \tag{4}$$

We can rewrite this inequality as follows:

$$300x + 400y - 300x \geq 1{,}300 - 300x,$$

$$400y \geq 1{,}300 - 300x,$$

$$\frac{1}{400}(400y) \geq \frac{1}{400}(1{,}300 - 300x),$$

$$y \geq \frac{13}{4} - \frac{3}{4}x,$$

or

$$y \geq \frac{^-3}{4}x + \frac{13}{4}.$$

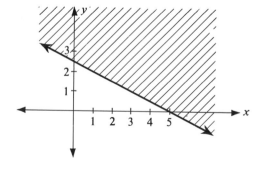

FIGURE 6-8.

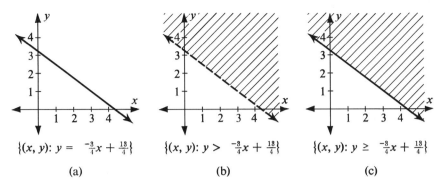

$\{(x, y): y = \tfrac{-3}{4}x + \tfrac{18}{4}\}$          $\{(x, y): y > \tfrac{-3}{4}x + \tfrac{18}{4}\}$          $\{(x, y): y \geq \tfrac{-3}{4}x + \tfrac{18}{4}\}$

(a)                                      (b)                                      (c)

FIGURE 6-9.

This inequality

$$y \geq \frac{^-3}{4}x + \frac{13}{4}$$

is equivalent to the inequality in (4). The graph of the set

$$\left\{(x, y) : y \geq \frac{^-3}{4}x + \frac{13}{4}\right\}$$

is the closed half-plane shown in Figure 6-9(c). It is the union of

$$\left\{(x, y) : y = \frac{^-3}{4}x + \frac{13}{4}\right\},$$

whose graph is the line in Figure 6-9(a), and

$$\left\{(x, y) : y > \frac{^-3}{4}x + \frac{13}{4}\right\},$$

whose graph is the open half-plane in Figure 6-9(b).

We can use the same procedure to obtain the graph of the set of points corresponding to the fifth constraint

$$x + y \leq 6.$$

This inequality can be rewritten as

$$x + y - x \leq 6 - x$$

or

$$y \leq 6 - x.$$

The graph of the set $\{(x, y): y \leq 6 - x\}$ is the closed half-plane shown in Figure 6-10(c). It is the union of the sets $\{(x, y): y = 6 - x\}$ and $\{(x, y): y < 6 - x\}$ whose graphs are shown in Figures 6-10(a) and (b), respectively.

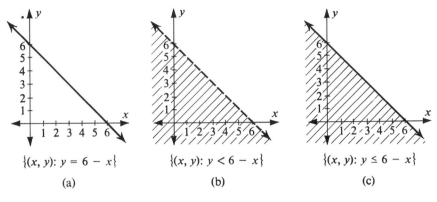

$\{(x, y): y = 6 - x\}$

(a)

$\{(x, y): y < 6 - x\}$

(b)

$\{(x, y): y \le 6 - x\}$

(c)

FIGURE 6-10.

If there are solutions to our problem, they must be coordinates of points which lie in the three half-planes corresponding to

$$\left\{(x, y): y \ge \frac{^{-}1}{2}x + \frac{5}{2}\right\}, \left\{(x, y): y \ge \frac{^{-}3}{4}x + \frac{13}{4}\right\}, \text{ and } \{(x, y): y \le 6 - x\}$$

and which also lie in the region $\{(x, y): x \ge 0\} \cap \{(x, y): y \ge 0\}$ shown in Figure 6-11(a). Figure 6-11(e) shows that region. It is actually the intersection

$$\{(x, y): x \ge 0\} \cap \{(x, y): y \ge 0\} \cap \left\{(x, y): y \ge \frac{^{-}1}{2}x + \frac{5}{2}\right\}$$

$$\cap \left\{(x, y): y \ge \frac{^{-}3}{4}x + \frac{13}{4}\right\} \cap \{(x, y): y \le 6 - x\}.$$

The graph of this intersection is a region called a *polygonal set*, or *polygonal region*. The intersection of a finite number of half-planes always forms such a region. A polygonal region may have either a finite area as in Figure 6-11(e) or an infinite area as shown in the shaded region of Figure 6-12. The latter region is formed by the intersection of three closed half-planes:

$$\{(x, y): x \ge 0\} \cap \{(x, y): y \ge 0\} \cap \{(x, y): y \ge 2 - x\}.$$

The points at which the sides or *boundaries* of a polygonal region meet are called *corners* or *vertices* as marked in Figure 6-12.

In general, a polygonal region is a region whose boundaries are *lines or parts of lines*. The regions in Figures 6-11(e) and 6-12 are special polygonal regions. That is, they are *convex* polygonal regions since if points *A and B* lie in the polygons, so does $\overline{AB}$, the line segment joining *A* and *B*. This is shown for the polygonal regions of Figures 6-11(e) and 6-12 in Figure 6-13. On the other hand, Figure 6-14 shows two regions that are *not* convex. *The intersection of a finite number of closed half-planes will always form a convex polygonal region.*

In the convex polygonal set resulting from our search for the solution of our sample linear programming problem, the boundaries are parts of the lines corresponding to the constraints of the problem. The points in the region

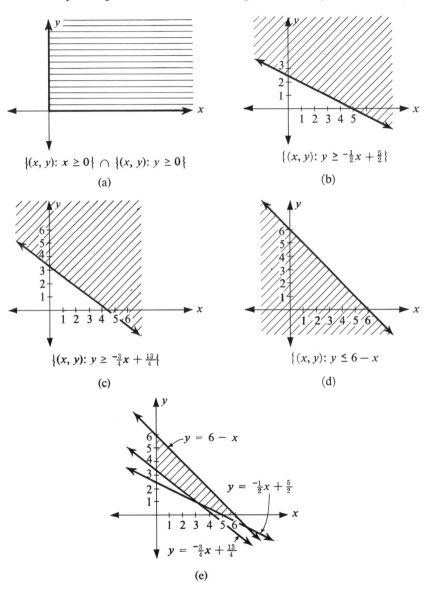

$\{(x, y): x \geq 0\} \cap \{(x, y): y \geq 0\}$

(a)

$\{(x, y): y \geq -\frac{1}{2}x + \frac{5}{2}\}$

(b)

$\{(x, y): y \geq -\frac{3}{4}x + \frac{13}{4}\}$

(c)

$\{(x, y): y \leq 6 - x$

(d)

$y = 6 - x$

$y = -\frac{1}{2}x + \frac{5}{2}$

$y = -\frac{3}{4}x + \frac{13}{4}$

(e)

FIGURE 6-11.

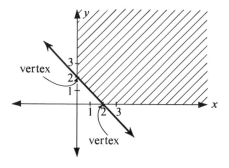

FIGURE 6-12.

which are not boundary points are called *interior points*. If our problem has a solution, i.e., a pair $(x, y)$ satisfying constraints and minimizing cost, it lies in the polygonal convex set formed by the intersection of the closed half-planes corresponding to the constraints. Thus, this region is often called the *region of feasible solutions*. Our job now is to pick from the infinite number of feasible solutions the one that makes our objective function

$$\text{cost} = 0.8x + 3y$$

a minimum. We shall show how this is done in the next section.

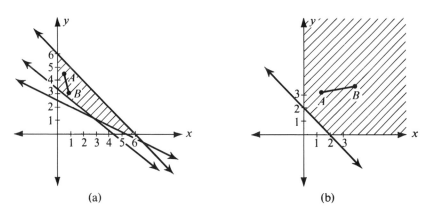

(a)                                             (b)

FIGURE 6-13.

*EXERCISES*

*For each of Exercises 1–10 sketch the set of points $\{(x, y)\}$ which satisfies the constraint(s).*

1.  $x \geq 3$.          2.  $y \geq 4$.          3.  $x \leq 3$.          4.  $y \leq 4$.
5.  $x \leq 3, y \leq 4$.   6.  $0 \leq x \leq 3$.   7.  $x \geq 3, y \leq 4$.

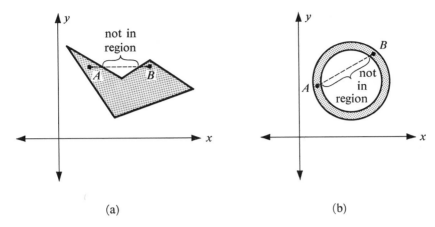

(a)                                    (b)

Figure 6-14.

8.  $x \geq 0, y \geq 0, x + y \leq 3$.
9.  $2x + 3y \leq 5, 0 \leq x \leq 4, 3x - y \geq 6$.
10. $y \leq 3x + 5, 3x + y \geq 6, 3x - y \geq {}^{-}2, x + y \leq 4$.

*State whether or not each of the shaded regions in Exercises 11–17 is (a) a convex region; (b) a convex polygonal region.*

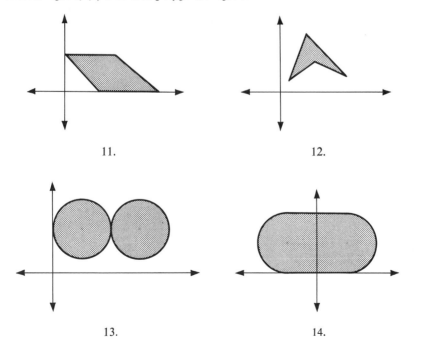

11.                                    12.

13.                                    14.

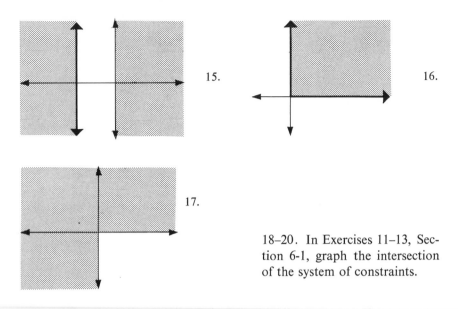

15.

16.

17.

18–20. In Exercises 11–13, Section 6-1, graph the intersection of the system of constraints.

────── 6-3    The Graphical Method

In this section we will continue our quest for the solution to the linear programming problem posed in Section 6-1. So far we have framed the problem and examined some of its characteristics. We have also represented the constraints of the problem graphically. Recall that the intersection of the half-planes corresponding to the constraints formed a convex polygonal region, the region of feasible solutions. If there is a pair of values $(x, y)$ which will minimize our objective function $cost = 0.8x + 3y$, it lies somewhere in this region. Where?

To answer this question we must examine some characteristics of linear forms and finite convex polygonal regions. First suppose that we have a line segment with distinct endpoints $(x_1, y_1)$ and $(x_2, y_2)$. If $f(x, y) = ax + by$ what can we say about the value of $f(r, s)$ where $P(r, s)$ is any point on the line segment joining $P_1(x_1, y_1)$ and $P_2(x_2, y_2)$? (See Figure 6-15.)

In Section 1-11 we learned that the line passing through $P_1$ and $P_2$ can be represented by one of the following equations:

$$x = k \tag{1}$$

or

$$y = mx + c. \tag{2}$$

Suppose (2) holds. Then $s = mr + c$. Thus,

$$\begin{aligned}
f(r, s) &= ar + bs \\
&= ar + b(mr + c) \\
&= (a + bm)r + bc. \tag{3}
\end{aligned}$$

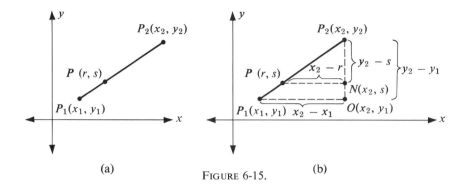

(a)                    FIGURE 6-15.                    (b)

From (3) we obtain

$$f(r, s) - f(x_1, y_1) = (a + bm)r + bc - [(a + bm)x_1 + bc]$$
$$= (a + bm)r - (a + bm)x_1$$
$$= (a + bm)(r - x_1) \qquad (4)$$

and

$$f(r, s) - f(x_2, y_2) = (a + bm)r + bc - [(a + bm)x_2 + bc]$$
$$= (a + bm)r - (a + bm)x_2$$
$$= (a + bm)(r - x_2). \qquad (5)$$

We can assume without loss of generality that $x_1 < x_2$. (Otherwise, $P_1$ and $P_2$ could be relabeled.) Then we must have $x_1 < r < x_2$ since $P$ lies between the distinct points $P_1$ and $P_2$. Thus $r - x_1 > 0$ and $r - x_2 < 0$.

If $a + bm > 0$   then   $(a + bm)(r - x_1) > 0$   since   $r - x_1 > 0$, and $(a + bm)(r - x_2) < 0$ since $r - x_2 < 0$. Thus from (4) we have

$$f(r, s) - f(x_1, y_1) > 0 \quad \text{or} \quad f(r, s) > f(x_1, y_1).$$

and from (5) we have

$$f(r, s) - f(x_2, y_2) < 0 \quad \text{or} \quad f(r, s) < f(x_2, y_2).$$

Combining these inequalities we have

$$f(x_1, y_1) < f(r, s) < f(x_2, y_2).$$

On the other hand if $a + bm < 0$, then

$$(a + bm)(r - x_1) < 0 \text{ since } r - x_1 > 0, \text{and } (a + bm)(r - x_2) > 0$$

since $r - x_2 < 0$. Again from (4) we have

$$f(r, s) - f(x_1, y_1) < 0 \quad \text{or} \quad f(r, s) < f(x_1, y_1)$$

and from (5) we have

$$f(r, s) - f(x_2, y_2) > 0 \quad \text{or} \quad f(r, s) > f(x_2, y_2).$$

Combining these inequalities we thus have

$$f(x_1, y_1) > f(r, s) > f(x_2, y_2).$$

In either case the value of $f$ at $P$ lies between that of $f$ at $P_1$ and $P_2$. The reader can use a similar argument to show that the same is true if (1) describes the line joining $P_1$ and $P_2$. (This is the case when $x_1 = x_2$.)

From this discussion we have the following theorem.

THEOREM 1. If a linear function assumes values $A$ and $B$ at the endpoints of a segment, then the values it assumes at points between the endpoints lie between $A$ and $B$.

Note that if $A = B$, that is, if the values of the linear function at the endpoints of the segment are equal, then the values at all points between the endpoints are equal (to $A = B$).

Now we are almost ready to find the maximum and minimum values assumed by a linear function at points of a finite convex polygonal region! We need to develop one more key theorem.

Let $P(x, y)$ be an interior point of a finite convex polygonal region as in Figure 6-16. Let $f(P)$ designate the value of the linear function $f$ at $P(x, y)$. Now consider any line $l$ which contains point $P$. Suppose $l$ intersects the boundaries of the polygon at $C$ and $D$ as shown in Figure 6-16. By Theorem 1, the value $f(P)$ is between the values $f(C)$ and $f(D)$.

Therefore $f$ attains its minimum and maximum on the boundary of the polygonal regions. Now suppose $D$ is a point of this boundary lying on the line segment joining the vertices $E$ and $G$. By Theorem 1 $f(D)$ lies between $f(E)$ and $f(G)$. This shows that on the boundary of a polygonal region $f$ attains its maximum and minimum at vertices.

Combined with the previous result we have the following theorem.

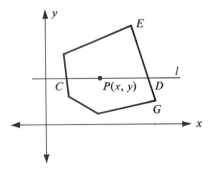

FIGURE 6-16.

THEOREM 2.   The maximum and minimum values of $f(x, y)$ in a finite convex polygonal region are attained at corner points of the polygon.

If $f(x, y)$ takes on the same value at more than one corner of the polygonal region, it must assume the same value at all points of the line determined by these two points. Therefore, it is possible to have a linear function assume its maximum or minimum value along an entire segment in a polygon. Such a segment may or may not be an edge of the polygon.

We are *finally* ready to solve the sample linear programming problem of Section 6-1. Practically, the results of our development mean that the following steps should be followed to find the maximum or minimum of a function $f(x, y) = ax + by$ over a finite convex polygonal region:

1.   Find the coordinates of the vertices of the convex polygonal region formed by the intersection of the half-planes corresponding to the constraints, either by graphing or by solving pairs of simultaneous equations.

2.   Find the value of the objective function $f(x, y) = ax + by$ at these vertices by substituting the coordinates of each point into $f(x, y)$.

3.   The largest of the values resulting is the maximum value attained by $f(x, y)$ on the convex polygonal region. The smallest of the values resulting is the minimum value attained by $f(x, y)$.

Note that these steps will work for the function

$$f(x, y) = ax + by + c,$$

where $a$, $b$, and $c$ are all real numbers. The addition of the number $c$ merely changes every value of the function including its maximum and minimum values by that amount.

Let us apply this method to the problem involving Mr. Paul's pills and capsules. For convenience, the graph of the intersection of the constraints is

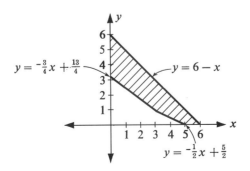

FIGURE 6-17.

reproduced in Figure 6-17. Recall that the four half-planes determined by the constraints of the problem are

$$\{(x, y): x \geq 0\},$$

$$\{(x, y): y \geq 0\},$$

$$\left\{(x, y): y \geq \frac{^-1}{2}x + \frac{5}{2}\right\},$$

and

$$\left\{(x, y): y \geq \frac{^-3}{4}x + \frac{13}{4}\right\}$$

and

$$\{(x, y): y \leq 6 - x\}.$$

First we must find the vertices of the convex polygonal region formed by their intersection. From Figure 6-17 it is apparent that the line $x = 0$ intersects the line $y = {}^-\frac{3}{4}x + \frac{13}{4}$. Solving the set of simultaneous equations

$$x = 0,$$

$$y = \frac{^-3}{4}x + \frac{13}{4}$$

is easy! When $x = 0$,

$$y = \frac{^-3}{4}(0) + \frac{13}{4} = \frac{13}{4}.$$

Thus, one vertex of the polygonal region is $(0, \frac{13}{4})$.

Further, the line $y = 0$ intersects the line $y = {}^-\frac{1}{2}x + \frac{5}{2}$. The solution of the set of simultaneous equations

$$y = 0,$$

$$y = \frac{^-1}{2}x + \frac{5}{2},$$

yields $x = 5$ and $y = 0$. Therefore, $(5, 0)$ is another vertex of the polygonal region.

The line $y = {}^-\frac{3}{4}x + \frac{13}{4}$ intersects the line $y = {}^-\frac{1}{2}x + \frac{5}{2}$. We can find out exactly where by solving the set of simultaneous equations

$$y = \frac{^-3}{4}x + \frac{13}{4},$$

$$y = \frac{^-1}{2}x + \frac{5}{2},$$

to obtain $x = 3$ and $y = 1$. Therefore, $(3, 1)$ is the third vertex of the polygonal region.

The line $y = 6 - x$ intersects the line $x = 0$. The point of intersection is given by the solution of the set of simultaneous equations

$$y = 6 - x,$$

$$x = 0.$$

The solution is $(0, 6)$, so the fourth vertex of the polygonal region is $(0, 6)$. Finally, the fifth vertex is the point of intersection of the lines $y = 6 - x$ and $y = 0$. The solution of the set of simultaneous equations

$$y = 6 - x,$$

$$y = 0$$

gives us this fifth vertex. It is $(6, 0)$.

We have found the five vertices algebraically. In the present problem, we could have easily read them from the graph in Figure 6-17. However, solving algebraically is exact, whereas it is easy to make a slight error in graphing lines which will throw off the coordinates of the vertices.

Remember that we want to *minimize* the objective function

$$\text{cost} = 0.8x + 3y.$$

According to Step (2) of the method developed above, we must substitute the coordinates of the vertices into this equation. We obtain

$$\left(0, \frac{13}{4}\right) : \text{cost} = 0.8(0) + 3\frac{(13)}{4} = \frac{39}{4} = 9.75,$$

$$(5, 0): \text{cost} = 0.8(5) + 3(0) = 4.00,$$

$$(3, 1): \text{cost} = 0.8(3) + 3(1) = 5.40,$$

$$(0, 6): \text{cost} = 0.8(0) + 3(6) = 18.00,$$

$$(6, 0): \text{cost} = 0.8(6) + 3(0) = 4.80.$$

The smallest value is 4.00, which corresponds to the coordinate $(5, 0)$. This is the minimum value of the objective function that we have been seeking! We see that Mr. Paul should take 5 Once-A-Day vitamin pills a day and 0 Vitality vitamin capsules a day in order to simultaneously obey his doctor's orders, minimize his cost (to 4 cents daily), and avoid taking more than 6 pills and capsules.

The technique we have developed in the first three sections is not very powerful since it can be conveniently applied only to very simple linear programming problems involving two or three variables. However, its presentation is helpful in developing insight into the nature of linear programming problems in general. In the next section we shall introduce a more useful method for solving linear programming problems.

*EXERCISES* ────────────────────────────────────────

*For the sets of constraints in Exercises 1–3, (a) Graph the polygonal region corresponding to the intersection of the half-planes. (b) From the graph in (a), give the coordinates of the vertices of the region. (c) Check your answer in (b) by solving pairs of simultaneous equations. (d) Maximize the objective function given. (e) Minimize the objective function given.*

1. $y \geq 1,$

$\qquad y \leq \dfrac{x}{2},$

$\qquad y \leq {}^-x + 4.$

$\quad f(x, y) = 2x - 3y.$

2. $y \leq {}^-2x + 16$

$\qquad y \geq \dfrac{x}{4} + \dfrac{1}{2},$

$\qquad 3x + 4y \geq 24,$

$\qquad y \leq x - 3.$

$\quad f(x, y) = 6x + 8y.$

3. $x \geq 0, y \geq 0,$

$\qquad 4x + y \geq 4,$

$\qquad 5x - 3y \leq 10,$

$\qquad y \leq \dfrac{4}{5}x + 1.$

$\quad f(x, y) = 8x - 3y.$

──── 6-4    Gauss-Jordan Complete Elimination Procedure

In this section we will begin a discussion of the *simplex method* for solving linear programming problems. This method can be developed by using only very simple mathematical ideas. Underlying the technique is an elimination procedure for solving systems of linear equations. We shall discuss this method, called the *Gauss-Jordan complete elimination procedure*, in this section.

Consider the following system of three linear equations in four unknowns, $r$, $s$, $t$, and $u$.

$$2r - s + t + u = 12,$$

$$r + s + 3t - u = 8,$$

$$3r - 2s + t + 4u = {}^-2.$$

Notice that we are now dealing with more general linear equations. Up to now our linear equations were of the form

$$ax + by = c.$$

However, any equation of the form

$$a_1 x_1 + a_2 x_2 + \cdots + a_n x_n = c,$$

where $c$ and the coefficients $a_i$ are real numbers, and the $x_i$ are variables, is considered a linear equation.

Suppose that we want to solve the system of equations above for $r$, $s$, and $t$ in terms of $u$. The first step in the solution is to detach the coefficients in the equation and arrange them in an array resembling a matrix as follows:

$$
\begin{array}{cccc|c}
r & s & t & u & \\
\hline
2 & {}^-1 & 1 & 1 & 12 \\
1 & 1 & 3 & {}^-1 & 8 \\
3 & {}^-2 & 1 & 4 & {}^-2
\end{array}
\qquad (1)
$$

Now we can eliminate the $t$ term from every row but one, say, the third. We can accomplish this by first multiplying every number in the third row by $^-1$. This is the same as multiplying both sides of the equation represented by the third row by $^-1$:

$$^-1(3r - 2s + t + 4u) = {}^-1({}^-2).$$

The resulting equation

$$^-3r + 2s - t - 4u = 2$$

is equivalent to the original. We can represent it in an array as before:

$$
\begin{array}{cccc|c}
r & s & t & u & \\
\hline
. & . & . & . & . \\
. & . & . & . & . \\
{}^-3 & 2 & {}^-1 & {}^-4 & 2
\end{array}
\quad \leftarrow \text{equivalent row}
$$

If we add the new third row to the first we obtain a new first row equivalent to the original:

$$
\begin{aligned}
^-3r + 2s - \;\; t - 4u &= 2 \\
+2r - \;\; s + \;\; t + \;\; u &= 12 \\
\hline
-\; r + \;\; s + 0t - 3u &= 14
\end{aligned}
$$

(Remember that if $a = b$ and $c = d$, $a + c = b + d$.) We can write

$$
\begin{array}{cccc|c}
r & s & t & u & \\
\hline
{}^-1 & 1 & 0 & {}^-3 & 14 \quad \leftarrow \text{new first row} \\
1 & 1 & 3 & {}^-1 & 8 \\
3 & {}^-2 & 1 & 4 & {}^-2
\end{array}
$$

There is a zero in the $t$ column of the first row. That means we have eliminated the $t$-term just as we wanted.

Next we want to eliminate the $t$ term in the second equation. To do this, first multiply the third equation by $^-3$. (The reason this is done will not be a mystery for long.) We obtain a new third equation,

$$^-9r + 6s - 3t - 12u = 6,$$

which is equivalent to the original equation $3r - 2s + t + 4u = {}^-2$. (Remember again that multiplying both sides of an equation by the same nonzero number produces an equation equivalent to the original.) As before we can represent it as

| $r$ | $s$ | $t$ | $u$ | |
|---|---|---|---|---|
| : | : | : | : | : |
| : | : | : | : | : |
| $^-9$ | 6 | $^-3$ | $^-12$ | 6 $\leftarrow$ equivalent row |

Now add this equivalent third row to the second. (Remember that we are really adding equations.) We obtain a new second row with the $t$-term eliminated.

| $r$ | $s$ | $t$ | $u$ | |
|---|---|---|---|---|
| $^-1$ | 1 | 0 | $^-3$ | 14 |
| $^-8$ | 7 | 0 | $^-13$ | 14 $\leftarrow$ new row    (2) |
| 3 | $^-2$ | 1 | 4 | $^-2$ |

The reason for multiplying the third row by 3 should now be apparent.

*The new matrix in* (2) *represents a system of linear equations which* is equivalent to the original system in (1). That is, it has the same solution set. In fact, in any system of equations if an equation is replaced by a new one obtained by adding it to a nonzero multiple of any other equation in the system, as we did above, an equivalent system results.

We have just completed an *iteration*, a procedure that enabled us to eliminate the value $t$ from all equations but one. First we selected a coefficient of $t$ in one of the equations as the one to keep. This coefficient is called the *pivot*. In our example we chose as pivot 1, the coefficient of $t$ in the third row of the original array in (1). Thus, the third row became the *pivotal row* and the third column became the *pivotal column*.

| $r$ | $s$ | $t$ | $u$ | |
|---|---|---|---|---|
| 2 | $^-1$ | 1 | 1 | 12    pivotal column |
| 1 | 1 | 3 | $^-1$ | 8 |
| 3 | $^-2$ | 1 | 4 | $^-2$ $\leftarrow$ pivotal row |

pivot

Conveniently, the value of the pivot was 1. Thus all we had to do was multiply, if necessary, the pivotal row by values chosen so that when the pivotal row was added to the other rows, values of 0 would appear in the pivotal column.

Now let us return to our new matrix and perform another iteration aimed, this time, at removing the $r$-coefficients from all rows but one. Let us designate $^-1$ in the first row as the pivot. (We do not use the 3 in the third row as pivot, for this might disturb the zeros we so carefully created in the $t$ column.)

$$
\begin{array}{c|cccc|c}
 & r & s & t & u & \\
\hline
 & ^-1 & 1 & 0 & ^-3 & 14 \\
 & ^-8 & 7 & 0 & ^-13 & 14 \\
\text{pivot} & 3 & ^-2 & 1 & 4 & ^-2
\end{array}
\quad \leftarrow \text{pivotal row}
$$

Next let us multiply all coefficients in the pivot row by $^-1$. (Remember that this gives us coefficients of an equivalent equation.)

$$
\begin{array}{c|cccc|c}
 & r & s & t & u & \\
\hline
 & 1 & ^-1 & 0 & 3 & ^-14 \\
 & ^-8 & 7 & 0 & ^-13 & 14 \\
\text{new pivot} & 3 & ^-2 & 1 & 4 & ^-2
\end{array}
\quad \leftarrow \text{new pivotal row} \qquad (3)
$$

Because the pivot element is now 1, it is easy to decide by what number to multiply the pivotal row before adding it to the other rows to eliminate the $r$-coefficients.

First we will eliminate the $r$-coefficient $^-8$ from the second row. To do this we multiply the new pivotal row by 8. We obtain an equivalent pivotal row:

$$
\begin{array}{cccc|c}
r & s & t & u & \\
\hline
8 & ^-8 & 0 & 24 & ^-112
\end{array}
\quad \leftarrow \text{equivalent pivotal row}
$$

Adding this new pivotal row to the second row in (3) gives us an array equivalent to (3) with an $r$-coefficient of 0 in the second row:

$$
\begin{array}{cccc|c}
r & s & t & u & \\
\hline
1 & ^-1 & 0 & 3 & ^-14 \\
0 & ^-1 & 0 & 11 & ^-98 \\
3 & ^-2 & 1 & 4 & ^-2
\end{array}
\quad \leftarrow \text{new second row}
$$

Next we want to eliminate the $r$-coefficient of 3 in the third row. To do this, we multiply the pivotal row by $^-3$ to obtain an equivalent pivotal row.

| $r$ | $s$ | $t$ | $u$ | |
|---|---|---|---|---|
| $^-3$ | 3 | 0 | $^-9$ | 42 |

← equivalent pivotal row

When we add this equivalent pivotal row to the third row we obtain a new array equivalent to (3).

| $r$ | $s$ | $t$ | $u$ | |
|---|---|---|---|---|
| 1 | $^-1$ | 0 | 3 | $^-14$ |
| 0 | $^-1$ | 0 | 11 | $^-98$ |
| 0 | 1 | 1 | $^-5$ | 40 |

(4)

← new third row

Now the third row, as well as the second, has an $r$-coefficient of 0. In other words, the $r$-term is eliminated from every equation but the first as we intended.

Finally, let us use the same techniques as above to eliminate the $s$-terms from all equations, but the second. (The reason for choosing the second equation should now be clear.) Thus, we choose $^-1$ as our pivot:

| | $r$ | $s$ | $t$ | $u$ | |
|---|---|---|---|---|---|
| | 1 | $^-1$ | 0 | 3 | $^-14$ |
| pivot | 0 | $(^-1)$ | 0 | 11 | $^-98$ |
| | 0 | 1 | 1 | $^-5$ | 40 |

The pivotal row is

| $r$ | $s$ | $t$ | $u$ | |
|---|---|---|---|---|
| 0 | $^-1$ | 0 | 11 | $^-98$ |

We can add it directly to the third row of (4) to eliminate the $s$-entry. The result is

| $r$ | $s$ | $t$ | $u$ | |
|---|---|---|---|---|
| 1 | $^-1$ | 0 | 3 | $^-14$ |
| 0 | $^-1$ | 0 | 11 | $^-98$ |
| 0 | 0 | 1 | 6 | $^-58$ |

← new third row

Next, noting that the $s$-entry to be eliminated in the first row is $^-1$, we multiply every entry in the pivotal row by $^-1$. This gives us an equivalent pivotal row with 1 as the pivot:

| | r | s | t | u | |
|---|---|---|---|---|---|
| pivot | 0 | (1) | 0 | $^-11$ | 98 | ← new pivotal row |

Addition of this new pivotal row to the first row gives us the new equivalent array:

| r | s | t | u | | |
|---|---|---|---|---|---|
| 1 | 0 | 0 | $^-8$ | 84 | ← new first row |
| 0 | $^-1$ | 0 | 11 | $^-98$ | |
| 0 | 0 | 1 | 6 | $^-58$ | |

For later convenience we multiply the pivotal row (the second row) in this array by $^-1$ so that the $s$-entry is 1. We obtain

| r | s | t | u | | |
|---|---|---|---|---|---|
| 1 | 0 | 0 | $^-8$ | 84 | |
| 0 | 1 | 0 | $^-11$ | 98 | (5) |
| 0 | 0 | 1 | 6 | $^-58$ | |

We have finally succeeded in eliminating $s$-coefficients from every equation but one! In fact, the three iterations we have performed have resulted in an array representing a system of three equations in which $r$-, $s$-, and $t$-coefficients each appear as 1 in only one of the three equations of the system, and as zeros in the other two equations. In fact the $r$, $s$, and $t$ columns are the unit vectors

$$\begin{pmatrix}1\\0\\0\end{pmatrix}, \begin{pmatrix}0\\1\\0\end{pmatrix}, \text{ and } \begin{pmatrix}0\\0\\1\end{pmatrix},$$

respectively.

The system of equations represented by (5) is

$$r \qquad -8u = 84,$$

$$s \quad -11u = 98, \qquad (6)$$

$$t + 6u = {}^-58.$$

This system in (6) is equivalent to the original system presented at the bebeginning of this section. We wanted to solve that system for $r$, $s$, and $t$ in terms of $u$. Now we can do just that very easily! We may solve the first equation in (6) for $r$, the second for $s$, and the third for $t$. We obtain

$$r = \quad 84 + 8u,$$

$$s = \quad 98 + 11u,$$

$$t = {}^-58 - 6u.$$

Obviously, we could assign an infinite number of values to $u$ and obtain an infinite number of solutions for $r$, $s$, and $t$. For instance, if $u = 1$, then

$$r = \quad 84 + \quad 8(1) = \quad 92,$$

$$s = \quad 98 + 11(1) = \quad 109,$$

$$t = {}^-58 - \quad 6(1) = {}^-64.$$

The simplest of the infinite number of possible solutions, however, is obtained by letting $u = 0$. Then

$$r = 84, \quad s = 98, \quad \text{and} \quad t = {}^-58.$$

This solution is often called the *basic solution* and $r$, $s$, and $t$ are called the *basic variables*. The *nonbasic variable* is $u$. Notice that the basic solutions appear in the right-hand column of the special array in (5)! This array is made "special" by the unit column vectors that appear in the columns corresponding to the basic variables.

We might also have solved our original system of three equations in four unknowns for three other variables besides $r$, $s$, and $t$, for instance, $r$, $s$, and $u$; $r$, $t$, and $u$; or $s$, $t$, and $u$. Then we could obtain other basic solutions by setting the nonbasic variable equal to 0.

In general, if we have a system of $n$ equations in $n + m$ unknowns, we can designate $m$ of the variables nonbasic and solve for the remaining basic variables in terms of the nonbasic variables. (For instance, if we have a system of 4 equations in $6 = 4 + 2$ unknowns, we could solve for four of the variables in terms of the other two.) Usually this solution will be unique.

Using the method we have described here will result in an array like (5), where the columns for the basic variables will be unit vectors. For the basic variable $r$ in our example, for instance, the $r$-column in (5) had all zeros except for a 1 in the first row and first column. And for the basic variable $s$, the second column in (5) had all zeros except for a 1 in the second row. The basic solution for each basic variable will appear in the right-hand column as we found in our example.

In the next section we will apply this technique, called the Gauss-Jordan Complete Elimination Procedure, to a sample linear programming problem.

*EXERCISES* —————————————————————————————

1.  Solve for $x$, $y$, and $z$ in terms of $u$ and then find the basic solution:

$$x - y + z + 2u = 5,$$
$$3x + y - 2z + u = 4,$$
$$^-2x + 3y + 3z - 5u = 10.$$

2.  Solve the system of equations in Exercise 1 for $x$, $y$ and $u$ in terms of $z$ and then find the basic solution.

3.  Solve for $x$, $y$, and $z$ in terms of $u$ and $v$ and then find the basic solution by setting $u$ and $v$ equal to 0.

$$x + 2y + z - u + v = 3,$$
$$3y - z + 2u - v = 7,$$
$$2x - y + 4z + 3v = {}^-2.$$

4.  Solve for $x$, $y$, $z$, and $u$ in terms of $a$ and $b$ and then find the basic solution by setting $a$ and $b$ equal to 0.

$$x + z - b = 7,$$
$$y + 2a = 5,$$
$$y + z - 2u + b = {}^-3,$$
$$^-2x + y + u = 6.$$

————— 6-5   The Simplex Method

In this section we shall apply the Gauss-Jordan Complete Elimination Procedure to the solution of linear programming problems. Consider the example below.

Grandma's Bakery, an auxiliary of Grandma's Candy Company, makes three kinds of cookies: chocolate chip, oatmeal, and sugar cookies. The bakery has found that each week it can sell no more than 1,500 dozen chocolate chip cookies, 1,200 dozen oatmeal cookies, and 1,000 dozen sugar cookies. Consequently, it never produces more than these respective amounts in a given week. The number of minutes required in each stage of production for a dozen of each type of cookie is shown in Table 6-1 along with the total number of hours available for each stage of production that week.

| Cookies | Minutes per dozen Blending | Baking | Packaging |
|---|---|---|---|
| Chocolate chip | 5 | 12 | 3 |
| Oatmeal | 4 | 15 | 2 |
| Sugar | 3 | 10 | 3 |
| Total hours available | 130 | 350 | 75 |

Table 6-1.

If Grandma's Bakery makes a profit of 10¢ per dozen on chocolate chip cookies, 12¢ per dozen on oatmeal cookies, and 8¢ per dozen on sugar cookies, how many dozen of each should it produce that week to maximize profits?

Here is an analysis of the problem:

Let $x$ = the number of dozens of chocolate chip cookies to be baked.

$y$ = the number of dozens of oatmeal cookies to be baked.

$z$ = the number of dozens of sugar cookies to be baked.

We want to find $x$, $y$, and $z$ so that

$$x \geq 0,\, y \geq 0,\, z \geq 0.$$

$$
\begin{aligned}
5x + 4y + 3z &\leq 7{,}800 &&(130 \times 60 = 7{,}800 \text{ minutes}), \\
12x + 15y + 10z &\leq 21{,}000 &&(350 \times 60 = 21{,}000 \text{ minutes}), \qquad (1) \\
3x + 2y + 3z &\leq 4{,}500 &&(\ 75 \times 60 = 4{,}500 \text{ minutes}),
\end{aligned}
$$

and so that

$$P \text{ (for profit)} = 10x + 12y + 8z$$

is maximum.

The system in (1) is a system of *inequalities*. We do not know how to solve such a system. However, the technique of the last section enables us to solve a system of equations. We can rewrite the system in (1) by introducing *slack variables* $r$, $s$, and $t$ to make the inequalities equations. Here is such a reformulation of (1):

Find $x \geq 0$, $y \geq 0$, $z \geq 0$, $r \geq 0$, $s \geq 0$, $t \geq 0$ so that

$$
\begin{aligned}
5x + 4y + 3z + r &\phantom{+ s + t} = 7{,}800, \\
12x + 15y + 10z \phantom{+r} + s &\phantom{+ t} = 21{,}000, \qquad (2) \\
3x + 2y + 3z \phantom{+r + s} + t &= 4{,}500,
\end{aligned}
$$

and so that

$$P = 10x + 12y + 8z + 0r + 0s + 0t \text{ is maximum.}$$

In fact we may rewrite the last equation as

$$^{-}10x - 12y - 8z + P = 0$$

and add it to the system in (2). Thus our final reformulation of the problem is as follows:

Find $x \geq 0$, $y \geq 0$, $z \geq 0$, $r \geq 0$, $s \geq 0$, $t \geq 0$ so that

$$
\begin{array}{rrrrrrl}
5x + & 4y + & 3z + r & & & = & 7,800, \\
12x + & 15y + & 10z & + s & & = & 21,000, \\
3x + & 2y + & 3z & & + t & = & 4,500, \\
-10x - & 12y - & 8z & & + P = & & 0,
\end{array}
\tag{3}
$$

and so that $P$ is maximum.

Any solution of the system of equations in (3) which also satisfies the requirement that $x \geq 0$, $y \geq 0$, $z \geq 0$, $r \geq 0$, $s \geq 0$, $t \geq 0$ is called a *feasible solution*. Any solution of (3) which maximizes $P$ is called an *optimal solution*.

Our job is to find the optimal feasible solution! There is a fundamental theorem in the theory of linear programming which says that *if there is an optimal feasible solution to a linear programming problem, then there is an optimal feasible solution which is also a basic solution*. (Roughly this theorem is a generalization of Theorem 2 in Section 6-3.) The simplex method is a systematic procedure for arriving at this optimal and feasible basic solution, if it exists. The method can also tell us when no solution exists.

The first step in the simplex method is to write an array, called a *simplex tableau*, corresponding to the system in (3):

| $x$ | $y$ | $z$ | $r$ | $s$ | $t$ | $P$ | |
|---|---|---|---|---|---|---|---|
| 5 | 4 | 3 | 1 | 0 | 0 | 0 | 7,800 |
| 12 | 15 | 10 | 0 | 1 | 0 | 0 | 21,000 |
| 3 | 2 | 3 | 0 | 0 | 1 | 0 | 4,500 |
| $-10$ | $-12$ | $-8$ | 0 | 0 | 0 | 1 | 0 |

The subarray boxed in below indicates that we already have a basic feasible (but perhaps not optimal) solution with $x$, $y$, and $z$ as nonbasic variables and $r$, $s$, $t$, and $P$ as basic variables.

| $x$ | $y$ | $z$ | $r$ | $s$ | $t$ | $P$ | |
|---|---|---|---|---|---|---|---|
| 5 | 4 | 3 | 1 | 0 | 0 | 0 | 7,800 |
| 12 | 15 | 10 | 0 | 1 | 0 | 0 | 21,000 |
| 3 | 2 | 3 | 0 | 0 | 1 | 0 | 4,500 |
| $-10$ | $-12$ | $-8$ | 0 | 0 | 0 | 1 | 0 |

(4)

That basic feasible solution is

$$x = 0, \ y = 0, \ z = 0, \ r = 7,800, \ s = 21,000, \ t = 4,500, \text{ and } P = 0.$$

The last row of array (4) tells us that we have the equation

$$^-10x - 12y - 8z + 0r + 0s + 0t + P = 0$$

or

$$10x + 12y + 8z - 0r - 0s - 0t = P. \tag{5}$$

Equation (5) indicates that the solution above does not give us maximum $P$ since we could increase the value of $P$ by increasing either $x$, $y$, or $z$, which currently have values of 0. Which should we increase, $x$, $y$, or $z$? Each unit increase in $y$ will result in an increase of 12 units for $P$, while a unit increase in $x$ will increase $P$ by 10 units and a unit increase in $z$ will increase $P$ by only 8 units. Therefore we should increase $y$ to get a maximum favorable effect on $P$.

If we increase $y$, leaving the values of $x$ and $z$ as 0, how are $r$, $s$, and $t$ affected? To see, we write the first three rows of the array in (4) as equations with $x$ and $z$ equal to zero as determined in the basic feasible solution above:

$$
\begin{aligned}
4y + r &= 7{,}800 \quad \text{or} \quad r = 7{,}800 - 4y, \\
15y + s &= 21{,}000 \quad \text{or} \quad s = 21{,}000 - 15y, \\
2y + t &= 4{,}500 \quad \text{or} \quad t = 4{,}500 - 2y.
\end{aligned}
\tag{6}
$$

The three equations in (6) tell us that any increase in $y$ will decrease $r$, $s$, and $t$. Remember now that we have required that

$$r \geq 0,\ s \geq 0,\ t \geq 0.$$

Therefore we must have

$$
\begin{aligned}
r &= 7{,}800 - 4y \geq 0 \quad \text{or} \quad 7{,}800 \geq 4y \quad \text{or} \quad 1{,}950 \geq y, \\
s &= 21{,}000 - 15y \geq 0 \quad \text{or} \quad 21{,}000 \geq 15y \quad \text{or} \quad 1{,}400 \geq y,
\end{aligned}
$$

and

$$t = 4{,}500 - 2y \geq 0 \quad \text{or} \quad 4{,}500 \geq 2y \quad \text{or} \quad 2{,}250 \geq y.$$

*All* of the three inequalities above must hold if $r$, $s$, and $t$ are to remain nonnegative. Thus, the allowable increase in $y$ cannot exceed the smallest of the numbers 1,950, 1,400, and 2,250. That is, if

$$y \leq 1{,}400,$$

then it would also be true that

$$y \leq 1{,}950 \quad \text{and} \quad y \leq 2{,}250.$$

We now know that the maximum increase we can make on $y$ is 1,400. If $y = 1{,}400$ then we know from (6) that

$$
\begin{aligned}
r &= 7{,}800 - 4(1{,}400) = 2{,}200, \\
s &= 21{,}000 - 15(1{,}400) = 0, \\
t &= 4{,}500 - 2(1{,}400) = 1{,}700.
\end{aligned}
$$

Thus our new basic feasible solution is

$$x = 0, \ y = 1,400, \ z = 0, \ r = 2,200, \ s = 0, \ t = 1,700$$

and

$$P = 10(0) + 12(1,400) + 8(0) - 0(2,200) - 0(0) - 0(1,700) = 16,800.$$

This new basic feasible solution has increased the value of $P$ from 0 to 16,800. That is an improvement!

We have gone to a lot of trouble to obtain this improvement. Luckily, there is a simpler way to get it. We saw in the last section that it is possible to obtain a new basic feasible solution for a system of $n$ equations in $n + m$ unknowns by using the Gauss-Jordan Complete Elimination Procedure. We can use this procedure after we have selected a pivot. This selection can be done as follows:

1.  Find the most negative entry in the last row of the simplex tableau. (This will yield the largest increase in profit $P$ per unit increase in the variable associated with this entry.) The variable associated with this entry is the variable to be introduced into the new basic feasible solution.

In our example the most negative entry was $^-12$. Therefore, the variable introduced was $y$.

2.  Divide each positive entry in the column corresponding to the last row's most negative entry into the corresponding element in the right-hand column of the array. (If all the entries in some column with a negative entry in the last row happen to be negative or zero, then the value of the objective function is said to be *infinitely maximum*. This is because the objective function could be made as large as desired by taking arbitrarily large values for the variable associated with these entries. For instance, see the three original equations in (6) and imagine 4, 15, and 2, the coefficients of $y$, as $^-4$, $^-15$, and $^-2$.)

For our example:

| $x$ | $y$ | $z$ | $r$ | $s$ | $t$ | $P$ | |
|---|---|---|---|---|---|---|---|
| 5 | 4 | 3 | 1 | 0 | 0 | 0 | $\dfrac{7,800}{4} = 1,950$ |
| 12 | 15 | 10 | 0 | 1 | 0 | 0 | $\dfrac{21,000}{15} = 1,400$ |
| 3 | 2 | 3 | 0 | 0 | 1 | 0 | $\dfrac{4,500}{2} = 2,250$ |
| $^-10$ | $^-12$ | $^-8$ | 0 | 0 | 0 | 1 | 0 |

↑
most negative
entry

3.   Choose as pivot the divisor that yields the smallest quotient.

In our example, the smallest quotient is 1,400. Thus the pivot is 15, the divisor.

4.   Perform a complete iteration using this pivot.

For our example the iteration is completed as follows:

Original array as it appears in (4):

|  | $x$ | $y$ | $z$ | $r$ | $s$ | $t$ | $P$ |  |
|---|---|---|---|---|---|---|---|---|
|  | 5 | 4 | 3 | 1 | 0 | 0 | 0 | 7,800 |
| pivot | 12 | (15) | 10 | 0 | 1 | 0 | 0 | 21,000 |
|  | 3 | 2 | 3 | 0 | 0 | 1 | 0 | 4,500 |
|  | $-10$ | $-12$ | $-8$ | 0 | 0 | 0 | 1 | 0 |

Division of second row by 15 yields equivalent array with new pivot of 1:

|  | $x$ | $y$ | $z$ | $r$ | $s$ | $t$ | $P$ |  |
|---|---|---|---|---|---|---|---|---|
|  | 5 | 4 | 3 | 1 | 0 | 0 | 0 | 7,800 |
| pivot | $\frac{4}{5}$ | (1) | $\frac{2}{3}$ | 0 | $\frac{1}{15}$ | 0 | 0 | 1,400 |
|  | 3 | 2 | 3 | 0 | 0 | 1 | 0 | 4,500 |
|  | $-10$ | $-12$ | $-8$ | 0 | 0 | 0 | 1 | 0 |

Elimination of $y$-entry in first row yields equivalent array:

| $x$ | $y$ | $z$ | $r$ | $s$ | $t$ | $P$ |  |
|---|---|---|---|---|---|---|---|
| $\frac{9}{5}$ | 0 | $\frac{1}{3}$ | 1 | $\frac{-4}{15}$ | 0 | 0 | 2,200 |
| $\frac{4}{5}$ | 1 | $\frac{2}{3}$ | 0 | $\frac{1}{15}$ | 0 | 0 | 1,400 |
| 3 | 2 | 3 | 0 | 0 | 1 | 0 | 4,500 |
| $-10$ | $-12$ | $-8$ | 0 | 0 | 0 | 1 | 0 |

Elimination of $y$-entry in third row yields equivalent array:

| $x$ | $y$ | $z$ | $r$ | $s$ | $t$ | $P$ |  |
|---|---|---|---|---|---|---|---|
| $\frac{9}{5}$ | 0 | $\frac{1}{3}$ | 1 | $\frac{-4}{15}$ | 0 | 0 | 2,200 |
| $\frac{4}{5}$ | 1 | $\frac{2}{3}$ | 0 | $\frac{1}{15}$ | 0 | 0 | 1,400 |
| $\frac{7}{5}$ | 0 | $\frac{5}{3}$ | 0 | $\frac{-2}{15}$ | 1 | 0 | 1,700 |
| $-10$ | $-12$ | $-8$ | 0 | 0 | 0 | 1 | 0 |

Elimination of $y$-entry in fourth row yields equivalent array:

| $x$ | $y$ | $z$ | $r$ | $s$ | $t$ | $P$ | |
|---|---|---|---|---|---|---|---|
| $\dfrac{9}{5}$ | $0$ | $\dfrac{1}{3}$ | $1$ | $\dfrac{-4}{15}$ | $0$ | $0$ | $2,200 = r$ |
| $\dfrac{4}{5}$ | $1$ | $\dfrac{2}{3}$ | $0$ | $\dfrac{1}{15}$ | $0$ | $0$ | $1,400 = y$ |
| $\dfrac{7}{5}$ | $0$ | $\dfrac{5}{3}$ | $0$ | $\dfrac{-2}{15}$ | $1$ | $0$ | $1,700 = t$ |
| $\dfrac{-2}{5}$ | $0$ | $0$ | $0$ | $\dfrac{4}{5}$ | $0$ | $1$ | $16,800 = P$ |

The arrows in the array indicate the new basic variables $y$, $r$, $t$, and $P$.

An examination of the last array above indicates that $P$ is not optimal. In particular, the fourth row has a negative entry in the $x$ column. This tells us that it is possible to increase $P$ still further. (Remember why we can conclude this! The last row stands for the equation

$$\frac{-2}{5}x + \frac{4}{5}s + P = 16,800$$

$$P = 16,800 + \frac{2}{5}x - \frac{4}{5}s.$$

The coefficient of $x$ is positive and therefore indicates that if we increase $x$ we will increase $P$ as well.)

We now repeat the same procedure as above. First we choose a pivot. We know it must be in the $x$-column; so we divide each positive entry in the $x$-column into the corresponding entry in the right-hand column as follows:

| $x$ | $y$ | $z$ | $r$ | $s$ | $t$ | $P$ | |
|---|---|---|---|---|---|---|---|
| $\dfrac{9}{5}$ | $0$ | $\dfrac{1}{3}$ | $1$ | $\dfrac{-4}{15}$ | $0$ | $0$ | $2,200 \div \dfrac{9}{5} = 1,222\dfrac{2}{9}$ |
| $\dfrac{4}{5}$ | $1$ | $\dfrac{2}{3}$ | $0$ | $\dfrac{1}{15}$ | $0$ | $0$ | $1,400 \div \dfrac{4}{5} = 1,750$ |
| pivot $\dfrac{7}{5}$ | $0$ | $\dfrac{5}{3}$ | $0$ | $\dfrac{-2}{15}$ | $1$ | $0$ | $1,700 \div \dfrac{7}{5} = 1,214\dfrac{2}{7}$ ← smallest quotient |
| $\dfrac{-2}{5}$ | $0$ | $0$ | $0$ | $\dfrac{4}{5}$ | $0$ | $1$ | $16,800$ |

The smallest quotient resulting is $1,214\frac{2}{7}$. This identifies the divisor, $\frac{7}{5}$, as the new pivot and the third row as the pivotal row.

Performing a complete iteration using this pivot gives us the array below.

| $x$ | $y$ | $z$ | $r$ | $s$ | $t$ | $P$ | |
|---|---|---|---|---|---|---|---|
| 0 | 0 | $\dfrac{-38}{21}$ | 1 | $\dfrac{-2}{21}$ | $\dfrac{-9}{7}$ | 0 | $14\dfrac{2}{7} = r$ |
| 0 | 1 | $\dfrac{-2}{7}$ | 0 | $\dfrac{1}{7}$ | $\dfrac{-4}{7}$ | 0 | $428\dfrac{4}{7} = y$ |
| 1 | 0 | $\dfrac{25}{21}$ | 0 | $\dfrac{-2}{21}$ | $\dfrac{5}{7}$ | 0 | $1{,}214\dfrac{2}{7} = x$ |
| 0 | 0 | $\dfrac{10}{21}$ | 0 | $\dfrac{16}{21}$ | $\dfrac{2}{7}$ | 1 | $17{,}285\dfrac{5}{7} = P$ |

↑    ↑         ↑              ↑

The arrows in the array indicate the new basic variables $r$, $y$, $x$, and $P$. The new value of $P$ is $17{,}285\frac{5}{7}$, an improvement over 16,800, the value of $P$ resulting from the previous iteration.

Is this value of $P$ the maximum we can obtain with our given constraints? Yes! The last row of the array above shows no negative entries, so $P$ cannot be increased further. In other words, the equation represented by the last row is

$$\frac{10}{21}z + \frac{16}{21}s + \frac{2}{7}t + P = 17{,}285\frac{5}{7}$$

or

$$17{,}285\frac{5}{7} - \frac{10}{21}z - \frac{16}{21}s - \frac{2}{7}t = P.$$

This equation clearly indicates that any increase in $z$, $s$, or $t$ would reduce the value of $P$.

Our problem is finally solved! The maximum profit that Grandma's Bakery can make the week in question is

$$17{,}285\tfrac{5}{7} \text{ cents or about \$172.86.}$$

To do this Grandma's should bake about $x = 1{,}214\frac{2}{7}$ dozen chocolate chip cookies and about $y = 428\frac{4}{7}$ oatmeal cookies. Note that the value of

$$P = 10x + 12y + 8z + 0r + 0s + 0t$$

when $x = 1{,}214\frac{2}{7}$ and $y = 428\frac{4}{7}$ is $17{,}285\frac{5}{7}$, the value of $P$ given in our array. Notice also that the value of the variable $r = 14\frac{2}{7}$ in our basic solution is dropped since $r$ was a fictitious slack variable. Actually this means that about $14\frac{2}{7}$ minutes of blending time will be unused that week. (Remember that $r$ was the slack variable added to the constraint dealing with blending time available.)

In this problem we have *maximized* a linear expression for $P$. However, many linear programming problems call for *minimizing* rather than maximizing. To do this we could maximize the linear expression $^-P$ and use the simplex method as we have in this section.

Without doubt you have noticed that the computation involved in solving linear programming problems using the simplex method is easy, but tedious. In addition, you probably have noticed the repetitive nature of the process. This characteristic makes computers very useful tools for solving linear programming problems with the simplex method, especially when the number of variables is large.

*EXERCISES* ——————————————————————

*Solve the following linear programming problems using the simplex method:*

1.  Maximize
    $$P = 50x + 40y$$
    so that
    $$x \geq 0, y \geq 0,$$
    $$2x + 3y \leq 240,$$
    $$2x + y \leq 120.$$

2.  Maximize
    $$P = 3x - 4y + z$$
    so that
    $$x \geq 0, y \geq 0, z \geq 0,$$
    $$x + y + z \leq 10,$$
    $$3x - y + 3z \leq 8,$$
    $$2x + y - 2z \leq 9.$$

3.  Minimize
    $$C = 2x + y$$
    so that
    $$x \geq 0, y \geq 0,$$
    $$x - y \leq 8,$$
    $$4x + 3y \leq 6.$$

4.  Minimize
    $$C = 3x - 2y + 4z$$
    so that
    $$x \geq 0, y \geq 0, z \geq 0,$$
    $$x + y \leq 6,$$
    $$3x + y - z \leq 10,$$
    $$y + 3z \leq 4.$$

5–6.  Use the simplex method to solve Exercises 11 and 13, Section 6-1.

7.  Norbert's Nut Company has 1000 pounds of peanuts, 500 pounds of cashews, and 200 pounds of filberts to use in the two different kinds of nut mixtures which it sells as appetizers. The proportions used for each product are shown below.

| Product \ Amount in ounces | Peanuts | Cashews | Filberts |
|---|---|---|---|
| Peanuts Galore | 24 | 4 | 4 |
| Marvelous Mix | 16 | 10 | 6 |

How many packages of each mixture should Norbert's Nut Company make in order to maximize profits if it makes a profit of $.80 from each package of Peanuts Galore and a profit of $.90 from each package of Marvelous Mix?

8. Mighty Manufacturing Company makes three products, zims, zams, and zips. Each product requires time on three machines as shown below.

| Hours Product | Machine A | Machine B | Machine C |
|---|---|---|---|
| Zim | 0 | 2 | 3 |
| Zam | 3 | 1 | 2 |
| Zip | 2 | 3 | 2 |

Each machine can run for 24 hours each day. If the company receives a profit of $5 for each zim, $6 for each zam, and $8 for each zip, how many of each should it produce to maximize profits?

—— 6-6    Degeneracy

In the simplex method we have just developed and applied, we obtained each basic feasible solution by first selecting a pivot. (You should have noticed that the column in which the pivot lies is the new basic variable to be introduced). To select this pivot we first examined the entries directly above some negative entry in the last row. Then we divided only those entries that were positive into the corresponding entries in the right-hand column of the array. The divisor producing the smallest quotient became the new pivot.

There are some problems that may arise. First, suppose that the smallest quotient is zero. This indicates that one of the basic variables has the value of 0. For example, examine the array below:

| | $x$ | $y$ | $r$ | $s$ | $C$ | |
|---|---|---|---|---|---|---|
| | 5 | 3 | 1 | 0 | 10 | $\dfrac{10}{5} = 2$ |
| pivot | 4 | ⁻1 | 0 | 1 | 0 | $\dfrac{0}{4} = 0$ |
| | ⁻4 | ⁻3 | 0 | 0 | 1 | 4 |

After the iteration is completed, the new variable will still have the value 0. (In the example above $s = 0$ before the iteration. After the iteration $x = 0$.) Further, the other basic variables will not change value. This situation does not help to improve the value of the objective function!

Problems may also arise when there is a tie between quotients for a smallest value. When this happens, the new basic variable takes on the value of this quotient. It also reduces to zero any other basic variable whose original value was used in computing the quotients involved in the tie. For instance, suppose $z$ is the pivotal column and a tie occurs in choosing the pivot:

$$
\begin{array}{ccccccc}
. & . & . & z & . & . & . \\
\hline
. & . & . & 6 & . & . & . \\
\\
. & . & . & 2 & . & . & . \\
\\
& & & \overset{\uparrow}{O} & & &
\end{array}
\quad
\left.
\begin{array}{c}
\dfrac{12}{6} = 2 \\[2mm]
\dfrac{4}{2} = 2
\end{array}
\right\} \leftarrow \text{tie!}
$$

most
negative
entry

Let us arbitrarily select 2 as the pivot. Multiplying the pivotal row by $\frac{1}{2}$ gives us

$$
\begin{array}{ccccccc|l}
. & . & . & z & . & . & . & \\
\hline
. & . & . & 6 & . & . & . & 12 \\
. & . & \nearrow & \textcircled{1} & . & . & . & 2 \leftarrow \text{(The new value of } z \text{ in the} \\
& \text{pivot} & & & & & & \quad \text{basic feasible solution.)}
\end{array}
$$

In the iteration, we multiply the pivotal row by $^-6$ and add it to the other row. This gives us:

$$
\begin{array}{ccccccc|l}
. & . & . & z & . & . & . & \\
\hline
. & . & . & 6-6=0 & . & . & . & 12 - 6 \cdot 2 = 0 \\
. & . & . & 1 & . & . & . & 2
\end{array}
$$

The zero in the right-hand column indicates that we are now back to the problem involving minimum ratios of zero, which we described above!

We say that *degeneracy* has occurred in the situations just presented. In both cases at least one of the basic variables has the value zero. A basic feasible solution in which some of the basic variables are zero is *called a degenerate basic feasible solution.*

What should be done when degeneracy occurs? Usually, it is best to ignore it and continue to introduce new variables. Eventually, the objective function will improve. Sometimes, a basic variable which was eliminated in a previous iteration will return. This occurrence is called *cycling*. There are methods to cope with this situation. However, we shall not discuss them here, since cycling is very rare in practical linear programming problems.

*EXERCISES* ——————————————————————

1.  Maximize
$$P = 2x + 5y$$
so that
$$x \geq 0, \, y \geq 0,$$
$$x + 2y \leq 10,$$
$$3x + 5y \leq 25.$$

2.  Maximize
$$P = 3x + y + z$$
so that
$$x \geq 0, \, y \geq 0, \, z \geq 0,$$
$$x + y \leq 5,$$
$$2x - z \leq 0,$$
$$y + 2z \leq 6.$$

—————— 6-7    Using Artificial Variables in the Simplex Method

In the first simplex tableau in (4) of our example in Section 6-5 we immediately had a basic feasible solution thanks to the presence of a set of unit column vectors in the columns corresponding to the basic variables. When such an initial basic feasible solution is not available, it is helpful to introduce one by using *artificial* variables.

Consider the following linear programming problem. Suppose we would like to find

$$x \geq 0 \quad \text{and} \quad y \geq 0$$

so that

$$3x + 2y \geq 8, \qquad 2y \geq 5 \tag{1}$$

and so that

$$K = x + 2y$$

is at a minimum.

To change the system in (1) from inequalities to equations we introduce the slack variables $r$ and $s$. We also let $C = {}^{-}K$, as suggested at the end of Section 6-5. Thus we can reformulate the problem as follows:

Find $x \geq 0, \, y \geq 0, \, r \geq 0,$ and $s \geq 0$
so that

$$3x + 2y - r = 8,$$
$$2y - s = 5, \tag{2}$$

and so that

$$C = {}^{-}x - 2y + 0r + 0s$$

is at a maximum.

Note that we must *subtract* $r$ and $s$ to change the $\geq$ to equal signs in (2). (In the example of the last section we were dealing with inequalities with $\leq$. Thus, in that situation we had to *add* slack variables.) Unfortunately, the negative coefficients before $r$ and $s$ resulting from the subtractions prevent the columns corresponding to the variables $r$ and $s$ from being unit vectors. Consequently, we have no initial basic feasible solution as shown by the array below which corresponds to (2).

| $x$ | $y$ | $r$ | $s$ | $C$ | |
|-----|-----|-----|-----|-----|-----|
| 3 | 2 | $^-1$ | 0 | 0 | 8 |
| 0 | 2 | 0 | $^-1$ | 0 | 5 |
| 1 | 2 | 0 | 0 | 1 | 0 |

However, we can remedy this situation by introducing two *artificial variables* $a$ and $b$ into the equations in (2) as follows:

$$3x + 2y - r \quad + a \quad = 8, \tag{3}$$
$$2y \quad - s \quad + b = 5,$$

To prevent the introduction of these variables from totally changing our problem, we subtract from $C$ the quantity $na + nb$, where $n$ is an unspecified but arbitrarily large positive number. (Since we are trying to maximize $C = {}^-K$, the subtraction of this arbitrarily large quantity from $C$ to form $C'$ will ensure that $C$ is maximized if $C'$ is maximized.) Thus,

$$C' = C - (na + nb) = {}^-x - 2y - na - nb.$$

We can rewrite this equation as

$$x + 2y + na + nb + C' = 0.$$

Our new problem can be reformulated as follows:
Find $x \geq 0$, $y \geq 0$, $r \geq 0$, $s \geq 0$, $a \geq 0$, $b \geq 0$ so that

$$3x + 2y - r \quad + a \quad = 8,$$
$$2y \quad - s \quad + b \quad = 5, \tag{4}$$
$$x + 2y \quad + na + nb + C' = 0,$$

and so that $C'$ is at a maximum.

The basic feasible solution to our original problem as stated in (2) (if it exists) will be a basic feasible solution for the artificial problem as stated in (4) with $a = b = 0$. Consequently, applying the simplex method to (4) will give us a basic feasible solution to (2) when $a = b = 0$, since the large negative coefficients $^-n$ in the expression for $C'$,

$$C' = {}^-x - 2y - na - nb,$$

will prevent $C'$ from reaching a maximum if $a > 0$ or $b > 0$. If $C'$ reaches a maximum before $a$ and $b$ are eliminated, this indicates the original problem has no feasible solution.

With this background, let us start our application of the simplex method to our artificial problem as formulated in (4). The first simplex tableau is:

| $x$ | $y$ | $r$ | $s$ | $a$ | $b$ | $C'$ | |
|---|---|---|---|---|---|---|---|
| 3 | 2 | $^-1$ | 0 | 1 | 0 | 0 | 8 |
| 0 | 2 | 0 | $^-1$ | 0 | 1 | 0 | 5 |
| 1 | 2 | 0 | 0 | $n$ | $n$ | 1 | 0 |

This array does not give us a basic feasible solution. In fact, at the moment there are no negative entries in the last row, so we cannot even proceed to find a pivot. Here is what can be done: First, add to the last row $^-n$ times the first row and $^-n$ times the second row. This gives us the equivalent array:

| $x$ | $y$ | $r$ | $s$ | $a$ | $b$ | $C'$ | |
|---|---|---|---|---|---|---|---|
| 3 | 2 | $^-1$ | 0 | 1 | 0 | 0 | $8 = a$ |
| 0 | 2 | 0 | $^-1$ | 0 | 1 | 0 | $5 = b$ |
| $^-3n + 1$ | $^-4n + 2$ | $n$ | $n$ | 0 | 0 | 1 | $^-13n = C'$ |

The unit vectors in the columns corresponding to $a$, $b$, and $C'$ as indicated by the arrows above give us our first basic feasible solution with $a$, $b$, and $C'$ as the basic variables. Of course, $C'$ is not at a maximum as indicated by the negative entries in the last row.

We can now continue as usual with the simplex method using the column of the most negative entry in the last row, $^-4n + 2$, as the pivotal column. The simplex tableaux for our example are shown below with appropriate remarks.

The pivot is 2:

| | $x$ | $y$ | $r$ | $s$ | $a$ | $b$ | $C'$ | |
|---|---|---|---|---|---|---|---|---|
| | 3 | 2 | $^-1$ | 0 | 1 | 0 | 0 | $\frac{8}{2} = 4$ |
| pivot | 0 | (2) | 0 | $^-1$ | 0 | 1 | 0 | $\frac{5}{2} = 2\frac{1}{2}$ |
| | $^-3n + 1$ | $^-4n + 2$ | $n$ | $n$ | 0 | 0 | 1 | $^-13n$ |

Division of the pivotal row by 2 yields a new equivalent array with pivot 1:

| | $x$ | $y$ | $r$ | $s$ | $a$ | $b$ | $C'$ | |
|---|---|---|---|---|---|---|---|---|
| | 3 | 2 | $^-1$ | 0 | 1 | 0 | 0 | 8 |
| pivot | 0 | (1) | 0 | $\dfrac{-1}{2}$ | 0 | $\dfrac{1}{2}$ | 0 | $\dfrac{5}{2}$ |
| | $^-3n+1$ | $^-4n+2$ | $n$ | $n$ | 0 | 0 | 1 | $^-13n$ |

Elimination of $y$-entries in first and third rows gives us the new equivalent array:

| | $x$ | $y$ | $r$ | $s$ | $a$ | $b$ | $C'$ | | |
|---|---|---|---|---|---|---|---|---|---|
| pivot | (3) | 0 | $^-1$ | 1 | 1 | $^-1$ | 0 | 3 | $= a$ |
| | 0 | 1 | 0 | $\dfrac{-1}{2}$ | 0 | $\dfrac{1}{2}$ | 0 | $\dfrac{5}{2}$ | $= y$ |
| | $^-3n+1$ | 0 | $n$ | $^-n+1$ | 0 | $2n-1$ | 1 | $^-3n-5 = C'$ | |

The negative entries in the last row of this array indicate that the value of $C'$ is not yet at a maximum. The most negative entry in the last row, $^-3n + 1$, indicates that the $x$-column should be taken as the pivotal column. The only positive element in that column is 3. It automatically becomes the new pivot.

Division of the elements of the pivotal row by 3 and elimination of the $x$-entries in the third row give us the new array:

| $x$ | $y$ | $r$ | $s$ | $a$ | $b$ | $C'$ | | |
|---|---|---|---|---|---|---|---|---|
| 1 | 0 | $\dfrac{-1}{3}$ | $\dfrac{1}{3}$ | $\dfrac{1}{3}$ | $\dfrac{-1}{3}$ | 0 | $1 = x$ | |
| 0 | 1 | 0 | $\dfrac{-1}{2}$ | 0 | $\dfrac{1}{2}$ | 0 | $\dfrac{5}{2} = y$ | |
| 0 | 0 | $\dfrac{1}{3}$ | $\dfrac{2}{3}$ | $n-\dfrac{1}{3}$ | $n-\dfrac{2}{3}$ | 1 | $^-6 = C'$ | |

The absence of negative entries in the last row indicates that the value for $C'$ is at a maximum. In addition, it no longer depends on $n$. Our final solution is $x = 1$, $y = \frac{5}{2}$, $C' = -6$, when $r = 0$, $s = 0$, $a = 0$, and $b = 0$. Since we let $C' = C - na - nb$ and $a = b = 0$, $C' = C$. But we also let $^-K = C$. Thus the minimum value of $K = {}^-(^-6) = 6$.

Admittedly, this problem could have been solved more easily using another method. However, it is a good example of how artificial variables can be used. The constraints of the problem all involved $\geq$. It is important to note that artificial variables can be used in systems whenever some of the inequalities are $\geq$ and others are $\leq$.

Consider, for example, the following linear programming problem. Find

$$x \geq 0 \quad \text{and} \quad y \geq 0$$

so that

$$x + y \leq 3,$$
$$2x - y \geq 4$$

and so that

$$P = 3x + 4y$$

is at a maximum. Using slack variables in both inequalities and an artificial variable in the second inequality, we can reformulate the problem as follows:

Find $x \geq 0$, $y \geq 0$, $r \geq 0$, $s \geq 0$ and $a \geq 0$ so that

$$x + y + r \qquad\quad = 3,$$
$$2x - y \qquad - s + a = 4,$$

and so that

$$P' = 3x + 4y + 0r + 0s - na$$

is at a maximum.

### EXERCISES

*Solve the following exercises using the simplex method.*

1.  Minimize

    $$N = 2x + y$$

    so that

    $$x \geq 0, \ y \geq 0,$$
    $$3x - \ y \geq 6,$$
    $$x + 2y \geq 5.$$

2.  Minimize

    $$P = x + y$$

    so that

    $$2x + \ y \geq 12,$$
    $$5x + 8y \geq 74,$$
    $$x + 6y \geq 24.$$

3.  Minimize

    $$C = 6x + 3y + 4z$$

    so that

    $$x \geq 0, \ y \geq 0, \ z \geq 0,$$
    $$x \geq 25,$$
    $$y \leq 60,$$
    $$z \leq 20,$$
    $$x + y + z \leq 150.$$

4.  Minimize

$$C = x + 2.5y + 3.5z + 4w + 5p + 4.5q$$

so that

$$x \geq 0, \ y \geq 0, \ z \geq 0, \ w \geq 0, \ p \geq 0, \ q \geq 0,$$
$$x + y \geq 40,$$
$$z + w + p + q \leq 35.$$

5.  Mr. Forest is going on a weekend hike and wants to carry only light-weight food. Consequently, he decides to limit his food supply to three different kinds of freeze dried meals. The table below gives the protein and calcium content in units of each type of meal packet together with the cost of each.

| Content<br>Packet | Protein | Calcium | Cost per<br>packet |
|---|---|---|---|
| A | 20 | 100 | $.25 |
| B | 15 | 400 | $.20 |
| C | 10 | 200 | $.15 |

The minimum daily adult requirement of protein is 70 units and of calcium is 800 units. How many packets of each food should Mr. Forest eat daily to meet these daily requirements and, simultaneously, *minimize the daily cost*?

6.  In Exercise 5, assume that the packets have the following weights:

| Packet | Weight in ounces |
|---|---|
| A | 6 |
| B | 4 |
| C | 3 |

How many packets of each food should Mr. Forest bring for each day of his hike to meet the minimum daily requirements while keeping the weight of his pack to a minimum?

7.  Rich Mining Company owns two mines. Mine A costs $350 an hour to operate, while Mine B costs $300 an hour to operate. The company needs at least 200 tons of high-grade ore, 500 tons of medium grade ore, and 400 tons of low grade ore. The production of the two mines is shown below. How many hours should each mine be worked to satisfy the company's requirements while keeping costs at a minimum?

| Production in<br>Mine        tons/hr | High grade | Medium grade | Low grade |
|---|---|---|---|
| A | 2 | 8 | 4 |
| B | 3 | 10 | 5 |

8.  Bob Banks has been given $1,200 by his father to invest in stocks on the condition that he purchase shares in only three companies: Space Applications Corporation, Computer Corporation of America, and Frank's Fish 'n Chips. In addition, Bob's father has stipulated that he may buy no more than 20 shares each of Computer Corporation of America and Frank's Fish 'n Chips and at least 25 shares of Space Applications Corporation. The current price per share of the three companies are listed below:

| Company | Price per share |
|---------|-----------------|
| Space Applications Corp. | $30 |
| Computer Corp. of America | $20 |
| Frank's Fish 'n Chips | $50 |

Find (a) the largest number of shares of stock that Bob Banks can purchase, (b) the smallest number of shares of stock that he can purchase.

9.  Edward Moore, a politician, is running for reelection to his U.S. Senate seat. There are three key cities in his state in which his political advisors recommend that he concentrate his time. The advisors estimate that every speech given in cities A, B, and C will gain for Moore 6,000, 3,000, and 4,000, respectively. Moore's heavy schedule in the Senate places the following restrictions on his campaign: He can give at most 6 appearances in city A and 2 appearances in city B. However, he can make at least 5 appearances in city C. How should Senator Moore allocate his time among the various cities to maximize the number of votes he gains if he can make at most 24 appearances in his home state during the campaign?

# Introduction to the Theory of Games    **7**

—— 7-1    Introduction

Before proceeding further the reader should be warned that this chapter is not going to tell him how to win at chess, make a fortune in the stock market, accomplish a diplomatic coup, or manage a sales campaign. The theory of games is not sufficiently developed to analyze thoroughly all competitive or conflict situations. The primary difficulty lies in constructing a mathematical model that adequately accounts for all the interrelationships present in a real game. Even if one is successful here the process of computerizing the model and obtaining desired results in a reasonable amount of time represents another formidable obstacle.

However, very judicious modeling has brought many economic, political, and social games within the scope of present-day game theory. By neglecting rather weak interrelationships the sizes of the models have been reduced to manageable levels.

In this chapter we shall discuss simple games with somewhat simplified assumptions. This chapter can nevertheless be rightly called an "Introduction to the Theory of Games," because the analysis of complicated games involves mathematical refinement more than the development of new concepts.

For our purposes a game will be a process whereby *players* use *strategies* to achieve *payoffs*. We shall restrict ourselves to games played by *two* participants. Before the game is played each participant independently formulates a strategy. This strategy is to be a complete strategy and determines his move under any contingency. That is, once a strategy is chosen the player has selected a course of action which anticipates every move of his opponent so that the play could be carried out by proxy. The game proceeds according to specified rules and at the end each player receives a payoff.

We shall denote the two players by $R$ and $J$, the two strategies by $x$ and $y$, and the two payoffs by $P$ and $Q$. Each payoff actually may be thought of as a function of the strategies, i.e., $P = P(x, y)$ and $Q = Q(x, y)$. (The nature of $P(x, y)$ and $Q(x, y)$ are, of course, determined by the rules of the game.) We shall make the further assumption that $Q = {}^-P$, i.e., whatever $R$ wins $J$ loses, and vice versa. Games of this type are called *zero-sum* games.

Finally, we assume $R$ has only a finite number of strategies to choose from, i.e., $x \in X$, where $X$ is a finite set of $m$ strategies. The same goes for $J$. That is, $y \in Y$, where $Y$ is a finite set of $n$ strategies. Such games can be analyzed using matrix theory. A *game matrix* is constructed so that each column represents a strategy of $R$, each row represents a strategy of $J$, and each element represents the payoff if the corresponding row and column strategies are chosen. A game matrix showing the payoffs $P$ to player $J$ under all possible pairs of strategies is shown in Figure 7-1.

$$
\begin{array}{c}
R \\
\begin{array}{cccc}
x_1 & x_2 & \cdots & x_m
\end{array} \\
J \quad
\begin{array}{c}
y_1 \\ y_2 \\ \vdots \\ \\ y_n
\end{array}
\left(
\begin{array}{cccc}
P(x_1, y_1) & P(x_2, y_1) & \cdots & P(x_m, y_1) \\
\cdot & & & \cdot \\
\cdot & \cdot & \cdot & \cdot \\
\cdot & & & \cdot \\
P(x_1, y_n) & & \cdots & P(x_m, y_n)
\end{array}
\right)
\end{array}
$$

Figure 7-1.

In the case of business transactions or betting games each element of the matrix in Figure 7-1 might be the actual cash $R$ pays to $J$ if the element is positive. (If the element is negative, $J$ pays $R$.) In the case of games like chess, tic-tac-toe, etc., where a player either wins, loses, or ties, the elements can be chosen as 1 if $J$ wins, 0 for a tie, and ${}^-1$ if $R$ wins.

—— 7-2    Strictly Determined Games

Consider the following example of a $2 \times 2$ game. Two players, Rex and Jon, play a game in which they simultaneously extend either 1 or 2 fingers from a closed fist. They agree that Jon will "pay" to Rex the difference

(number of fingers shown by Jon) − (number of fingers shown by Rex)

if this difference is negative. If the difference is positive, Rex will "pay" Jon this amount. This game can be represented by the $2 \times 2$ *game matrix* in Figure 7-2. There the rows represent Jon's choices and the columns represent Rex's choices. The entries represent the differences in numbers of fingers as defined above. For instance, the entry of $^-1$ in Jon's 1-row and Rex's 2-column is the difference $1 - 2 = {}^-1$. Thus $^-1$ is the payoff. This corre-

$$
\begin{array}{c}
\text{Rex} \\
\text{number of } \overset{\rightarrow}{\downarrow} \quad 1 \quad 2 \\
\text{fingers shown} \quad 1 \quad \begin{pmatrix} 0 & {}^-1 \\ & \\ 1 & 0 \end{pmatrix} \\
\text{Jon} \qquad\qquad \\
2 \quad
\end{array}
$$

FIGURE 7-2.

sponds to the case when Jon shows 1 finger and Rex shows 2 fingers. Since the difference is negative, Jon pays Rex 1. Thus Jon loses 1 and Rex wins 1. Note that this is a zero-sum game since the sum of Jon's gains plus the sum of Rex's gains will always be 0 as the game continues. (Here we interpret a *loss* as a *negative gain*.)

An examination of the game matrix indicates that Jon's best strategy is to show 2 fingers, since at the *worst* he would neither win nor lose as indicated by the 0 entry in the second column. On the other hand, Rex's best strategy is to show 2 fingers as well, since at worst he would neither win nor lose, as indicated by the 0 entry in the second row. The payoff when both Rex and Jon play their best strategies is called the *value of the game*. In this case the value is 0, as shown by the circled entry in Figure 7-3. When the value of the game is zero, the game is called *fair*.

$$
\begin{array}{c}
\text{Rex} \\
\text{best strategy (guarantees best gain if} \\
\downarrow \quad \text{Jon is free to use all strategies)} \\
\begin{pmatrix} 0 & {}^-1 \\ 1 & ⓪ \end{pmatrix} \\
\text{Jon} \\
\text{(guarantees} \qquad \text{best strategy} \rightarrow \\
\text{least loss if} \\
\text{Rex is free to use all strategies)}
\end{array}
$$

FIGURE 7-3.

We develop a variation for setting up a game matrix to make all this somewhat more relevant by applying the discussion to the real world in a conflict situation between a husband and wife team who like to kayak. In order to be specific we will name them Dick and Gail. Dick is a notorious runner of wild water rivers while Gail prefers less dramatic action with more time for scenery, conversation, and relaxation. They will both be out of town at different meetings, and agree to drive Highway M enroute home. They are to drive until they meet and then proceed to the nearest river from their meeting point. It turns out that the rivers available on the route to be driven range in difficulty from class 1 (a quiet afternoon float) to class 5 (the kind of water better left to the movies). However, due to timing and other factors the only rivers that will fall near meeting points are rivers classed as 2, 3, 4, or 5. More than that, if $A$ and $B$ are known time options, the meeting places will call for rivers classed as indicated in the cells of the game matrix in Figure 7-4.

$$
\begin{array}{c}
\text{Gail} \\
\begin{array}{cc} A & B \end{array}
\end{array}
$$

Dick $\begin{array}{c} A \\ B \end{array} \begin{pmatrix} 4 & 3 \\ 5 & 2 \end{pmatrix}$ 
③ greatest row minimum
2

5    ③    least column maximum

FIGURE 7-4.

A little study shows that if Gail selects strategy $B$ she need fear no river worse than a 3, while Dick sees that if he plays strategy $A$ he will have no river easier than a 3. The optimal strategy for each in this case is the strategy indicated by the circled numbers.

Games such as our examples are called *strictly determined*, since neither Dick nor Gail would be inclined to alter strategy even if the "opponent's" strategy were known. Each strategy is completely determined independent of the other.

One distinguishing feature of the matrix for a strictly determined game is an entry that is the smallest entry in its row and the largest entry in its column. In our first example, this was the 0 circled in Figure 7-3. Such an entry is called a *saddle point*. The value of a saddle point entry may occur in other places in the game matrix, but at the saddle point it must be a row minimum and a column maximum. Consider for example the game matrix:

$$
\begin{pmatrix}
\boxed{1} & \boxed{1} & 0 & 2 \\
\boxed{1} & \boxed{1} & 0 & \boxed{1} \\
\boxed{1} & {}^{-}1 & 1 & 0 \\
3 & 2 & ① & 1
\end{pmatrix}
\begin{array}{l}
0 \quad \text{row minimum} \\
0 \\
{}^{-}1 \\
1 \leftarrow \text{greatest row minimum}
\end{array}
$$

column
maximum    3    2    1    2
                    ↑
                  least
                 column
                maximum

The saddle point 1 is circled. Notice that it occurs in other rows, besides the fourth, and other columns besides the third as indicated by the boxed entries in the matrix. However, there is only one position in the matrix where it is both a row minimum and a column maximum. Thus, a saddle point is simultaneously the *greatest* row minimum (maximin) and *least* column maximum (minimax). It can be shown that *when a game has a saddle point, the optimal strategy for both players is to select a row in which the saddle point is the minimum and a column in which the saddle point is the maximum.* When a game has a saddle point, it is the *value* of the game. (A game may have more than one entry which is a saddle point, but in this event all such entries will be numerically equal.)

To find a saddle point of any game matrix, first circle the minimum value(s) in each row. Then check to see whether any one of the numbers circled is a maximum value in its column. For instance, consider the matrix in Figure 7-5. A minimum value in each row is circled. Since none of these circled numbers is a maximum of its column, the matrix has no saddle point.

$$\begin{pmatrix} ① & 2 & 5 \\ 2 & -2 & 7 \\ 4 & 6 & ③ \end{pmatrix}$$

FIGURE 7-5.

In fact, in most game matrices no saddle point exists. When this is the case the game is said to be *nonstrictly determined*. If the game is played only once no optimal strategies exist and game theory has no advice on how to play the game. For example, consider Figure 7-6. Clearly $R$ (and $J$) cannot

$$R$$

$$J \quad \begin{matrix} & x_1 & x_2 \\ y_1 & \begin{pmatrix} 0 & 1 \\ y_2 & 1 & 0 \end{pmatrix} \end{matrix}$$

FIGURE 7-6.

prefer one strategy over the other, because the game matrix would remain unchanged if the strategies were relabeled. Thus game theory cannot present $J$ with an optimal strategy. $J$ may as well choose row 1 simply to play the game.

Now let us consider an extremely simple example from business and examine how it can be analyzed using what we know about game theory.

Suppose Alabama Baked Chicken and Chuck's Fish 'n Chips are each trying to decide whether to build a new restaurant on the north side of the city (N) or the south side (S). If both decide to build on the north side or south side both firms estimate the difference (Alabama Baked Chicken sales minus Chuck's sales) in sales will be negative four thousand and positive five thousand, respectively. (See Figure 7-7.)

Chuck's Fish 'n Chips

$$\begin{array}{c} & N \quad S \\ \text{Alabama Baked Chicken} \quad \begin{array}{c} N \\ S \end{array} \begin{pmatrix} ^-4 & \\ & 5 \end{pmatrix} \end{array}$$

FIGURE 7-7.

If Alabama Baked Chicken decides to build on the north side and Chuck's decides to build on the south side it is estimated that Alabama Baked Chicken sales will trail Chuck's sales by two thousand dollars. (See Figure 7-8.)

Chuck's Fish 'n Chips

$$\begin{array}{c} & N \quad S \\ \text{Alabama Baked Chicken} \quad \begin{array}{c} N \\ S \end{array} \begin{pmatrix} & ^-2 \\ & \end{pmatrix} \end{array}$$

FIGURE 7-8.

Finally, it is predicted that Alabama Baked Chicken sales will be seven thousand dollars more than Chuck's if it builds on the south side and Chuck's

Chuck's Fish 'n Chips

$$\begin{array}{c} & N \quad S \\ \text{Alabama Baked Chicken} \quad \begin{array}{c} N \\ S \end{array} \begin{pmatrix} & \\ 7 & \end{pmatrix} \end{array}$$

FIGURE 7-9.

builds on the north side. (See Figure 7-9.) The final "game" matrix is shown in Figure 7-10. The 5 circled in the game matrix is the saddle point. This

Chuck's Fish 'n Chips

$$\begin{array}{c} & N \quad S \\ \text{Alabama Baked Chicken} \quad \begin{array}{c} N \\ S \end{array} \begin{pmatrix} ^-4 & ^-2 \\ 7 & ⑤ \end{pmatrix} \end{array}$$

FIGURE 7-10.

indicates that for optimal competition both firms should build on the south side. Note that the game is not fair since its value is 5, not 0. In fact, it is unfair to Chuck's, since Alabama Baked Chicken would always choose to build on the south side (and thus always choose the second row) because they would always make more money than Chuck's there. Chuck's, on the other hand, would always be faced with trailing Alabama Baked Chicken sales as indicated by the positive entries of   5 and   7 in the matrix. However, that firm, if wise, would choose to build on the south side (and thus choose the second column) since their sales would then trail Alabama Baked Chicken by less. Note that optimal strategy for each business in this game produces the best possible competition against the other business, rather than highest possible gross sales.

### EXERCISES ───────────────────────────────────────

*Find the saddle point in each game matrix if one exists.*

1. $\begin{pmatrix} 1 & 0 \\ 3 & ^-1 \end{pmatrix}$
    2. $\begin{pmatrix} 0 & ^-1 \\ 1 & 0 \end{pmatrix}$

3. $\begin{pmatrix} 5 & 7 \\ 6 & 9 \end{pmatrix}$
    4. $\begin{pmatrix} 0 & \dfrac{1}{2} \\ \dfrac{5}{4} & \dfrac{3}{4} \end{pmatrix}$

5. $\begin{pmatrix} 0 & ^-1 \\ 2 & 3 \end{pmatrix}$

6. Rex and Jon decide to play the following game. Rex is to hide a half dollar in one hand and a quarter in the other. If Jon correctly guesses the coin held in Rex's left hand he receives the coin. If Jon guesses wrong, Rex pays the difference   between the guess and the coin held. (If this difference is negative, Jon pays Rex.) What is the game value? How much should Jon pay to play if the game is to be fair.

7. At dinner Rex and Jon dispose of extra dessert by the horse-n-goggle method. Each exposes from 0–5 fingers from a clinched fist. If the count of extended fingers is odd Jon wins, if the count is even Rex wins the dessert. Is there an optimal strategy for either?

### ─── 7-3   Strategies

When a game that is played over and over has a saddle point, both participants should, for best results, choose the row and column intersecting at this saddle point without fail. A strategy such as this in which one row (or column) is picked all the time is called a *pure strategy*. This row or column is assigned probability one and all the others are assigned probability zero.

For instance, consider once again the example of the last section, and assume now that Rex and Jon play their game repeatedly. The game matrix, shown in Figure 7-11, had the saddle point 0. We know that Jon's

$$\text{Rex}$$

$$\text{Jon} \begin{pmatrix} 0 & ^-1 \\ 1 & 0 \end{pmatrix}$$

↖saddle point

FIGURE 7-11.

optimal strategy was to continually play the row with the saddle point, row 2. We can represent the strategy chosen by Jon as the row vector

$$(p_1 \; p_2)$$

where $p_1$ gives the probability that Jon will play the first row and $p_2$ gives the probability that Jon will play the second row. Thus $p_1 + p_2 = 1$ and Jon's *optimal strategy* can be written as

$$(0 \; 1).$$

The 1 in the *second* position and the 0 in the first position indicate that Jon should *always* choose the *second* row to maximize his payoff. Because the vector (0 1) has an entry of 1 and all other entries 0, (0 1) is said to represent a pure strategy.

Similarly, we can represent the strategy chosen by Rex as the column vector

$$\begin{pmatrix} q_1 \\ q_2 \end{pmatrix},$$

where $q_1$ gives the probability that Rex will choose the first column and $q_2$ gives the probability that Rex will choose the second column for best results. Again, the sum of $q_1$ and $q_2$ should be 1. Rex's *optimal strategy* can be represented by the column vector

$$\begin{pmatrix} 0 \\ 1 \end{pmatrix},$$

since his payoff is maximized by always choosing the second column.

Next reconsider the game matrix of the last section shown for reference in Figure 7-12. Since no saddle point exists, the game is nonstrictly determined.

$$R$$

$$\begin{array}{cc} & x_1 \quad x_2 \end{array}$$

$$J \quad \begin{array}{c} y_1 \\ y_2 \end{array} \begin{pmatrix} 0 & 1 \\ 1 & 0 \end{pmatrix}$$

FIGURE 7-12.

In such cases we decided that game theory has no advice on optimal strategies when the game is played only once.

However, let us now assume the above game is played many times. If $R$ consistently chooses $x_1$, $J$ will certainly notice and consistently play $y_2$. This means that in order to avoid losing 1 every game $R$ must change his strategy to $x_2$ often enough to keep $J$ from guessing his strategy. For example, $R$ could choose his strategy by flipping a coin (heads for $x_1$, tails for $x_2$). This would be likely to keep $J$ from winning too often.

This analysis shows that for games without saddle points which are played many times there may be such a thing as an optimal strategy if we expand our definition of strategy to include the possibility of choosing different rows (columns) for each play according to some predetermined rule. This "generalized" strategy is called a *mixed strategy* and is often defined by specifying for each strategy a probability that it will be picked on any given play of the game.

Now consider the general $2 \times 2$ matrix in Figure 7-13. Assume that it

$$\text{Jon} \quad \begin{pmatrix} a_{11} & a_{12} \\ a_{21} & a_{22} \end{pmatrix}$$

Rex

FIGURE 7-13.

defines a $2 \times 2$ game. Also assume that the strategies of players Jon and Rex are

$$(p_1 \ p_2) \quad \text{and} \quad \begin{pmatrix} q_1 \\ q_2 \end{pmatrix},$$

respectively. Then the probability that $a_{11}$ will be the payoff is $p_1 q_1$; for, if $p_1$ is the probability that Jon will choose row 1, and $q_1$ is the probability that Rex will choose column 1, then (since these are independent events), the probability that row 1 and column 1 will be chosen is the product of the separate probabilities. (See Section 4-3.) Similarly, the probabilities that $a_{12}$, $a_{21}$, and $a_{22}$ will be the payoffs are $p_1 q_2$, $p_2 q_1$, and $p_2 q_2$, respectively. Thus, the *expectation* of the game is

$$p_1 q_1 a_{11} + p_1 q_2 a_{12} + p_2 q_1 a_{21} + p_2 q_2 a_{22}.$$

This number is yielded by the matrix product

$$\text{Expectation} = (p_1 \ p_2) \begin{pmatrix} a_{11} & a_{12} \\ a_{21} & a_{22} \end{pmatrix} \begin{pmatrix} q_1 \\ q_2 \end{pmatrix}.$$

If the strategies $(p_1 \ p_2)$ and $\begin{pmatrix} q_1 \\ q_2 \end{pmatrix}$ are optimal this expectation is the value of the game. For the first example of this section the game value is

$$(0\ 1)\begin{pmatrix} 0 & {}^-1 \\ 1 & 0 \end{pmatrix}\begin{pmatrix} 0 \\ 1 \end{pmatrix} = (0 + 1\ 0 + 0)\begin{pmatrix} 0 \\ 1 \end{pmatrix}$$

$$= (1\ 0)\begin{pmatrix} 0 \\ 1 \end{pmatrix}$$

$$= 0,$$

just as we concluded previously for the case when Rex and Jon both play their optimal strategies.

In the next section we will examine a way to find the optimal strategies for nonstrictly determined games. Then we will be able to find the value of games without saddle points such as in the second example of this section.

*EXERCISES* ────────────────────────────────────────

Determine the optimal strategy and game values of each of the following.

1. $\begin{pmatrix} 1 & 4 \\ 2 & 3 \end{pmatrix}$.      2. $\begin{pmatrix} 0 & 1 \\ 2 & 3 \end{pmatrix}$.      3. $\begin{pmatrix} 1 & 3 \\ {}^-3 & 1 \end{pmatrix}$.

4. $\begin{pmatrix} {}^-1 & {}^-1 \\ 0 & 2 \end{pmatrix}$.      5. $\begin{pmatrix} {}^-2 & 2 \\ 1 & 1 \end{pmatrix}$.

───── 7-4    Nonstrictly Determined 2 × 2 Games

We have already investigated optimal strategies for 2 × 2 games when the corresponding game matrices have saddle points. In such cases the games are strictly determined and the optimal strategies are pure.

Now let us investigate optimal strategies for 2 × 2 games when the corresponding matrices have no saddle points. In such cases the games are nonstrictly determined and the optimal strategies are mixed. Suppose that the game matrix shown in Figure 7-14 has no saddle point, where Jon and

Rex

$$\text{Jon} \begin{pmatrix} w & x \\ y & z \end{pmatrix}$$

FIGURE 7-14.

Rex are the players. It can be shown that the optimal strategy for Jon, represented by the row vector $(p_1\ p_2)$, is given by

$$p_1 = \frac{z - y}{w + z - x - y} \quad \text{and} \quad p_2 = \frac{w - x}{w + z - x - y}.$$

The optimal strategy for $R$, represented by the column vector $\begin{pmatrix} q_1 \\ q_2 \end{pmatrix}$, is given by

$$q_1 = \frac{z - x}{w + z - x - y} \quad \text{and} \quad q_2 = \frac{w - y}{w + z - x - y}.$$

The value $V$ of the game is

$$V = \frac{wz - xy}{w + z - x - y}.$$

For instance, if the game matrix is

$$\begin{matrix} & \text{Rex} \\ \text{Jon} & \begin{pmatrix} 3 & {}^-4 \\ {}^-2 & {}^-1 \end{pmatrix} \end{matrix}$$

then

$$p_1 = \frac{{}^-1 - ({}^-2)}{3 + {}^-1 - ({}^-4) - ({}^-2)} = \frac{1}{8},$$

$$p_2 = \frac{3 - ({}^-4)}{3 + {}^-1 - ({}^-4) - ({}^-2)} = \frac{7}{8},$$

$$q_1 = \frac{{}^-1 - ({}^-4)}{3 + {}^-1 - ({}^-4) - ({}^-2)} = \frac{3}{8},$$

and

$$q_2 = \frac{3 - ({}^-2)}{3 + {}^-1 - ({}^-4) - ({}^-2)} = \frac{5}{8}.$$

Thus, the optimal strategy for Jon is to choose the first row $\frac{1}{8}$ of the time and the second row $\frac{7}{8}$ of the time. The optimal strategy for Rex is to choose the first column $\frac{3}{8}$ of the time and the second column $\frac{5}{8}$ of the time. The value $V$ of the game is

$$V = \frac{3 \cdot {}^-1 - {}^-4 \cdot {}^-2}{3 + {}^-1 - ({}^-4) - ({}^-2)} = \frac{{}^-11}{8}.$$

Since $V \neq 0$, the game is unfair. In fact, it is biased for Rex, since Rex wins when the matrix entries are negative.

Sometimes it is possible to reduce a game matrix larger than 2 × 2 to a 2 × 2 game matrix by eliminating certain rows and columns. For instance, consider the 3 × 3 game matrix of Figure 7-15.

$$\begin{matrix} & \text{Rex} \\ \text{Jon} & \begin{pmatrix} 4 & {}^-1 & 1 \\ 2 & 2 & {}^-4 \\ 3 & {}^-2 & {}^-1 \end{pmatrix} \end{matrix}$$

FIGURE 7-15.

Notice that every element of the first row is as large or larger than the corresponding elements of the third row. The row with larger elements, the first row, is said to *dominate* the row with smaller elements, the third row. Since player Jon pays player Rex for negative payoffs and wins more for larger positive payoffs, he would prefer to play the first row with its larger values, rather than the third row. For this reason the row that is *dominated*, in this case the third row, can be eliminated without affecting the optimal strategies and value of the game. This gives us the game matrix of Figure 7-16.

$$
\text{Jon}\quad \begin{pmatrix} 4 & ^-1 & 1 \\ 2 & 2 & ^-4 \end{pmatrix}.
$$

Rex

FIGURE 7-16.

In our new game matrix notice that every element of the first column is as large or larger than each corresponding element of the second column, i.e. the first column dominates the second. Clearly Rex would much prefer to play the column with smaller elements to minimize his losses and maximize his wins. (Remember that Rex must pay when the matrix entries are positive. The smaller the entries, the less he pays! Also recall that Rex wins when the matrix entries are negative.) Thus the *dominating column*, here the first column, can be eliminated without affecting the optimal strategies and value of the game. (Note that a dominat*ed* row is eliminated, but a dominat*ing* column is eliminated.) Our new game matrix is shown in Figure 7-17.

$$
\text{Jon}\quad \begin{pmatrix} ^-1 & 1 \\ 2 & ^-4 \end{pmatrix}.
$$

Rex

FIGURE 7-17.

Now the techniques we have already developed for finding the optimal strategies and values for $2 \times 2$ game matrices can be used. The strategies used depend, of course, on whether or not the game is strictly determined. Here, inspection of the matrix entries yields no saddle point. To obtain the optimal strategies and game value, we must thus use the technique shown in the present section.

*EXERCISES* ─────────────────────────────────────

*Determine the optimal strategies and the game value for each of the following games:*

1. $\begin{pmatrix} 3 & 0 \\ 2 & 4 \end{pmatrix}$.

2. $\begin{pmatrix} 4 & 1 \\ 3 & 2 \end{pmatrix}$.

3. $\begin{pmatrix} 3 & 1 \\ 2 & 4 \end{pmatrix}$.

4. $\begin{pmatrix} 2 & ^-1 \\ ^-1 & 2 \end{pmatrix}$.

5. $\begin{pmatrix} 1 & 10 \\ 9 & 12 \end{pmatrix}$.

6. $\begin{pmatrix} 1 & 10 \\ ^-1 & 12 \end{pmatrix}$.

7. $\begin{pmatrix} 3 & 1 \\ 0 & 2 \end{pmatrix}$.

8. $\begin{pmatrix} 7 & 4 \\ 3 & 5 \end{pmatrix}$.

9. $\begin{pmatrix} 5 & 2 \\ 1 & 3 \end{pmatrix}$.

10. $\begin{pmatrix} 9 & 0 \\ 6 & 12 \end{pmatrix}$.

11. $\begin{pmatrix} 1 & 4 & 0 \\ 2 & 0 & 1 \end{pmatrix}$.

12. $\begin{pmatrix} 3 & 5 \\ 4 & 2 \\ 2 & 1 \end{pmatrix}$.

13. $\begin{pmatrix} 4 & 1 & 0 \\ 1 & 4 & 3 \\ 0 & 3 & 2 \end{pmatrix}$.

14. $\begin{pmatrix} 4 & 1 & 2 \\ 3 & 5 & 1 \\ 2 & 1 & 1 \end{pmatrix}$.

───── 7-5   2 × m and m × 2 Games

In this section we will consider games which result in $2 \times m$ or $m \times 2$ game matrices, where $m > 2$. For example, the matrix

$$\begin{pmatrix} 3 & 1 & ^-3 \\ ^-4 & 5 & 2 \end{pmatrix}$$

might correspond to a $2 \times m$ game matrix, where $m = 3$.

On the other hand, the matrix

$$\begin{pmatrix} 3 & ^-4 \\ 1 & 5 \\ ^-3 & 2 \\ 0 & 3 \end{pmatrix}$$

might correspond to an $m \times 2$ game matrix, where $m = 4$.

If $2 \times m$ or $m \times 2$ game matrices are strictly determined or can be reduced to $2 \times 2$ games, then we already know how to find the optimal strategies and game values. If not, the optimal strategies and game values can be found by using graphs. As an example, consider the $2 \times 3$ game matrix of Figure 7-18. Check to see first of all that there is no saddle point

Rex

Jon $\begin{pmatrix} 7 & 4 & 1 \\ ^-2 & 3 & 6 \end{pmatrix}$

FIGURE 7-18.

and that there are no dominating rows and columns.

Also recall that $V$ is the value of the game which good play (that is, use of optimal strategies) will guarantee in the long run *if both players* use their optimal strategies. Since Jon wins if the entries of the game matrix are *positive*, his winnings will be greater than or equal to $V$ if he uses his optimal strategy and Rex does not. (Remember that the bigger $V$ is, the better it is for Jon.) Since Rex wins if the entries of the game matrix are *negative*, his winnings will be smaller than or equal to $V$ if he uses his optimal strategy and Jon does not. (Remember that the smaller $V$ is, the better it is for Rex.)

With these comments in mind, we can say that

$$\text{Jon's winnings} \geq V$$

and

$$\text{Rex's winnings} \leq V.$$

Now denote by $(p \ \ 1 - p)$ the optimal strategy for Jon. (This is a suitable representation of the probability vector, since the sum of the entries must be 1.) If Rex plays the first column, then Jon's winnings, the vector product shown by arrows below,

$$(\overrightarrow{p \ \ 1 - p})\begin{pmatrix} 7 & 4 & 1 \\ -2 & 3 & 6 \end{pmatrix}$$

will be greater than or equal to $V$:

$$(p \ \ 1 - p)\begin{pmatrix} 7 \\ -2 \end{pmatrix} \geq V,$$

$$7p - 2 + 2p \geq V,$$

or

$$9p - 2 \geq V. \tag{1}$$

Similarly, if Rex plays the second column, then Jon's winnings, the vector product shown by arrows below,

$$(\overrightarrow{p \ \ 1 - p})\begin{pmatrix} 7 & 4 & 1 \\ -2 & 3 & 6 \end{pmatrix}$$

will be greater than or equal to $V$:

$$(p \ \ 1 - p)\begin{pmatrix} 4 \\ 3 \end{pmatrix} \geq V,$$

$$4p + 3 - 3p \geq V,$$

or

$$p + 3 \geq V. \tag{2}$$

And if Rex plays the third column, then Jon's winnings, the vector product shown by arrows below,

$$(\overrightarrow{p \ \ 1 - p})\begin{pmatrix} 7 & 4 & 1 \\ -2 & 3 & 6 \end{pmatrix}$$

will be greater than or equal to $V$:

$$(p \quad 1-p)\binom{1}{6} \geq V,$$

$$p + 6 - 6p \qquad \geq V,$$

$$^{-}5p + 6 \qquad \geq V. \tag{3}$$

Now graph each of the inequalities in (1), (2), and (3) on the same pair of coordinate axes as shown in Figure 7-19. The shaded region in Figure 7-19

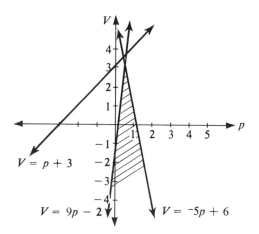

FIGURE 7-19.

is the intersection of the three half-planes determined by inequalities (1), (2), and (3). It represents the possible values of the game $V$ (winnings for Jon) corresponding to the different columns Rex could play. Figure 7-19 shows that the maximum value of $V$ in the shaded region corresponds to the intersection of the lines $V = {}^{-}5p + 6$ and $V = 9p - 2$. There $V = 3\frac{1}{7}$ and $p = \frac{4}{7}$. Thus, the optimal strategy for Jon is $(\frac{4}{7} \ \frac{3}{7})$ and the value of the game is $3\frac{1}{7}$.

To find the optimal strategy for Rex we can use the first method of Section 7-4. First note that the optimal strategy for Jon was determined by the intersection of the lines whose equations were computed from the first and third columns of the game matrix

$$\begin{pmatrix} \downarrow & & \downarrow \\ 7 & 4 & 1 \\ ^{-}2 & 3 & 6 \end{pmatrix}.$$

Consider the $2 \times 2$ matrix formed with these two column vectors,

$$\begin{pmatrix} 7 & 1 \\ ^{-}2 & 6 \end{pmatrix} = \begin{pmatrix} w & x \\ y & z \end{pmatrix}.$$

Now use the formulas for $q_1$ and $q_2$ in Section 7-4 to find the optimal strategy $\begin{pmatrix} q_1 \\ q_2 \end{pmatrix}$ for Rex based on this $2 \times 2$ submatrix of the original game matrix:

$$q_1 = \frac{z - x}{w + z - x - y} = \frac{6 - 1}{7 + 6 - 1 - (^-2)} = \frac{5}{14},$$

$$q_2 = \frac{w - y}{w + z - x - y} = \frac{7 - (^-2)}{7 + 6 - 1 - (^-2)} = \frac{9}{14}.$$

Thus Rex's optimum strategy is

$$\begin{pmatrix} \dfrac{5}{14} \\ 0 \\ \dfrac{9}{14} \end{pmatrix}.$$

Here is a short cut for finding the optimal strategies for a game matrix. Reconsider the $2 \times 3$ games matrix in Figure 7-20. The first step is to check

$$\text{Rex}$$

$$\text{Jon} \begin{pmatrix} 7 & 4 & 1 \\ ^-2 & 3 & 6 \end{pmatrix}$$

FIGURE 7-20.

for a saddle point and dominating rows or columns. If a saddle point exists the game is strictly determined and the optimal strategies are pure. If there are dominated rows or dominating columns, they should be eliminated. Since we have already decided that no saddle points and no dominated rows or dominating columns exist for this example, we can proceed.

We next construct a "graph" of the game by taking two parallel axes which we will call $A$ and $B$. On the $A$ axis we mark 7, the entry in the first row, first column of the game matrix. On the $B$ axis we mark $^-2$, the entry in the second row, first column of the game matrix. Then we connect these points as shown in Figure 7-21.

Figure 7-22 shows the result of repeating this procedure for the second and third columns of the game matrix. The dots trace the segments bounding the *bottom* of the graph and locate the lowest point of intersection of the segments. The two segments are those corresponding to the first and third columns of the game matrix:

$$\begin{pmatrix} \downarrow & & \downarrow \\ 7 & 4 & 1 \\ ^-2 & 3 & 6 \end{pmatrix}.$$

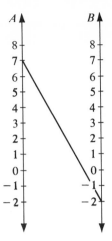

FIGURE 7-21.

They indicate that the 2 × 2 matrix

$$\begin{pmatrix} 7 & 1 \\ -2 & 6 \end{pmatrix}$$

is the one that should be used to determine Rex's optimal mixed strategy as we did above. Notice this is the same as the result we obtained using the method described at the beginning of this section.

If the game were m × 2 for Jon we could solve it similarly. However, instead of examining the lower bounds we would trace the *upper* bounds, since Jon wishes to maximize the game value. Instead of selecting the highest

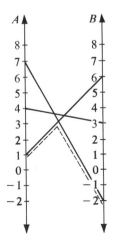

FIGURE 7-22.

point of intersection we would find the lowest as determined by the upper bounds. This point would identify two line segments and we could then determine the mixed strategies for play.

*EXERCISES* ──────────────────────────────────────

*Determine the optimal strategies and game values for each of the following games:*

1. $\begin{pmatrix} 6 & 5 & 7 & 1 \\ 2 & 4 & 3 & 5 \end{pmatrix}$.

2. $\begin{pmatrix} 1 & 3 & 0 & 2 & 1 \\ 2 & 1 & 2 & 4 & 3 \end{pmatrix}$.

3. $\begin{pmatrix} 5 & 1 \\ 2 & ^-1 \\ ^-1 & 6 \\ 1 & 2 \\ 3 & 4 \end{pmatrix}$.

4. $\begin{pmatrix} 3 & 1 \\ 5 & 2 \\ 2 & ^-1 \\ ^-1 & 3 \\ 7 & 1 \\ 1 & 0 \\ ^-1 & 2 \end{pmatrix}$.

────── 7-6   3 × 3 Games

In a 3 × 3 game, as might be expected from previous experience, the players should first examine the game matrix for a saddle point. If one is found, the game strategy is determined. If no saddle point exists, a check of the matrix for dominance should be carried out. If a player fails to do either of these and misses either a saddle point or reduction via dominance he will be punished for his error, since the procedure about to be developed will not work when one of the preceding techniques succeeds.

We begin with the game matrix of Figure 7-23. A check for a saddle

Rex

$$\text{Jon} \begin{pmatrix} 2 & 5 & 4 \\ 5 & 2 & 3 \\ 7 & 1 & ^-3 \end{pmatrix}$$

FIGURE 7-23.

point is fruitless, so we examine dominance by row and by column. Again no row or column dominance is evident.

To establish the best mixed strategy for the game we follow the procedure below. We begin with Rex. First, from the game matrix of Figure 7-24,

Rex

$$\text{Jon} \begin{pmatrix} 2 & 5 & 4 \\ 5 & 2 & 3 \\ 7 & 1 & ^-3 \end{pmatrix}$$

FIGURE 7-24.

we obtain the difference matrix whose elements are found by subtracting each row from the preceding row. We obtain

$$\begin{pmatrix} -3 & 3 & 1 \\ -2 & 1 & 6 \end{pmatrix}.$$

We now wish to determine Rex's optimum strategy

$$\begin{pmatrix} q_1 \\ q_2 \\ q_3 \end{pmatrix},$$

where

$$q_1 = \frac{a}{a+b+c}; \quad q_2 = \frac{b}{a+b+c}; \quad \text{and} \quad q_3 = \frac{c}{a+b+c}.$$

To compute $a$ in the expression for $q_1$, the probability that Rex should play column 1 in his optimum strategy, strike out column 1 in the difference matrix

$$\begin{pmatrix} -3 & 3 & 1 \\ -2 & 1 & 6 \end{pmatrix}$$

and find the absolute value of the difference between the product of the diagonal elements

$$\begin{pmatrix} -3 & 3 & 1 \\ -2 & 1 & 6 \end{pmatrix}$$

This is the value of $a$:

$$a = |3 \cdot 6 - 1 \cdot 1| = |17| = 17.$$

To find the values of $b$ and $c$ in the expressions for $q_2$ and $q_3$, strike out columns 2 and 3, respectively, in the difference matrix. Then find the absolute value of the difference between the products of the diagonal elements as before. We have for $b$:

$$\begin{pmatrix} -3 & 3 & 1 \\ -2 & 1 & 6 \end{pmatrix} \quad b = |{}^-3 \cdot 6 - 1 \cdot {}^-2| = |{}^-16| = 16.$$

For $c$ we have:

$$\begin{pmatrix} -3 & 3 & 1 \\ -2 & 1 & 6 \end{pmatrix} \quad c = |{}^-3 \cdot 1 - 3 \cdot {}^-2| = |3| = 3.$$

Thus

$$q_1 = \frac{17}{17 + 16 + 3} = \frac{17}{36},$$

$$q_2 = \frac{16}{17 + 16 + 3} = \frac{16}{36},$$

$$q_3 = \frac{3}{17 + 16 + 3} = \frac{3}{36}.$$

Rex's optimum strategy is

$$\begin{pmatrix} \dfrac{17}{36} \\[2mm] \dfrac{16}{36} \\[2mm] \dfrac{3}{36} \end{pmatrix}.$$

We can find similarly Jon's optimum strategy

$$(p_1 \; p_2 \; p_3),$$

where

$$p_1 = \frac{d}{d + e + f}; \; p_2 = \frac{e}{d + e + f}; \quad \text{and} \quad p_3 = \frac{f}{d + e + f}.$$

We start with the original game matrix (Figure 7-25). We find the difference

$$\text{Rex}$$
$$\text{Jon} \begin{pmatrix} 2 & 5 & 4 \\ 5 & 2 & 3 \\ 7 & 1 & ^-3 \end{pmatrix}.$$

Figure 7-25.

matrix by subtracting each column from the preceding one. This difference matrix is

$$\begin{pmatrix} ^-3 & 1 \\ 3 & ^-1 \\ 6 & 4 \end{pmatrix}.$$

To find the value of $d$ in the expression for $p_1$, the probability that Jon should play row 1 in his optimum strategy, cross out the first row in the difference matrix and find the absolute value of the difference between the products of the diagonal elements as before:

$$\begin{pmatrix} {}^-3 & 1 \\ 3 & {}^-1 \\ 6 & 4 \end{pmatrix}.$$

We have

$$d = |3 \cdot 4 - {}^-1 \cdot 6| = |18| = 18.$$

To compute the values of e and f, strike out rows 2 and 3, respectively, in the difference matrix and find the absolute value of the difference between the products of the diagonal elements as we did previously. For e we have

$$\begin{pmatrix} {}^-3 & 1 \\ 3 & {}^-1 \\ 6 & 4 \end{pmatrix} \quad e = |{}^-3 \cdot 4 - 1 \cdot 6| = |{}^-18| = 18.$$

And for f we have

$$\begin{pmatrix} {}^-3 & 1 \\ 3 & {}^-1 \\ 6 & 4 \end{pmatrix} \quad f = |{}^-3 \cdot {}^-1 - 1 \cdot 3| = 0.$$

Thus,

$$p_1 = \frac{18}{18 + 18 + 0} = \frac{18}{36},$$

$$p_2 = \frac{18}{18 + 18 + 0} = \frac{18}{36},$$

and

$$p_3 = \frac{0}{18 + 18 + 0} = \frac{0}{36} \quad \text{or} \quad 0.$$

Jon's optimum strategy is thus

$$\begin{pmatrix} \frac{18}{36} & \frac{18}{36} & 0 \end{pmatrix}.$$

To check our results, we **begin** by multiplying Rex's optimum strategy

$$\begin{pmatrix} \frac{17}{36} \\ \frac{16}{36} \\ \frac{3}{36} \end{pmatrix}$$

by each row and Jon's optimum strategy

$$\begin{pmatrix} \dfrac{18}{36} & \dfrac{18}{36} & 0 \end{pmatrix}$$

by each column. If we have found the correct optimum strategies, all products will be identical, and therefore equal the value of the game.

We have for Rex, if Jon plays rows 1, 2, and 3 respectively,

$$\text{Row 1:} \quad (2 \quad 5 \quad 4) \begin{pmatrix} \dfrac{17}{36} \\ \dfrac{16}{36} \\ \dfrac{3}{36} \end{pmatrix} = \dfrac{34 + 80 + 12}{36} = \dfrac{126}{36}.$$

$$\text{Row 2:} \quad (5 \quad 2 \quad 3) \begin{pmatrix} \dfrac{17}{36} \\ \dfrac{16}{36} \\ \dfrac{3}{36} \end{pmatrix} = \dfrac{85 + 32 + 9}{36} = \dfrac{126}{36}.$$

$$\text{Row 3:} \quad (7 \quad 1 \quad {}^-3) \begin{pmatrix} \dfrac{17}{36} \\ \dfrac{16}{36} \\ \dfrac{3}{36} \end{pmatrix} = \dfrac{119 + 16 + {}^-9}{36} = \dfrac{126}{36}.$$

The game value for Rex is $\frac{126}{36}$ or $\frac{7}{2}$.

Similarly we have for Jon, if Rex plays columns 1, 2, and 3 respectively,

$$\text{Column 1:} \quad \begin{pmatrix} \dfrac{18}{36} & \dfrac{18}{36} & 0 \end{pmatrix} \begin{pmatrix} 2 \\ 5 \\ 7 \end{pmatrix} = \dfrac{36 + 90}{36} = \dfrac{126}{36}.$$

$$\text{Column 2:} \quad \begin{pmatrix} \dfrac{18}{36} & \dfrac{18}{36} & 0 \end{pmatrix} \begin{pmatrix} 5 \\ 2 \\ 1 \end{pmatrix} = \dfrac{90 + 36}{36} = \dfrac{126}{36}.$$

$$\text{Column 3: } \begin{pmatrix} \dfrac{18}{36} & \dfrac{18}{36} & 0 \end{pmatrix} \begin{pmatrix} 4 \\ 3 \\ -3 \end{pmatrix} = \frac{72 + 54}{36} = \frac{126}{36}.$$

The game value for Jon is also $\frac{126}{36}$ or $\frac{7}{2}$. We have thus determined the optimal mixed strategies for each player. Since the value of the game is positive, the game is biased in favor of Jon.

The reader should be cautioned that this method of solving a $3 \times 3$ game works if and only if the above row and column checks result in identical answers. When the saddle point, dominated row or column, or difference matrix methods do not check there are other procedures that can be used. (See J. D. Williams' *The Compleat Strategyst* for a useful technique.) You can also use the simplex method from linear programming. In the next section you will see how to set up linear programs for a $3 \times 3$ game. From a practical point of view, it is best to go to a computer for the computation. Certainly you will want computer assistance for any game matrix exceeding $3 \times 3$.

## ———— *7–7   General Solution to 3 × 3 Games

Now we explore the solution to a general $3 \times 3$ game. (It can be shown that every $3 \times 3$ game has a solution.) Usually in practice you would not try to solve such a problem yourself. You would proceed to the computer center and apply one of the programs already available for such problems. Most computer centers are set up to handle such problems on a routine basis.

We begin by setting up the game matrix

$$\text{Rex}$$
$$\text{Jon} \begin{pmatrix} a_{11} & a_{12} & a_{13} \\ a_{21} & a_{22} & a_{23} \\ a_{31} & a_{32} & a_{33} \end{pmatrix}.$$

We assume $a_{ij} > 0$, otherwise we can add an arbitrary $k$ to each $a_{ij}$ until $\dot{a}_{ij} > 0$ for every $i, j$. (Adding the *same* constant to every entry will not alter the strategic character of the game.)

Now suppose Rex has a mixed strategy described by the vector

$$\begin{pmatrix} q_1 \\ q_2 \\ q_3 \end{pmatrix},$$

and suppose $V$ is the game value. We have

$$a_{11}q_1 + a_{12}q_2 + a_{13}q_3 \le V, \tag{1}$$

$$a_{21}q_1 + a_{22}q_2 + a_{23}q_3 \le V, \tag{2}$$

$$a_{31}q_1 + a_{32}q_2 + a_{33}q_3 \le V. \tag{3}$$

(Remember the reason for the $\leq$ from Section 7-5.) Dividing both sides of (1) by $V$ we obtain

$$\frac{a_{11}q_1}{V} + \frac{a_{12}q_2}{V} + \frac{a_{13}q_3}{V} \leq 1,$$

and, similarly

$$\frac{a_{21}q_1}{V} + \frac{a_{22}q_2}{V} + \frac{a_{23}q_3}{V} \leq 1,$$

$$\frac{a_{31}q_1}{V} + \frac{a_{32}q_2}{V} + \frac{a_{33}q_3}{V} \leq 1.$$

Let

$$x_1 = \frac{q_1}{V}, \ x_2 = \frac{q_2}{V}, \ x_3 = \frac{q_3}{V}.$$

Note that $a_{ij} > 0$ implies $V > 0$, hence each $x_i$ is nonnegative. Also notice that

$$x_1 + x_2 + x_3 = \frac{1}{V},$$

since

$$q_1 + q_2 + q_3 = 1.$$

Since $V$ is the amount Rex pays to Jon, Rex will want to minimize $V$ (or equivalently maximize $1/V$). We can thus find a solution to our game as a solution of the following linear programming problem:

Find $x_1 \geq 0$, $x_2 \geq 0$, $x_3 \geq 0$ such that

$$a_{11}x_1 + a_{12}x_2 + a_{13}x_3 \leq 1,$$
$$a_{21}x_1 + a_{22}x_2 + a_{23}x_3 \leq 1,$$
$$a_{31}x_1 + a_{32}x_2 + a_{33}x_3 \leq 1,$$

and $x_1 + x_2 + x_3$ is a maximum.

It is possible to obtain a solution by the simplex method you saw in Section 6-5.

A similar linear programming problem can be set up for Jon. The value of $V$ for Jon's program, however, must turn out to be the same as that for Rex's.

## EXERCISES

*Find the optimal strategies and game values for each of the following games. Use any method you wish.*

1. 
$$\text{Jon} \begin{pmatrix} 1 & 3 \\ 0 & 2 \\ {}^-1 & 0 \end{pmatrix}. \quad \text{Rex}$$

2. 
$$\text{Jon} \begin{pmatrix} {}^-2 & 5 & 0 \\ 2 & {}^-3 & {}^-1 \end{pmatrix}. \quad \text{Rex}$$

3. 
$$\text{Jon} \begin{pmatrix} 4 & 8 & 4 \\ 0 & 2 & 6 \\ 10 & 3 & 3 \end{pmatrix}. \quad \text{Rex}$$

Rex

4. Jon $\begin{pmatrix} 3 & 1 & ^-2 \\ 1 & 5 & 2 \\ ^-1 & 2 & 8 \end{pmatrix}$.

Rex

5. Jon $\begin{pmatrix} 8 & 3 & 0 \\ 2 & 6 & 2 \\ ^-2 & ^-1 & ^-1 \end{pmatrix}$.

6. Jon wants a puppy and is trying to argue his inflexible father into getting him the dog. Being blessed with the wits of a youngster he cons his father into the following game.

   Jon and his father are each to choose a number between 1 and 3 inclusive and independently of each other. If they select the same number, father tabulates that value for himself. If they choose different numbers, Jon tabulates his own number for himself. After 10 plays the high scorer gets his way with reference to the puppy.

   a. Construct the game matrix.
   b. Calculate optimal strategies and game value.
   c. What do you predict?

7. Rex and Jon like to play a Chinese game consisting of three items—worm, man, chicken. They play by shaking their hand and throwing out 1 or 2 or 3 fingers. 1 finger is worm, 2 man, and 3 chicken. A tie is a draw. Now worms eat man, so in the case of 1–2, 1 wins; man eats chicken, so in the case of 2–3, 2 wins; finally chickens eat worms so a 3–1 allows 3 to win.

   What are the best strategies for Rex and Jon?

# APPENDIX I: $\Sigma$ NOTATION

This appendix is intended to give the student an introduction to $\Sigma$ notation and its uses in computation. We begin by listing a variety of statements of equality. Each statement should be read in detail. *Every deposit of ink has meaning.*

$$\sum_{i=1}^{3} = x_1 + x_2 + x_3 .$$

The symbol '$\Sigma$' denotes a sum. The index $i$ denotes the subscript of the first term of the sum and the numeral at the top of the $\Sigma$ denotes the subscript of the final term of the sum. All counting numbers between the two are also used as subscripts as indicated. Additional examples are:

$$\sum_{i=1}^{7} x_i = x_1 + x_2 + x_3 + x_4 + x_5 + x_6 + x_7 .$$

$$\sum_{i=1}^{n} x_i = x_1 + x_2 + x_3 + \cdots + x_n .$$

$$\sum_{i=5}^{9} x_i = x_5 + x_6 + x_7 + x_8 + x_9 .$$

$$\sum_{i=1}^{3} x_i + \sum_{i=4}^{7} x_i = (x_1 + x_2 + x_3) + (x_4 + x_5 + x_6 + x_7)$$

$$= x_1 + x_2 + x_3 + x_4 + x_5 + x_6 + x_7$$

$$= \sum_{i=1}^{7} x_i .$$

$$\sum_{i=1}^{3} (x_i + y_i) = (x_1 + y_1) + (x_2 + y_2) + (x_3 + y_3)$$

$$= (x_1 + x_2 + x_3) + (y_1 + y_2 + y_3)$$

$$= \sum_{i=1}^{3} x_i + \sum_{i=1}^{3} y_i .$$

$$\sum_{i=1}^{3} i^r = 1^r + 2^r + 3^r .$$

$$\sum_{i=1}^{3} 5x_i = 5x_1 + 5x_2 + 5x_3$$

$$= 5(x_1 + x_2 + x_3)$$

$$= 5 \sum_{i=1}^{3} x_i .$$

$$\sum_{i=1}^{3} 5(x_i + y_i) = 5(x_1 + y_1) + 5(x_2 + y_2) + 5(x_3 + y_3)$$

$$= 5x_1 + 5y_1 + 5x_2 + 5y_2 + 5x_3 + 5y_3$$

$$= 5(x_1 + x_2 + x_3) + 5(y_1 + y_2 + y_3)$$

$$= 5\sum_{i=1}^{3} x_i + 5\sum_{i=1}^{3} y_i$$

$$= 5\sum_{i=1}^{3} (x_i + y_i).$$

$$\sum_{i=1}^{3} 1 = 1 + 1 + 1 = 3 \cdot 1 = 3.$$

Next we will consider more complicated forms for computation. First note that

$$\sum_{i=1}^{3} x_i(x_i + 1) = x_1(x_1 + 1) + x_2(x_2 + 1) + x_3(x_3 + 1)$$

$$= x_1^2 + x_1 + x_2^2 + x_2 + x_3^2 + x_3$$

$$= (x_1^2 + x_2^2 + x_3^2) + (x_1 + x_2 + x_3)$$

$$= \sum_{i=1}^{3} x_i^2 + \sum_{i=1}^{3} x_i.$$

Similarly we see that

$$\sum_{i=1}^{3} (x_i - 1)(x_i + 1) = (x_1 - 1)(x_1 + 1) + (x_2 - 1)(x_2 + 1) + (x_3 - 1)(x_3 + 1)$$

$$= (x_1^2 - 1) + (x_2^2 - 1) + (x_3^2 - 1)$$

$$= (x_1^2 + x_2^2 + x_3^2) - 3$$

$$= \sum_{i=1}^{3} x_i^2 - 3$$

$$= \sum_{i=1}^{3} x_i^2 - \sum_{i=1}^{3} 1.$$

(*Note:* For any constant $k$, we define $\sum_{i=1}^{n} k$ to be the sum of $n$ $k$'s, $k + k + k + \cdots k = n \cdot k$.)

Now we extend the notation index to the general case, the sum of $n$ terms.

$$\sum_{i=1}^{n} x_i = x_1 + x_2 + x_3 + \cdots + x_n.$$

$$\sum_{i=1}^{n} x_i^2 = x_1^2 + x_2^2 + x_3^2 + \cdots + x_n^2.$$

$$\sum_{i=1}^{n}(x_i + y_i)^2 = (x_1 + y_1)^2 + (x_2 + y_2)^2 + \cdots + (x_n + y_n)^2.$$

$$= (x_1^2 + 2x_1y_1 + y_1^2) + (x_2^2 + 2x_2y_2 + y_2^2) + \cdots$$

$$+ (x_n^2 + 2x_ny_n + y_n^2)$$

$$= (x_1^2 + x_2^2 + \cdots + x_n^2) + (2x_1y_1 + \cdots + 2x_ny_n)$$

$$+ (y_1^2 + \cdots + y_n^2)$$

$$= \sum_{i=1}^{n} x_i^2 + 2\sum_{i=1}^{n} x_i y_i + \sum_{i=1}^{n} y_i^2.$$

$$\sum_{i=1}^{n} ax_i = a\sum_{i=1}^{n} x_i = ax_1 + ax_2 + \cdots + ax_n.$$

$$\sum_{i=1}^{n} x_i(x_i - 1) = x_1^2 - x_1 + x_2^2 - x_2 + \cdots + x_n^2 - x_n$$

$$= (x_1^2 + x_2^2 + \cdots + x_n^2) - (x_1 + x_2 + \cdots + x_n)$$

$$= \sum_{i=1}^{n} x_i^2 - \sum_{i=1}^{n} x_i.$$

## EXERCISES

*Write out term by term each of the sums in Exercises 1 through 7.*

1. $\sum_{i=1}^{4} x_i.$

2. $\sum_{i=1}^{4} 3x_i.$

3. $\sum_{i=1}^{4} (x_i - y_i).$

4. $7\sum_{i=1}^{4} x_i.$

5. $3\sum_{i=1}^{4} x_i.$

6. $3\sum_{i=1}^{4} (x_i - y_i).$

7. $\sum_{i=1}^{3} 5.$

*Write each of the expressions in Exercises 8 through 11 in $\sum$ notation.*

8. $x_1 + x_2 + x_3 + x_4.$

9. $ax_1 + ax_2 + ax_3$ (two ways).

10. $(x_1 + y_1) + (x_2 + y_2) + (x_3 + y_3) + (x_4 + y_4)$ (two ways).

11. $(x_1^2 + x_2^2 + x_3^2) - (x_1 + x_2 + x_3)$ (two ways).

*Write out term by term each of the sums in Exercises 12 through 15.*

12. $\sum_{i=1}^{3} (x_i + 1)^2.$

13. $\sum_{i=1}^{3} x_i^2(x_i - 1).$

14. $\sum_{i=1}^{3} (mx_i + ny_i).$

15. $\sum_{i=1}^{7} k.$

*Write each of the expressions in Exercises 16 through 19 in $\sum$ notation.*

16.  $2 + 4 + 6 + 8 + \cdots + 2 \cdot n.$        17.  $1 + 4 + 16 + 25 + \cdots + n^2.$

18.  $x^1 + x^2 + x^3 + \cdots + x^n.$         19.  $x_1^2 + x_2^2 + x_3^2 + \cdots + x_n^2.$

*Write out term by term each of the sums in Exercises 20 through 23.*

20.  $\displaystyle\sum_{i=1}^{5} \frac{1}{x^i}.$        21.  $\displaystyle\sum_{i=1}^{3} \frac{1}{x_i^2}.$

22.  $\displaystyle\sum_{i=1}^{4} \frac{1}{i}.$         23.  $\displaystyle\sum_{i=1}^{6} \frac{1}{3^i}.$

*Write each of the expressions in Exercises 24 through 26 in $\sum$ notation.*

24.  $\dfrac{x_1 + x_2 + x_3 + x_4 + x_5 + x_6 + x_7}{7}.$

25.  $\dfrac{x}{2} + \dfrac{x^2}{4} + \dfrac{x^3}{8} + \dfrac{x^4}{16}.$

26.  $\dfrac{x_1}{1+2} + \dfrac{x_2}{2+3} + \dfrac{x_3}{3+4} + \dfrac{x_4}{4+5} + \dfrac{x_5}{5+6}.$

| $n$ | $n^2$ | $\sqrt{n}$ | $n^3$ | $\sqrt[3]{n}$ | $n$ | $n^2$ | $\sqrt{n}$ | $n^3$ | $\sqrt[3]{n}$ |
|---|---|---|---|---|---|---|---|---|---|
| 1 | 1 | 1.000 | 1 | 1.000 | 51 | 2,601 | 7.141 | 132,651 | 3.708 |
| 2 | 4 | 1.414 | 8 | 1.260 | 52 | 2,704 | 7.211 | 140,608 | 3.733 |
| 3 | 9 | 1.732 | 27 | 1.442 | 53 | 2,809 | 7.280 | 148,877 | 3.756 |
| 4 | 16 | 2.000 | 64 | 1.587 | 54 | 2,916 | 7.348 | 157,464 | 3.780 |
| 5 | 25 | 2.236 | 125 | 1.710 | 55 | 3,025 | 7.416 | 166,375 | 3.803 |
| 6 | 36 | 2.449 | 216 | 1.817 | 56 | 3,136 | 7.483 | 175,616 | 3.826 |
| 7 | 49 | 2.646 | 343 | 1.913 | 57 | 3,249 | 7.550 | 185,193 | 3.849 |
| 8 | 64 | 2.828 | 512 | 2.000 | 58 | 3,364 | 7.616 | 195,112 | 3.871 |
| 9 | 81 | 3.000 | 729 | 2.080 | 59 | 3,481 | 7.681 | 205,379 | 3.893 |
| 10 | 100 | 3.162 | 1,000 | 2.154 | 60 | 3,600 | 7.746 | 216,000 | 3.915 |
| 11 | 121 | 3.317 | 1,331 | 2.224 | 61 | 3,721 | 7.810 | 226,981 | 3.936 |
| 12 | 144 | 3.464 | 1,728 | 2.289 | 62 | 3,844 | 7.874 | 238,328 | 3.958 |
| 13 | 169 | 3.606 | 2,197 | 2.351 | 63 | 3,969 | 7.937 | 250,047 | 3.979 |
| 14 | 196 | 3.742 | 2,744 | 2.410 | 64 | 4,096 | 8.000 | 262,144 | 4.000 |
| 15 | 225 | 3.873 | 3,375 | 2.466 | 65 | 4,225 | 8.062 | 274,625 | 4.021 |
| 16 | 256 | 4.000 | 4,096 | 2.520 | 66 | 4,356 | 8.124 | 287,496 | 4.041 |
| 17 | 289 | 4.123 | 4,913 | 2.571 | 67 | 4,489 | 8.185 | 300,763 | 4.062 |
| 18 | 324 | 4.243 | 5,832 | 2.621 | 68 | 4,624 | 8.246 | 314,432 | 4.082 |
| 19 | 361 | 4.359 | 6,859 | 2.668 | 69 | 4,761 | 8.307 | 328,509 | 4.102 |
| 20 | 400 | 4.472 | 8,000 | 2.714 | 70 | 4,900 | 8.367 | 343,000 | 4.121 |
| 21 | 441 | 4.583 | 9,261 | 2.759 | 71 | 5,041 | 8.426 | 357,911 | 4.141 |
| 22 | 484 | 4.690 | 10,648 | 2.802 | 72 | 5,184 | 8.485 | 373,248 | 4.160 |
| 23 | 529 | 4.796 | 12,167 | 2.844 | 73 | 5,329 | 8.544 | 389,017 | 4.179 |
| 24 | 576 | 4.899 | 13,824 | 2.884 | 74 | 5,476 | 8.602 | 405,224 | 4.198 |
| 25 | 625 | 5.000 | 15,625 | 2.924 | 75 | 5,625 | 8.660 | 421,875 | 4.217 |
| 26 | 676 | 5.099 | 17,576 | 2.962 | 76 | 5,776 | 8.718 | 438,976 | 4.236 |
| 27 | 729 | 5.196 | 19,683 | 3.000 | 77 | 5,929 | 8.775 | 456,533 | 4.254 |
| 28 | 784 | 5.292 | 21,952 | 3.037 | 78 | 6,084 | 8.832 | 474,552 | 4.273 |
| 29 | 841 | 5.385 | 24,389 | 3.072 | 79 | 6,241 | 8.888 | 493,039 | 4.291 |
| 30 | 900 | 5.477 | 27,000 | 3.107 | 80 | 6,400 | 8.944 | 512,000 | 4.309 |
| 31 | 961 | 5.568 | 29,791 | 3.141 | 81 | 6,561 | 9.000 | 531,441 | 4.327 |
| 32 | 1,024 | 5.657 | 32,768 | 3.175 | 82 | 6,724 | 9.055 | 551,368 | 4.344 |
| 33 | 1,089 | 5.745 | 35,937 | 3.208 | 83 | 6,889 | 9.110 | 571,787 | 4.362 |
| 34 | 1,156 | 5.831 | 39,304 | 3.240 | 84 | 7,056 | 9.165 | 592,704 | 4.380 |
| 35 | 1,225 | 5.916 | 42,875 | 3.271 | 85 | 7,225 | 9.220 | 614,125 | 4.397 |
| 36 | 1,296 | 6.000 | 46,656 | 3.302 | 86 | 7,396 | 9.274 | 636,056 | 4.414 |
| 37 | 1,369 | 6.083 | 50,653 | 3.332 | 87 | 7,569 | 9.327 | 658,503 | 4.431 |
| 38 | 1,444 | 6.164 | 54,872 | 3.362 | 88 | 7,744 | 9.381 | 681,472 | 4.448 |
| 39 | 1,521 | 6.245 | 59,319 | 3.391 | 89 | 7,921 | 9.434 | 704,969 | 4.465 |
| 40 | 1,600 | 6.325 | 64,000 | 3.420 | 90 | 8,100 | 9.487 | 729,000 | 4.481 |
| 41 | 1,681 | 6.403 | 68,921 | 3.448 | 91 | 8,281 | 9.539 | 753,571 | 4.498 |
| 42 | 1,764 | 6.481 | 74,088 | 3.476 | 92 | 8,464 | 9.592 | 778,688 | 4.514 |
| 43 | 1,849 | 6.557 | 79,507 | 3.503 | 93 | 8,649 | 9.644 | 804,357 | 4.531 |
| 44 | 1,936 | 6.633 | 85,184 | 3.530 | 94 | 8,836 | 9.695 | 830,584 | 4.547 |
| 45 | 2,025 | 6.708 | 91,125 | 3.557 | 95 | 9,025 | 9.747 | 857,375 | 4.563 |
| 46 | 2,116 | 6.782 | 97,336 | 3.583 | 96 | 9,216 | 9.798 | 884,736 | 4.579 |
| 47 | 2,209 | 6.856 | 103,823 | 3.609 | 97 | 9,409 | 9.849 | 912,673 | 4.595 |
| 48 | 2,304 | 6.928 | 110,592 | 3.634 | 98 | 9,604 | 9.899 | 941,192 | 4.610 |
| 49 | 2,401 | 7.000 | 117,649 | 3.659 | 99 | 9,801 | 9.950 | 970,299 | 4.626 |
| 50 | 2,500 | 7.071 | 125,000 | 3.684 | 100 | 10,000 | 10.000 | 1,000,000 | 4.642 |

# APPENDIX III: TERMS OF BINOMIAL DISTRIBUTION

Each three-digit entry in the table should be read with a decimal preceding it. For entries 0+, the probability is less than 0.0005, but greater than 0.

$$\binom{n}{x} p^x q^{n-x}$$

| $n$ | $x$ | .01 | .05 | .10 | .20 | .30 | .40 | .50 | .60 | .70 | .80 | .90 | .95 | .99 | $x$ |
|---|---|---|---|---|---|---|---|---|---|---|---|---|---|---|---|
| 2 | 0 | 980 | 902 | 810 | 640 | 490 | 360 | 250 | 160 | 090 | 040 | 010 | 002 | 0+ | 0 |
|   | 1 | 020 | 095 | 180 | 320 | 420 | 480 | 500 | 480 | 420 | 320 | 180 | 095 | 020 | 1 |
|   | 2 | 0+ | 002 | 010 | 040 | 090 | 160 | 250 | 360 | 490 | 640 | 810 | 902 | 980 | 2 |
| 3 | 0 | 970 | 857 | 729 | 512 | 343 | 216 | 125 | 064 | 027 | 008 | 001 | 0+ | 0+ | 0 |
|   | 1 | 029 | 135 | 243 | 384 | 441 | 432 | 375 | 288 | 189 | 096 | 027 | 007 | 0+ | 1 |
|   | 2 | 0+ | 007 | 027 | 096 | 189 | 288 | 375 | 432 | 441 | 384 | 243 | 135 | 029 | 2 |
|   | 3 | 0+ | 0+ | 001 | 008 | 027 | 064 | 125 | 216 | 343 | 512 | 729 | 857 | 970 | 3 |
| 4 | 0 | 961 | 815 | 656 | 410 | 240 | 130 | 062 | 026 | 008 | 002 | 0+ | 0+ | 0+ | 0 |
|   | 1 | 039 | 171 | 292 | 410 | 412 | 346 | 250 | 154 | 076 | 026 | 004 | 0+ | 0+ | 1 |
|   | 2 | 001 | 014 | 049 | 154 | 265 | 346 | 375 | 346 | 265 | 154 | 049 | 014 | 001 | 2 |
|   | 3 | 0+ | 0+ | 004 | 026 | 076 | 154 | 250 | 346 | 412 | 410 | 292 | 171 | 039 | 3 |
|   | 4 | 0+ | 0+ | 0+ | 002 | 008 | 026 | 062 | 130 | 240 | 410 | 656 | 815 | 961 | 4 |
| 5 | 0 | 951 | 774 | 590 | 328 | 168 | 078 | 031 | 010 | 002 | 0+ | 0+ | 0+ | 0+ | 0 |
|   | 1 | 048 | 204 | 328 | 410 | 360 | 259 | 156 | 077 | 028 | 006 | 0+ | 0+ | 0+ | 1 |
|   | 2 | 001 | 021 | 073 | 205 | 309 | 346 | 312 | 230 | 132 | 051 | 008 | 001 | 0+ | 2 |
|   | 3 | 0+ | 001 | 008 | 051 | 132 | 230 | 312 | 346 | 309 | 205 | 073 | 021 | 001 | 3 |
|   | 4 | 0+ | 0+ | 0+ | 006 | 028 | 077 | 156 | 259 | 360 | 410 | 328 | 204 | 048 | 4 |
|   | 5 | 0+ | 0+ | 0+ | 0+ | 002 | 010 | 031 | 078 | 168 | 328 | 590 | 774 | 951 | 5 |
| 6 | 0 | 941 | 735 | 531 | 262 | 118 | 047 | 016 | 004 | 001 | 0+ | 0+ | 0+ | 0+ | 0 |
|   | 1 | 057 | 232 | 354 | 393 | 303 | 187 | 094 | 037 | 010 | 002 | 0+ | 0+ | 0+ | 1 |
|   | 2 | 001 | 031 | 098 | 246 | 324 | 311 | 234 | 138 | 060 | 015 | 001 | 0+ | 0+ | 2 |
|   | 3 | 0+ | 002 | 015 | 082 | 185 | 276 | 312 | 276 | 185 | 082 | 015 | 002 | 0+ | 3 |
|   | 4 | 0+ | 0+ | 001 | 015 | 060 | 138 | 234 | 311 | 324 | 246 | 098 | 031 | 001 | 4 |
|   | 5 | 0+ | 0+ | 0+ | 002 | 010 | 037 | 094 | 187 | 303 | 393 | 354 | 232 | 057 | 5 |
|   | 6 | 0+ | 0+ | 0+ | 0+ | 001 | 004 | 016 | 047 | 118 | 262 | 531 | 735 | 941 | 6 |
| 7 | 0 | 932 | 698 | 478 | 210 | 082 | 028 | 008 | 002 | 0+ | 0+ | 0+ | 0+ | 0+ | 0 |
|   | 1 | 066 | 257 | 372 | 267 | 247 | 131 | 055 | 017 | 004 | 0+ | 0+ | 0+ | 0+ | 1 |
|   | 2 | 002 | 041 | 124 | 275 | 318 | 261 | 164 | 077 | 025 | 004 | 0+ | 0+ | 0+ | 2 |
|   | 3 | 0+ | 004 | 023 | 115 | 227 | 290 | 273 | 194 | 097 | 029 | 003 | 0+ | 0+ | 3 |
|   | 4 | 0+ | 0+ | 003 | 029 | 097 | 194 | 273 | 290 | 227 | 115 | 023 | 004 | 0+ | 4 |
|   | 5 | 0+ | 0+ | 0+ | 004 | 025 | 077 | 164 | 261 | 318 | 275 | 124 | 041 | 002 | 5 |
|   | 6 | 0+ | 0+ | 0+ | 0+ | 004 | 017 | 055 | 131 | 247 | 367 | 372 | 257 | 066 | 6 |
|   | 7 | 0+ | 0+ | 0+ | 0+ | 0+ | 002 | 008 | 028 | 082 | 210 | 478 | 698 | 932 | 7 |

$$\binom{n}{x} p^x q^{n-x}$$

| n | x | .01 | .05 | .10 | .20 | .30 | .40 | p .50 | .60 | .70 | .80 | .90 | .95 | .99 | x |
|---|---|-----|-----|-----|-----|-----|-----|-----|-----|-----|-----|-----|-----|-----|---|
| 8 | 0 | 923 | 663 | 430 | 168 | 058 | 017 | 004 | 001 | 0+ | 0+ | 0+ | 0+ | 0+ | 0 |
|   | 1 | 075 | 279 | 383 | 336 | 198 | 090 | 031 | 008 | 001 | 0+ | 0+ | 0+ | 0+ | 1 |
|   | 2 | 003 | 051 | 149 | 294 | 296 | 209 | 109 | 041 | 010 | 001 | 0+ | 0+ | 0+ | 2 |
|   | 3 | 0+ | 005 | 033 | 147 | 254 | 279 | 219 | 124 | 047 | 009 | 0+ | 0+ | 0+ | 3 |
|   | 4 | 0+ | 0+ | 005 | 046 | 136 | 232 | 273 | 232 | 136 | 046 | 005 | 0+ | 0+ | 4 |
|   | 5 | 0+ | 0+ | 0+ | 009 | 047 | 124 | 219 | 279 | 254 | 147 | 033 | 005 | 0+ | 5 |
|   | 6 | 0+ | 0+ | 0+ | 001 | 010 | 041 | 109 | 209 | 296 | 294 | 149 | 051 | 003 | 6 |
|   | 7 | 0+ | 0+ | 0+ | 0+ | 001 | 008 | 031 | 090 | 198 | 336 | 383 | 279 | 075 | 7 |
|   | 8 | 0+ | 0+ | 0+ | 0+ | 0+ | 001 | 004 | 017 | 058 | 168 | 430 | 663 | 923 | 8 |
| 9 | 0 | 914 | 630 | 387 | 134 | 040 | 010 | 002 | 0+ | 0+ | 0+ | 0+ | 0+ | 0+ | 0 |
|   | 1 | 083 | 299 | 387 | 302 | 156 | 060 | 018 | 004 | 0+ | 0+ | 0+ | 0+ | 0+ | 1 |
|   | 2 | 003 | 063 | 172 | 302 | 267 | 161 | 070 | 021 | 004 | 0+ | 0+ | 0+ | 0+ | 2 |
|   | 3 | 0+ | 008 | 045 | 176 | 267 | 251 | 164 | 074 | 021 | 003 | 0+ | 0+ | 0+ | 3 |
|   | 4 | 0+ | 001 | 007 | 066 | 172 | 251 | 246 | 167 | 074 | 017 | 001 | 0+ | 0+ | 4 |
|   | 5 | 0+ | 0+ | 001 | 017 | 074 | 167 | 146 | 251 | 172 | 066 | 007 | 001 | 0+ | 5 |
|   | 6 | 0+ | 0+ | 0+ | 003 | 021 | 074 | 164 | 251 | 267 | 176 | 045 | 008 | 0+ | 6 |
|   | 7 | 0+ | 0+ | 0+ | 0+ | 004 | 021 | 070 | 161 | 267 | 302 | 172 | 063 | 003 | 7 |
|   | 8 | 0+ | 0+ | 0+ | 0+ | 0+ | 004 | 018 | 060 | 156 | 302 | 387 | 299 | 083 | 8 |
|   | 9 | 0+ | 0+ | 0+ | 0+ | 0+ | 0+ | 002 | 010 | 040 | 134 | 387 | 630 | 914 | 9 |
| 10 | 0 | 904 | 599 | 349 | 107 | 028 | 006 | 001 | 0+ | 0+ | 0+ | 0+ | 0+ | 0+ | 0 |
|   | 1 | 091 | 315 | 387 | 268 | 121 | 040 | 010 | 002 | 0+ | 0+ | 0+ | 0+ | 0+ | 1 |
|   | 2 | 004 | 075 | 194 | 302 | 233 | 121 | 044 | 011 | 001 | 0+ | 0+ | 0+ | 0+ | 2 |
|   | 3 | 0+ | 010 | 057 | 201 | 267 | 215 | 117 | 042 | 009 | 001 | 0+ | 0+ | 0+ | 3 |
|   | 4 | 0+ | 001 | 011 | 088 | 200 | 251 | 205 | 111 | 037 | 006 | 0+ | 0+ | 0+ | 4 |
|   | 5 | 0+ | 0+ | 001 | 026 | 103 | 201 | 246 | 201 | 103 | 026 | 001 | 0+ | 0+ | 5 |
|   | 6 | 0+ | 0+ | 0+ | 006 | 037 | 111 | 205 | 251 | 200 | 088 | 011 | 001 | 0+ | 6 |
|   | 7 | 0+ | 0+ | 0+ | 001 | 009 | 042 | 117 | 215 | 267 | 201 | 057 | 010 | 0+ | 7 |
|   | 8 | 0+ | 0+ | 0+ | 0+ | 001 | 011 | 044 | 121 | 233 | 302 | 194 | 075 | 004 | 8 |
|   | 9 | 0+ | 0+ | 0+ | 0+ | 0+ | 002 | 010 | 040 | 121 | 268 | 387 | 315 | 091 | 9 |
|   | 10 | 0+ | 0+ | 0+ | 0+ | 0+ | 0+ | 001 | 006 | 028 | 107 | 349 | 599 | 904 | 10 |
| 11 | 0 | 895 | 569 | 314 | 086 | 020 | 004 | 0+ | 0+ | 0+ | 0+ | 0+ | 0+ | 0+ | 0 |
|   | 1 | 099 | 329 | 384 | 236 | 093 | 027 | 005 | 001 | 0+ | 0+ | 0+ | 0+ | 0+ | 1 |
|   | 2 | 005 | 087 | 213 | 295 | 200 | 089 | 027 | 005 | 001 | 0+ | 0+ | 0+ | 0+ | 2 |
|   | 3 | 0+ | 014 | 071 | 221 | 257 | 177 | 081 | 023 | 004 | 0+ | 0+ | 0+ | 0+ | 3 |
|   | 4 | 0+ | 001 | 016 | 111 | 220 | 236 | 161 | 070 | 017 | 002 | 0+ | 0+ | 0+ | 4 |
|   | 5 | 0+ | 0+ | 002 | 039 | 132 | 221 | 226 | 147 | 057 | 010 | 0+ | 0+ | 0+ | 5 |
|   | 6 | 0+ | 0+ | 0+ | 010 | 057 | 147 | 226 | 221 | 132 | 039 | 002 | 0+ | 0+ | 6 |
|   | 7 | 0+ | 0+ | 0+ | 002 | 017 | 070 | 161 | 236 | 220 | 111 | 016 | 001 | 0+ | 7 |
|   | 8 | 0+ | 0+ | 0+ | 0+ | 004 | 023 | 081 | 177 | 257 | 221 | 071 | 014 | 0+ | 8 |
|   | 9 | 0+ | 0+ | 0+ | 0+ | 001 | 005 | 027 | 089 | 200 | 295 | 213 | 087 | 005 | 9 |

$$\binom{n}{x} p^x q^{n-x}$$

| n | x | .01 | .05 | .10 | .20 | .30 | .40 | p .50 | .60 | .70 | .80 | .90 | .95 | .99 | x |
|---|---|---|---|---|---|---|---|---|---|---|---|---|---|---|---|
| | 10 | 0+ | 0+ | 0+ | 0+ | 0+ | 001 | 005 | 027 | 093 | 236 | 384 | 329 | 099 | 10 |
| | 11 | 0+ | 0+ | 0+ | 0+ | 0+ | 0+ | 0+ | 004 | 020 | 086 | 314 | 569 | 895 | 11 |
| 12 | 0 | 886 | 540 | 282 | 069 | 014 | 002 | 0+ | 0+ | 0+ | 0+ | 0+ | 0+ | 0+ | 0 |
| | 1 | 107 | 341 | 377 | 206 | 071 | 017 | 003 | 0+ | 0+ | 0+ | 0+ | 0+ | 0+ | 1 |
| | 2 | 006 | 099 | 230 | 283 | 168 | 064 | 016 | 002 | 0+ | 0+ | 0+ | 0+ | 0+ | 2 |
| | 3 | 0+ | 017 | 085 | 236 | 240 | 142 | 054 | 012 | 001 | 0+ | 0+ | 0+ | 0+ | 3 |
| | 4 | 0+ | 002 | 021 | 133 | 231 | 213 | 121 | 042 | 008 | 001 | 0+ | 0+ | 0+ | 4 |
| | 5 | 0+ | 0+ | 004 | 053 | 158 | 227 | 193 | 101 | 029 | 003 | 0+ | 0+ | 0+ | 5 |
| | 6 | 0+ | 0+ | 0+ | 016 | 079 | 177 | 226 | 177 | 079 | 016 | 0+ | 0+ | 0+ | 6 |
| | 7 | 0+ | 0+ | 0+ | 003 | 029 | 101 | 193 | 227 | 258 | 053 | 004 | 0+ | 0+ | 7 |
| | 8 | 0+ | 0+ | 0+ | 001 | 008 | 042 | 121 | 213 | 231 | 133 | 021 | 002 | 0+ | 8 |
| | 9 | 0+ | 0+ | 0+ | 0+ | 001 | 012 | 054 | 142 | 240 | 236 | 085 | 017 | 0+ | 9 |
| 12 | 10 | 0+ | 0+ | 0+ | 0+ | 0+ | 002 | 016 | 064 | 168 | 283 | 230 | 099 | 006 | 10 |
| | 11 | 0+ | 0+ | 0+ | 0+ | 0+ | 0+ | 003 | 017 | 071 | 206 | 377 | 341 | 107 | 11 |
| | 12 | 0+ | 0+ | 0+ | 0+ | 0+ | 0+ | 0+ | 002 | 014 | 069 | 282 | 540 | 886 | 12 |
| 13 | 0 | 878 | 513 | 254 | 055 | 010 | 001 | 0+ | 0+ | 0+ | 0+ | 0+ | 0+ | 0+ | 0 |
| | 1 | 115 | 351 | 367 | 179 | 054 | 011 | 002 | 0+ | 0+ | 0+ | 0+ | 0+ | 0+ | 1 |
| | 2 | 007 | 111 | 245 | 268 | 139 | 045 | 010 | 001 | 0+ | 0+ | 0+ | 0+ | 0+ | 2 |
| | 3 | 0+ | 021 | 100 | 246 | 218 | 111 | 035 | 006 | 001 | 0+ | 0+ | 0+ | 0+ | 3 |
| | 4 | 0+ | 003 | 028 | 154 | 234 | 184 | 087 | 024 | 003 | 0+ | 0+ | 0+ | 0+ | 4 |
| | 5 | 0+ | 0+ | 006 | 069 | 180 | 221 | 157 | 066 | 014 | 001 | 0+ | 0+ | 0+ | 5 |
| | 6 | 0+ | 0+ | 001 | 023 | 103 | 197 | 209 | 131 | 044 | 006 | 0+ | 0+ | 0+ | 6 |
| | 7 | 0+ | 0+ | 0+ | 006 | 044 | 131 | 209 | 197 | 103 | 023 | 001 | 0+ | 0+ | 7 |
| | 8 | 0+ | 0+ | 0+ | 001 | 014 | 066 | 157 | 221 | 180 | 069 | 006 | 0+ | 0+ | 8 |
| | 9 | 0+ | 0+ | 0+ | 0+ | 003 | 024 | 087 | 184 | 234 | 154 | 028 | 003 | 0+ | 9 |
| | 10 | 0+ | 0+ | 0+ | 0+ | 001 | 006 | 035 | 111 | 218 | 246 | 100 | 021 | 0+ | 10 |
| | 11 | 0+ | 0+ | 0+ | 0+ | 0+ | 001 | 010 | 045 | 139 | 268 | 245 | 111 | 007 | 11 |
| | 12 | 0+ | 0+ | 0+ | 0+ | 0+ | 0+ | 002 | 011 | 054 | 179 | 367 | 351 | 115 | 12 |
| | 13 | 0+ | 0+ | 0+ | 0+ | 0+ | 0+ | 0+ | 001 | 010 | 055 | 254 | 513 | 878 | 13 |
| 14 | 0 | 869 | 488 | 229 | 044 | 001 | 0+ | 0+ | 0+ | 0+ | 0+ | 0+ | 0+ | 0+ | 0 |
| | 1 | 123 | 359 | 356 | 154 | 041 | 007 | 001 | 0+ | 0+ | 0+ | 0+ | 0+ | 0+ | 1 |
| | 2 | 008 | 123 | 257 | 250 | 113 | 032 | 006 | 001 | 0+ | 0+ | 0+ | 0+ | 0+ | 2 |
| | 3 | 0+ | 026 | 114 | 250 | 194 | 085 | 022 | 003 | 0+ | 0+ | 0+ | 0+ | 0+ | 3 |
| | 4 | 0+ | 004 | 035 | 172 | 229 | 155 | 061 | 014 | 001 | 0+ | 0+ | 0+ | 0+ | 4 |
| | 5 | 0+ | 0+ | 008 | 086 | 196 | 207 | 122 | 041 | 007 | 0+ | 0+ | 0+ | 0+ | 5 |
| | 6 | 0+ | 0+ | 001 | 032 | 126 | 207 | 183 | 092 | 023 | 002 | 0+ | 0+ | 0+ | 6 |
| | 7 | 0+ | 0+ | 0+ | 009 | 062 | 157 | 209 | 157 | 062 | 009 | 0+ | 0+ | 0+ | 7 |
| | 8 | 0+ | 0+ | 0+ | 002 | 023 | 092 | 183 | 207 | 126 | 032 | 001 | 0+ | 0+ | 8 |
| | 9 | 0+ | 0+ | 0+ | 0+ | 007 | 041 | 122 | 207 | 196 | 086 | 008 | 0+ | 0+ | 9 |

$$\binom{n}{x} p^x q^{n-x}$$

| $n$ | $x$ | .01 | .05 | .10 | .20 | .30 | .40 | $p$ .50 | .60 | .70 | .80 | .90 | .95 | .99 | $x$ |
|---|---|---|---|---|---|---|---|---|---|---|---|---|---|---|---|
| | 10 | 0+ | 0+ | 0+ | 0+ | 001 | 014 | 061 | 155 | 229 | 172 | 035 | 004 | 0+ | 10 |
| | 11 | 0+ | 0+ | 0+ | 0+ | 0+ | 003 | 022 | 085 | 194 | 250 | 114 | 026 | 0+ | 11 |
| | 12 | 0+ | 0+ | 0+ | 0+ | 0+ | 001 | 006 | 032 | 113 | 250 | 257 | 123 | 008 | 12 |
| | 13 | 0+ | 0+ | 0+ | 0+ | 0+ | 0+ | 001 | 007 | 041 | 154 | 356 | 329 | 123 | 13 |
| | 14 | 0+ | 0+ | 0+ | 0+ | 0+ | 0+ | 0+ | 001 | 007 | 044 | 229 | 488 | 869 | 14 |
| 15 | 0 | 860 | 463 | 206 | 035 | 005 | 0+ | 0+ | 0+ | 0+ | 0+ | 0+ | 0+ | 0+ | 0 |
| | 1 | 130 | 366 | 343 | 132 | 031 | 005 | 0+ | 0+ | 0+ | 0+ | 0+ | 0+ | 0+ | 1 |
| | 2 | 009 | 135 | 267 | 231 | 092 | 022 | 003 | 0+ | 0+ | 0+ | 0+ | 0+ | 0+ | 2 |
| | 3 | 0+ | 031 | 129 | 250 | 170 | 063 | 014 | 002 | 0+ | 0+ | 0+ | 0+ | 0+ | 3 |
| | 4 | 0+ | 005 | 043 | 188 | 219 | 127 | 042 | 007 | 001 | 0+ | 0+ | 0+ | 0+ | 4 |
| | 5 | 0+ | 001 | 010 | 103 | 206 | 186 | 092 | 024 | 003 | 0+ | 0+ | 0+ | 0+ | 5 |
| | 6 | 0+ | 0+ | 002 | 043 | 147 | 207 | 153 | 061 | 012 | 001 | 0+ | 0+ | 0+ | 6 |
| | 7 | 0+ | 0+ | 0+ | 014 | 081 | 177 | 196 | 118 | 035 | 003 | 0+ | 0+ | 0+ | 7 |
| | 8 | 0+ | 0+ | 0+ | 003 | 035 | 118 | 196 | 177 | 081 | 014 | 0+ | 0+ | 0+ | 8 |
| | 9 | 0+ | 0+ | 0+ | 001 | 012 | 061 | 153 | 207 | 147 | 043 | 002 | 0+ | 0+ | 9 |
| 15 | 10 | 0+ | 0+ | 0+ | 0+ | 003 | 024 | 092 | 186 | 206 | 103 | 010 | 001 | 0+ | 10 |
| | 11 | 0+ | 0+ | 0+ | 0+ | 001 | 007 | 042 | 127 | 219 | 188 | 043 | 005 | 0+ | 11 |
| | 12 | 0+ | 0+ | 0+ | 0+ | 0+ | 002 | 014 | 063 | 170 | 250 | 129 | 031 | 0+ | 12 |
| | 13 | 0+ | 0+ | 0+ | 0+ | 0+ | 0+ | 003 | 022 | 092 | 231 | 267 | 135 | 009 | 13 |
| | 14 | 0+ | 0+ | 0+ | 0+ | 0+ | 0+ | 0+ | 005 | 031 | 132 | 343 | 366 | 130 | 14 |
| | 15 | 0+ | 0+ | 0+ | 0+ | 0+ | 0+ | 0+ | 0+ | 005 | 035 | 206 | 463 | 860 | 15 |
| 16 | 0 | 851 | 440 | 185 | 028 | 003 | 0+ | 0+ | 0+ | 0+ | 0+ | 0+ | 0+ | 0+ | 0 |
| | 1 | 138 | 371 | 329 | 113 | 023 | 003 | 0+ | 0+ | 0+ | 0+ | 0+ | 0+ | 0+ | 1 |
| | 2 | 010 | 146 | 275 | 211 | 073 | 015 | 002 | 0+ | 0+ | 0+ | 0+ | 0+ | 0+ | 2 |
| | 3 | 0+ | 036 | 142 | 246 | 146 | 047 | 009 | 001 | 0+ | 0+ | 0+ | 0+ | 0+ | 3 |
| | 4 | 0+ | 006 | 051 | 200 | 201 | 101 | 028 | 004 | 0+ | 0+ | 0+ | 0+ | 0+ | 4 |
| | 5 | 0+ | 001 | 014 | 120 | 210 | 162 | 067 | 014 | 001 | 0+ | 0+ | 0+ | 0+ | 5 |
| | 6 | 0+ | 0+ | 003 | 055 | 165 | 198 | 122 | 039 | 006 | 0+ | 0+ | 0+ | 0+ | 6 |
| | 7 | 0+ | 0+ | 0+ | 020 | 101 | 189 | 175 | 084 | 119 | 001 | 0+ | 0+ | 0+ | 7 |
| | 8 | 0+ | 0+ | 0+ | 006 | 049 | 142 | 196 | 142 | 049 | 006 | 0+ | 0+ | 0+ | 8 |
| | 9 | 0+ | 0+ | 0+ | 001 | 019 | 084 | 175 | 189 | 101 | 020 | 0+ | 0+ | 0+ | 9 |
| | 10 | 0+ | 0+ | 0+ | 0+ | 006 | 039 | 122 | 198 | 165 | 055 | 003 | 0+ | 0+ | 10 |
| | 11 | 0+ | 0+ | 0+ | 0+ | 001 | 014 | 067 | 162 | 210 | 120 | 014 | 001 | 0+ | 11 |
| | 12 | 0+ | 0+ | 0+ | 0+ | 0+ | 004 | 028 | 101 | 204 | 200 | 051 | 006 | 0+ | 12 |
| | 13 | 0+ | 0+ | 0+ | 0+ | 0+ | 001 | 009 | 047 | 146 | 246 | 142 | 036 | 0+ | 13 |
| | 14 | 0+ | 0+ | 0+ | 0+ | 0+ | 0+ | 002 | 015 | 073 | 211 | 275 | 146 | 010 | 14 |
| | 15 | 0+ | 0+ | 0+ | 0+ | 0+ | 0+ | 0+ | 003 | 023 | 113 | 329 | 371 | 138 | 15 |
| | 16 | 0+ | 0+ | 0+ | 0+ | 0+ | 0+ | 0+ | 0+ | 003 | 028 | 185 | 440 | 851 | 16 |
| 17 | 0 | 843 | 418 | 167 | 023 | 002 | 0+ | 0+ | 0+ | 0+ | 0+ | 0+ | 0+ | 0+ | 0 |

$$\binom{n}{x}p^x q^{n-x}$$

| n | x | .01 | .05 | .10 | .20 | .30 | .40 | .50 | .60 | .70 | .80 | .90 | .95 | .99 | x |
|---|---|-----|-----|-----|-----|-----|-----|-----|-----|-----|-----|-----|-----|-----|---|
| | 1 | 145 | 374 | 315 | 096 | 017 | 002 | 0+ | 0+ | 0+ | 0+ | 0+ | 0+ | 0+ | 1 |
| | 2 | 012 | 158 | 280 | 191 | 058 | 010 | 001 | 0+ | 0+ | 0+ | 0+ | 0+ | 0+ | 2 |
| | 3 | 001 | 041 | 156 | 239 | 125 | 034 | 005 | 0+ | 0+ | 0+ | 0+ | 0+ | 0+ | 3 |
| | 4 | 0+ | 008 | 060 | 209 | 187 | 080 | 018 | 002 | 0+ | 0+ | 0+ | 0+ | 0+ | 4 |
| | 5 | 0+ | 001 | 017 | 136 | 208 | 138 | 047 | 008 | 001 | 0+ | 0+ | 0+ | 0+ | 5 |
| | 6 | 0+ | 0+ | 004 | 068 | 178 | 184 | 094 | 024 | 003 | 0+ | 0+ | 0+ | 0+ | 6 |
| | 7 | 0+ | 0+ | 001 | 027 | 120 | 193 | 148 | 057 | 009 | 0+ | 0+ | 0+ | 0+ | 7 |
| | 8 | 0+ | 0+ | 0+ | 008 | 064 | 161 | 185 | 107 | 028 | 002 | 0+ | 0+ | 0+ | 8 |
| | 9 | 0+ | 0+ | 0+ | 002 | 028 | 107 | 185 | 161 | 064 | 008 | 0+ | 0+ | 0+ | 9 |
| | 10 | 0+ | 0+ | 0+ | 0+ | 009 | 057 | 148 | 193 | 120 | 027 | 001 | 0+ | 0+ | 10 |
| | 11 | 0+ | 0+ | 0+ | 0+ | 003 | 024 | 094 | 184 | 178 | 068 | 004 | 0+ | 0+ | 11 |
| | 12 | 0+ | 0+ | 0+ | 0+ | 001 | 008 | 047 | 138 | 208 | 136 | 017 | 001 | 0+ | 12 |
| | 13 | 0+ | 0+ | 0+ | 0+ | 0+ | 002 | 018 | 080 | 187 | 209 | 060 | 008 | 0+ | 13 |
| | 14 | 0+ | 0+ | 0+ | 0+ | 0+ | 0+ | 005 | 034 | 125 | 239 | 156 | 041 | 001 | 14 |
| | 15 | 0+ | 0+ | 0+ | 0+ | 0+ | 0+ | 001 | 010 | 058 | 191 | 280 | 158 | 012 | 15 |
| | 16 | 0+ | 0+ | 0+ | 0+ | 0+ | 0+ | 0+ | 002 | 017 | 096 | 315 | 374 | 145 | 16 |
| | 17 | 0+ | 0+ | 0+ | 0+ | 0+ | 0+ | 0+ | 0+ | 002 | 023 | 167 | 418 | 843 | 17 |
| 18 | 0 | 835 | 397 | 150 | 018 | 002 | 0+ | 0+ | 0+ | 0+ | 0+ | 0+ | 0+ | 0+ | 0 |
| | 1 | 152 | 376 | 300 | 081 | 013 | 001 | 0+ | 0+ | 0+ | 0+ | 0+ | 0+ | 0+ | 1 |
| | 2 | 013 | 168 | 284 | 172 | 046 | 007 | 001 | 0+ | 0+ | 0+ | 0+ | 0+ | 0+ | 2 |
| | 3 | 001 | 047 | 168 | 230 | 105 | 025 | 003 | 0+ | 0+ | 0+ | 0+ | 0+ | 0+ | 3 |
| | 4 | 0+ | 009 | 070 | 215 | 168 | 061 | 012 | 001 | 0+ | 0+ | 0+ | 0+ | 0+ | 4 |
| | 5 | 0+ | 001 | 022 | 151 | 202 | 115 | 033 | 004 | 0+ | 0+ | 0+ | 0+ | 0+ | 5 |
| | 6 | 0+ | 0+ | 005 | 082 | 187 | 166 | 071 | 015 | 001 | 0+ | 0+ | 0+ | 0+ | 6 |
| | 7 | 0+ | 0+ | 001 | 035 | 138 | 189 | 121 | 037 | 005 | 0+ | 0+ | 0+ | 0+ | 7 |
| | 8 | 0+ | 0+ | 0+ | 012 | 081 | 173 | 167 | 077 | 015 | 001 | 0+ | 0+ | 0+ | 8 |
| | 9 | 0+ | 0+ | 0+ | 003 | 039 | 128 | 185 | 128 | 039 | 003 | 0+ | 0+ | 0+ | 9 |
| | 10 | 0+ | 0+ | 0+ | 001 | 015 | 077 | 167 | 173 | 081 | 012 | 0+ | 0+ | 0+ | 10 |
| | 11 | 0+ | 0+ | 0+ | 0+ | 005 | 037 | 121 | 189 | 138 | 035 | 001 | 0+ | 0+ | 11 |
| | 12 | 0+ | 0+ | 0+ | 0+ | 001 | 015 | 071 | 166 | 187 | 082 | 005 | 0+ | 0+ | 12 |
| | 13 | 0+ | 0+ | 0+ | 0+ | 0+ | 004 | 033 | 115 | 202 | 151 | 022 | 001 | 0+ | 13 |
| | 14 | 0+ | 0+ | 0+ | 0+ | 0+ | 001 | 012 | 061 | 168 | 215 | 070 | 009 | 0+ | 14 |
| | 15 | 0+ | 0+ | 0+ | 0+ | 0+ | 0+ | 003 | 025 | 105 | 230 | 168 | 047 | 001 | 15 |
| | 16 | 0+ | 0+ | 0+ | 0+ | 0+ | 0+ | 001 | 007 | 046 | 172 | 284 | 168 | 013 | 16 |
| | 17 | 0+ | 0+ | 0+ | 0+ | 0+ | 0+ | 0+ | 001 | 013 | 081 | 300 | 376 | 152 | 17 |
| | 18 | 0+ | 0+ | 0+ | 0+ | 0+ | 0+ | 0+ | 0+ | 002 | 018 | 150 | 397 | 835 | 18 |
| 19 | 0 | 826 | 377 | 135 | 014 | 001 | 0+ | 0+ | 0+ | 0+ | 0+ | 0+ | 0+ | 0+ | 0 |
| | 1 | 159 | 377 | 285 | 068 | 009 | 001 | 0+ | 0+ | 0+ | 0+ | 0+ | 0+ | 0+ | 1 |
| | 2 | 014 | 179 | 285 | 154 | 036 | 005 | 0+ | 0+ | 0+ | 0+ | 0+ | 0+ | 0+ | 2 |

$$\binom{n}{x} p^x q^{n-x}$$

| $n$ | $x$ | .01 | .05 | .10 | .20 | .30 | .40 | $p$ .50 | .60 | .70 | .80 | .90 | .95 | .99 | $x$ |
|---|---|---|---|---|---|---|---|---|---|---|---|---|---|---|---|
| | 3 | 001 | 053 | 180 | 218 | 087 | 017 | 002 | 0+ | 0+ | 0+ | 0+ | 0+ | 0+ | 3 |
| | 4 | 0+ | 011 | 080 | 218 | 149 | 047 | 007 | 001 | 0+ | 0+ | 0+ | 0+ | 0+ | 4 |
| | 5 | 0+ | 002 | 027 | 164 | 192 | 093 | 022 | 002 | 0+ | 0+ | 0+ | 0+ | 0+ | 5 |
| | 6 | 0+ | 0+ | 007 | 095 | 192 | 145 | 052 | 008 | 001 | 0+ | 0+ | 0+ | 0+ | 6 |
| | 7 | 0+ | 0+ | 001 | 044 | 153 | 180 | 096 | 024 | 002 | 0+ | 0+ | 0+ | 0+ | 7 |
| | 8 | 0+ | 0+ | 0+ | 017 | 098 | 180 | 144 | 053 | 008 | 0+ | 0+ | 0+ | 0+ | 8 |
| | 9 | 0+ | 0+ | 0+ | 005 | 051 | 146 | 176 | 098 | 022 | 001 | 0+ | 0+ | 0+ | 9 |
| | 10 | 0+ | 0+ | 0+ | 001 | 022 | 098 | 176 | 146 | 051 | 005 | 0+ | 0+ | 0+ | 10 |
| | 11 | 0+ | 0+ | 0+ | 0+ | 008 | 053 | 144 | 180 | 098 | 017 | 0+ | 0+ | 0+ | 11 |
| | 12 | 0+ | 0+ | 0+ | 0+ | 002 | 024 | 096 | 180 | 153 | 044 | 001 | 0+ | 0+ | 12 |
| | 13 | 0+ | 0+ | 0+ | 0+ | 001 | 008 | 052 | 145 | 192 | 095 | 007 | 0+ | 0+ | 13 |
| | 14 | 0+ | 0+ | 0+ | 0+ | 0+ | 002 | 022 | 093 | 192 | 164 | 027 | 002 | 0+ | 14 |
| | 15 | 0+ | 0+ | 0+ | 0+ | 0+ | 001 | 007 | 047 | 149 | 218 | 080 | 011 | 0+ | 15 |
| | 16 | 0+ | 0+ | 0+ | 0+ | 0+ | 0+ | 002 | 017 | 087 | 218 | 180 | 053 | 001 | 16 |
| | 17 | 0+ | 0+ | 0+ | 0+ | 0+ | 0+ | 0+ | 005 | 036 | 154 | 285 | 179 | 014 | 17 |
| | 18 | 0+ | 0+ | 0+ | 0+ | 0+ | 0+ | 0+ | 001 | 009 | 068 | 285 | 377 | 159 | 18 |
| | 19 | 0+ | 0+ | 0+ | 0+ | 0+ | 0+ | 0+ | 0+ | 001 | 014 | 135 | 377 | 826 | 19 |
| 20 | 0 | 818 | 358 | 122 | 012 | 001 | 0+ | 0+ | 0+ | 0+ | 0+ | 0+ | 0+ | 0+ | 0 |
| | 1 | 165 | 377 | 270 | 058 | 007 | 0+ | 0+ | 0+ | 0+ | 0+ | 0+ | 0+ | 0+ | 1 |
| | 2 | 016 | 189 | 285 | 137 | 028 | 003 | 0+ | 0+ | 0+ | 0+ | 0+ | 0+ | 0+ | 2 |
| | 3 | 001 | 060 | 190 | 205 | 072 | 012 | 001 | 0+ | 0+ | 0+ | 0+ | 0+ | 0+ | 3 |
| | 4 | 0+ | 013 | 090 | 218 | 130 | 035 | 005 | 0+ | 0+ | 0+ | 0+ | 0+ | 0+ | 4 |
| | 5 | 0+ | 002 | 032 | 175 | 179 | 075 | 015 | 001 | 0+ | 0+ | 0+ | 0+ | 0+ | 5 |
| | 6 | 0+ | 0+ | 009 | 109 | 192 | 124 | 037 | 005 | 0+ | 0+ | 0+ | 0+ | 0+ | 6 |
| | 7 | 0+ | 0+ | 002 | 055 | 164 | 166 | 074 | 015 | 001 | 0+ | 0+ | 0+ | 0+ | 7 |
| | 8 | 0+ | 0+ | 0+ | 022 | 114 | 180 | 120 | 035 | 004 | 0+ | 0+ | 0+ | 0+ | 8 |
| | 9 | 0+ | 0+ | 0+ | 007 | 065 | 160 | 160 | 071 | 012 | 0+ | 0+ | 0+ | 0+ | 9 |
| | 10 | 0+ | 0+ | 0+ | 002 | 031 | 117 | 176 | 117 | 031 | 002 | 0+ | 0+ | 0+ | 10 |
| | 11 | 0+ | 0+ | 0+ | 0+ | 012 | 071 | 160 | 160 | 065 | 007 | 0+ | 0+ | 0+ | 11 |
| | 12 | 0+ | 0+ | 0+ | 0+ | 004 | 035 | 120 | 180 | 114 | 022 | 0+ | 0+ | 0+ | 12 |
| | 13 | 0+ | 0+ | 0+ | 0+ | 001 | 015 | 074 | 166 | 164 | 055 | 002 | 0+ | 0+ | 13 |
| | 14 | 0+ | 0+ | 0+ | 0+ | 0+ | 005 | 037 | 124 | 192 | 109 | 009 | 0+ | 0+ | 14 |
| | 15 | 0+ | 0+ | 0+ | 0+ | 0+ | 001 | 015 | 075 | 179 | 175 | 032 | 002 | 0+ | 15 |
| | 16 | 0+ | 0+ | 0+ | 0+ | 0+ | 0+ | 005 | 025 | 130 | 218 | 090 | 013 | 0+ | 16 |
| | 17 | 0+ | 0+ | 0+ | 0+ | 0+ | 0+ | 001 | 012 | 072 | 205 | 190 | 060 | 001 | 17 |
| | 18 | 0+ | 0+ | 0+ | 0+ | 0+ | 0+ | 0+ | 003 | 028 | 137 | 285 | 189 | 016 | 18 |
| | 19 | 0+ | 0+ | 0+ | 0+ | 0+ | 0+ | 0+ | 0+ | 007 | 058 | 270 | 377 | 165 | 19 |
| | 20 | 0+ | 0+ | 0+ | 0+ | 0+ | 0+ | 0+ | 0+ | 001 | 012 | 122 | 358 | 818 | 20 |

# APPENDIX IV: CUMULATIVE TERMS OF BINOMIAL DISTRIBUTION

Each three-digit entry in the table should be read with a decimal preceding it. For entries, $0+$, the probability is less than 0.0005, but greater than 0. For entries $1-$, the probability is larger than 0.9995 but less than 1.

$$\sum_{x=r}^{n} \binom{n}{x} p^x q^{n-x}.$$

| $n$ | $r$ | .01 | .05 | .10 | .20 | .30 | .40 | $p$ .50 | .60 | .70 | .80 | .90 | .95 | .99 | $r$ |
|---|---|---|---|---|---|---|---|---|---|---|---|---|---|---|---|
| 2 | 0 | 1 | 1 | 1 | 1 | 1 | 1 | 1 | 1 | 1 | 1 | 1 | 1 | 1 | 0 |
|  | 1 | 020 | 098 | 190 | 360 | 510 | 640 | 750 | 840 | 910 | 960 | 990 | 998 | 1− | 1 |
|  | 2 | 0+ | 002 | 010 | 040 | 090 | 160 | 250 | 360 | 490 | 640 | 810 | 902 | 980 | 2 |
| 3 | 0 | 1 | 1 | 1 | 1 | 1 | 1 | 1 | 1 | 1 | 1 | 1 | 1 | 1 | 0 |
|  | 1 | 030 | 143 | 271 | 488 | 657 | 784 | 875 | 936 | 973 | 992 | 999 | 1− | 1− | 1 |
|  | 2 | 0+ | 007 | 028 | 104 | 216 | .352 | 500 | 648 | 784 | 896 | 972 | 993 | 1− | 2 |
|  | 3 | 0+ | 0+ | 001 | 008 | 027 | 064 | 125 | 216 | 343 | 512 | 729 | 857 | 970 | 3 |
| 4 | 0 | 1 | 1 | 1 | 1 | 1 | 1 | 1 | 1 | 1 | 1 | 1 | 1 | 1 | 0 |
|  | 1 | 039 | 185 | 344 | 590 | 760 | 870 | 938 | 974 | 992 | 998 | 1− | 1− | 1− | 1 |
|  | 2 | 001 | 014 | 052 | 181 | 348 | 535 | 688 | 821 | 916 | 973 | 996 | 1− | 1− | 2 |
|  | 3 | 0+ | 0+ | 004 | 027 | 084 | 179 | 312 | 475 | 652 | 819 | 948 | 986 | 999 | 3 |
|  | 4 | 0+ | 0+ | 0+ | 002 | 008 | 026 | 062 | 130 | 240 | 410 | 656 | 815 | 961 | 4 |
| 5 | 0 | 1 | 1 | 1 | 1 | 1 | 1 | 1 | 1 | 1 | 1 | 1 | 1 | 1 | 0 |
|  | 1 | 049 | 226 | 410 | 672 | 832 | 922 | 969 | 990 | 998 | 1− | 1− | 1− | 1− | 1 |
|  | 2 | 001 | 023 | 081 | 263 | 472 | 663 | 812 | 913 | 969 | 993 | 1− | 1− | 1− | 2 |
|  | 3 | 0+ | 001 | 009 | 058 | 163 | 317 | 500 | 683 | 837 | 942 | 991 | 999 | 1− | 3 |
|  | 4 | 0+ | 0+ | 0+ | 007 | 031 | 087 | 188 | 337 | 528 | 737 | 919 | 977 | 999 | 4 |
|  | 5 | 0+ | 0+ | 0+ | 0+ | 002 | 010 | 031 | 078 | 168 | 328 | 590 | 774 | 951 | 5 |
| 6 | 0 | 1 | 1 | 1 | 1 | 1 | 1 | 1 | 1 | 1 | 1 | 1 | 1 | 1 | 0 |
|  | 1 | 059 | 265 | 469 | 738 | 882 | 953 | 984 | 996 | 999 | 1− | 1− | 1− | 1− | 1 |
|  | 2 | 001 | 033 | 114 | 345 | 580 | 767 | 891 | 959 | 989 | 998 | 1− | 1− | 1− | 2 |
|  | 3 | 0+ | 002 | 016 | 099 | 256 | 456 | 656 | 821 | 930 | 983 | 999 | 1− | 1− | 3 |
|  | 4 | 0+ | 0+ | 001 | 017 | 070 | 179 | 344 | 544 | 744 | 901 | 984 | 998 | 1− | 4 |
|  | 5 | 0+ | 0+ | 0+ | 002 | 011 | 041 | 109 | 233 | 420 | 655 | 886 | 967 | 999 | 5 |
|  | 6 | 0+ | 0+ | 0+ | 0+ | 001 | 004 | 016 | 047 | 118 | 262 | 531 | 735 | 941 | 6 |
| 7 | 0 | 1 | 1 | 1 | 1 | 1 | 1 | 1 | 1 | 1 | 1 | 1 | 1 | 1 | 0 |
|  | 1 | 068 | 302 | 522 | 790 | 918 | 972 | 992 | 998 | 1− | 1− | 1− | 1− | 1− | 1 |
|  | 2 | 002 | 044 | 150 | 423 | 671 | 841 | 938 | 981 | 996 | 1− | 1− | 1− | 1− | 2 |
|  | 3 | 0+ | 004 | 026 | 148 | 353 | 580 | 773 | 904 | 971 | 995 | 1− | 1− | 1− | 3 |
|  | 4 | 0+ | 0+ | 003 | 033 | 126 | 290 | 500 | 710 | 874 | 967 | 997 | 1− | 1− | 4 |
|  | 5 | 0+ | 0+ | 0+ | 005 | 029 | 096 | 227 | 420 | 647 | 852 | 974 | 996 | 1− | 5 |

$$\sum_{x=r}^{n}\binom{n}{x}p^x q^{n-x}$$

| n | r | .01 | .05 | .10 | .20 | .30 | .40 | .50 | .60 | .70 | .80 | .90 | .95 | .99 | r |
|---|---|-----|-----|-----|-----|-----|-----|-----|-----|-----|-----|-----|-----|-----|---|
|  | 6 | 0+ | 0+ | 0+ | 0+ | 004 | 019 | 062 | 159 | 329 | 577 | 850 | 956 | 998 | 6 |
|  | 7 | 0+ | 0+ | 0+ | 0+ | 0+ | 002 | 008 | 028 | 082 | 210 | 478 | 698 | 932 | 7 |
| 8 | 0 | 1 | 1 | 1 | 1 | 1 | 1 | 1 | 1 | 1 | 1 | 1 | 1 | 1 | 0 |
|  | 1 | 077 | 337 | 570 | 832 | 942 | 983 | 996 | 999 | 1− | 1− | 1− | 1− | 1− | 1 |
|  | 2 | 003 | 057 | 187 | 497 | 745 | 894 | 965 | 991 | 999 | 1− | 1− | 1− | 1− | 2 |
|  | 3 | 0+ | 006 | 038 | 203 | 448 | 685 | 855 | 950 | 989 | 999 | 1− | 1− | 1− | 3 |
|  | 4 | 0+ | 0+ | 005 | 056 | 194 | 406 | 637 | 826 | 942 | 990 | 1− | 1− | 1− | 4 |
|  | 5 | 0+ | 0+ | 0+ | 010 | 058 | 174 | 363 | 594 | 806 | 944 | 995 | 1− | 1− | 5 |
|  | 6 | 0+ | 0+ | 0+ | 001 | 011 | 050 | 145 | 315 | 552 | 797 | 962 | 994 | 1− | 6 |
|  | 7 | 0+ | 0+ | 0+ | 0+ | 001 | 009 | 035 | 106 | 255 | 503 | 813 | 943 | 997 | 7 |
|  | 8 | 0+ | 0+ | 0+ | 0+ | 0+ | 001 | 004 | 017 | 058 | 168 | 430 | 663 | 923 | 8 |
| 9 | 0 | 1 | 1 | 1 | 1 | 1 | 1 | 1 | 1 | 1 | 1 | 1 | 1 | 1 | 0 |
|  | 1 | 086 | 370 | 613 | 866 | 960 | 990 | 998 | 1− | 1− | 1− | 1− | 1− | 1− | 1 |
|  | 2 | 003 | 071 | 225 | 564 | 804 | 929 | 980 | 996 | 1− | 1− | 1− | 1− | 1− | 2 |
|  | 3 | 0+ | 008 | 053 | 262 | 537 | 768 | 910 | 975 | 996 | 1− | 1− | 1− | 1− | 3 |
|  | 4 | 0+ | 001 | 008 | 086 | 270 | 517 | 746 | 901 | 975 | 997 | 1− | 1− | 1− | 4 |
|  | 5 | 0+ | 0+ | 001 | 020 | 099 | 267 | 500 | 733 | 901 | 980 | 999 | 1− | 1− | 5 |
|  | 6 | 0+ | 0+ | 0+ | 003 | 025 | 099 | 254 | 483 | 730 | 914 | 992 | 999 | 1− | 6 |
|  | 7 | 0+ | 0+ | 0+ | 0+ | 004 | 025 | 090 | 232 | 463 | 738 | 947 | 992 | 1− | 7 |
|  | 8 | 0+ | 0+ | 0+ | 0+ | 0+ | 004 | 020 | 071 | 196 | 436 | 775 | 929 | 997 | 8 |
|  | 9 | 0+ | 0+ | 0+ | 0+ | 0+ | 0+ | 002 | 010 | 040 | 134 | 387 | 630 | 914 | 9 |
| 10 | 0 | 1 | 1 | 1 | 1 | 1 | 1 | 1 | 1 | 1 | 1 | 1 | 1 | 1 | 0 |
|  | 1 | 096 | 401 | 651 | 893 | 972 | 994 | 999 | 1− | 1− | 1− | 1− | 1− | 1− | 1 |
|  | 2 | 004 | 086 | 264 | 624 | 851 | 954 | 989 | 998 | 1− | 1− | 1− | 1− | 1− | 2 |
|  | 3 | 0+ | 012 | 070 | 322 | 617 | 833 | 945 | 988 | 998 | 1− | 1− | 1− | 1− | 3 |
|  | 4 | 0+ | 001 | 013 | 121 | 350 | 618 | 828 | 945 | 989 | 999 | 1− | 1− | 1− | 4 |
|  | 5 | 0+ | 0+ | 002 | 033 | 150 | 367 | 623 | 834 | 953 | 994 | 1− | 1− | 1− | 5 |
|  | 6 | 0+ | 0+ | 0+ | 006 | 047 | 166 | 377 | 633 | 850 | 967 | 998 | 1− | 1− | 6 |
|  | 7 | 0+ | 0+ | 0+ | 001 | 011 | 055 | 172 | 382 | 650 | 879 | 987 | 999 | 1− | 7 |
|  | 8 | 0+ | 0+ | 0+ | 0+ | 002 | 012 | 055 | 167 | 383 | 678 | 930 | 988 | 1− | 8 |
|  | 9 | 0+ | 0+ | 0+ | 0+ | 0+ | 002 | 011 | 046 | 149 | 376 | 736 | 914 | 996 | 9 |
|  | 10 | 0+ | 0+ | 0+ | 0+ | 0+ | 0+ | 001 | 006 | 028 | 107 | 349 | 599 | 904 | 10 |
| 11 | 0 | 1 | 1 | 1 | 1 | 1 | 1 | 1 | 1 | 1 | 1 | 1 | 1 | 1 | 0 |
|  | 1 | 105 | 431 | 686 | 914 | 980 | 996 | 1− | 1− | 1− | 1− | 1− | 1− | 1− | 1 |
|  | 2 | 005 | 102 | 303 | 678 | 887 | 970 | 994 | 999 | 1− | 1− | 1− | 1− | 1− | 2 |
|  | 3 | 0+ | 015 | 090 | 383 | 687 | 881 | 967 | 994 | 999 | 1− | 1− | 1− | 1− | 3 |
|  | 4 | 0+ | 002 | 019 | 161 | 430 | 704 | 887 | 971 | 996 | 1− | 1− | 1− | 1− | 4 |
|  | 5 | 0+ | 0+ | 003 | 050 | 210 | 467 | 726 | 901 | 978 | 998 | 1− | 1− | 1− | 5 |
|  | 6 | 0+ | 0+ | 0+ | 012 | 078 | 247 | 500 | 753 | 922 | 988 | 1− | 1− | 1− | 6 |

$$\sum_{x=r}^{n} \binom{n}{x} p^x q^{n-x}$$

| n | r | .01 | .05 | .10 | .20 | .30 | .40 | .50 | .60 | .70 | .80 | .90 | .95 | .99 | r |
|---|---|-----|-----|-----|-----|-----|-----|-----|-----|-----|-----|-----|-----|-----|---|
|    | 7  | 0+  | 0+  | 0+  | 002 | 022 | 099 | 274 | 533 | 790 | 950 | 997 | 1−  | 1−  | 7  |
|    | 8  | 0+  | 0+  | 0+  | 0+  | 004 | 029 | 113 | 296 | 570 | 839 | 981 | 998 | 1−  | 8  |
|    | 9  | 0+  | 0+  | 0+  | 0+  | 001 | 006 | 033 | 119 | 313 | 617 | 910 | 985 | 1−  | 9  |
|    | 10 | 0+  | 0+  | 0+  | 0+  | 0+  | 001 | 006 | 030 | 113 | 322 | 697 | 898 | 995 | 10 |
|    | 11 | 0+  | 0+  | 0+  | 0+  | 0+  | 0+  | 0+  | 004 | 020 | 086 | 314 | 569 | 895 | 11 |
| 12 | 0  | 1   | 1   | 1   | 1   | 1   | 1   | 1   | 1   | 1   | 1   | 1   | 1   | 1   | 0  |
|    | 1  | 114 | 460 | 718 | 931 | 986 | 998 | 1−  | 1−  | 1−  | 1−  | 1−  | 1−  | 1−  | 1  |
|    | 2  | 006 | 118 | 341 | 725 | 915 | 980 | 997 | 1−  | 1−  | 1−  | 1−  | 1−  | 1−  | 2  |
|    | 3  | 0+  | 020 | 111 | 442 | 747 | 917 | 981 | 997 | 1−  | 1−  | 1−  | 1−  | 1−  | 3  |
|    | 4  | 0+  | 002 | 026 | 205 | 507 | 775 | 927 | 985 | 998 | 1−  | 1−  | 1−  | 1−  | 4  |
|    | 5  | 0+  | 0+  | 004 | 073 | 276 | 562 | 806 | 943 | 991 | 999 | 1−  | 1−  | 1−  | 5  |
|    | 6  | 0+  | 0+  | 001 | 019 | 118 | 335 | 613 | 842 | 961 | 996 | 1−  | 1−  | 1−  | 6  |
|    | 7  | 0+  | 0+  | 0+  | 004 | 039 | 158 | 387 | 665 | 882 | 981 | 999 | 1−  | 1−  | 7  |
|    | 8  | 0+  | 0+  | 0+  | 001 | 009 | 057 | 194 | 438 | 724 | 927 | 996 | 1−  | 1−  | 8  |
|    | 9  | 0+  | 0+  | 0+  | 0+  | 002 | 015 | 073 | 225 | 493 | 795 | 974 | 998 | 1−  | 9  |
| 12 | 10 | 0+  | 0+  | 0+  | 0+  | 0+  | 003 | 019 | 083 | 253 | 558 | 889 | 980 | 1−  | 10 |
|    | 11 | 0+  | 0+  | 0+  | 0+  | 0+  | 0+  | 003 | 020 | 085 | 275 | 659 | 882 | 994 | 11 |
|    | 12 | 0+  | 0+  | 0+  | 0+  | 0+  | 0+  | 0+  | 002 | 014 | 069 | 282 | 540 | 886 | 12 |
| 13 | 0  | 1   | 1   | 1   | 1   | 1   | 1   | 1   | 1   | 1   | 1   | 1   | 1   | 1   | 0  |
|    | 1  | 122 | 487 | 746 | 945 | 990 | 999 | 1−  | 1−  | 1−  | 1−  | 1−  | 1−  | 1−  | 1  |
|    | 2  | 007 | 135 | 379 | 766 | 936 | 687 | 998 | 1−  | 1−  | 1−  | 1−  | 1−  | 1−  | 2  |
|    | 3  | 0+  | 025 | 134 | 498 | 798 | 942 | 989 | 999 | 1−  | 1−  | 1−  | 1−  | 1−  | 3  |
|    | 4  | 0+  | 003 | 034 | 253 | 579 | 831 | 954 | 992 | 999 | 1−  | 1−  | 1−  | 1−  | 4  |
|    | 5  | 0+  | 0+  | 006 | 099 | 346 | 647 | 867 | 968 | 996 | 1−  | 1−  | 1−  | 1−  | 5  |
|    | 6  | 0+  | 0+  | 001 | 030 | 165 | 426 | 709 | 902 | 982 | 999 | 1−  | 1−  | 1−  | 6  |
|    | 7  | 0+  | 0+  | 0+  | 007 | 062 | 229 | 500 | 771 | 938 | 993 | 1−  | 1−  | 1−  | 7  |
|    | 8  | 0+  | 0+  | 0+  | 001 | 018 | 098 | 291 | 574 | 835 | 970 | 999 | 1−  | 1−  | 8  |
|    | 9  | 0+  | 0+  | 0+  | 0+  | 004 | 032 | 133 | 353 | 654 | 901 | 994 | 1−  | 1−  | 9  |
|    | 10 | 0+  | 0+  | 0+  | 0+  | 001 | 008 | 046 | 169 | 421 | 747 | 966 | 997 | 1−  | 10 |
|    | 11 | 0+  | 0+  | 0+  | 0+  | 0+  | 001 | 011 | 058 | 202 | 502 | 866 | 975 | 1−  | 11 |
|    | 12 | 0+  | 0+  | 0+  | 0+  | 0+  | 0+  | 002 | 013 | 064 | 234 | 621 | 865 | 993 | 12 |
|    | 13 | 0+  | 0+  | 0+  | 0+  | 0+  | 0+  | 0+  | 001 | 010 | 055 | 254 | 513 | 878 | 13 |
| 14 | 0  | 1   | 1   | 1   | 1   | 1   | 1   | 1   | 1   | 1   | 1   | 1   | 1   | 1   | 0  |
|    | 1  | 131 | 512 | 771 | 956 | 993 | 999 | 1−  | 1−  | 1−  | 1−  | 1−  | 1−  | 1−  | 1  |
|    | 2  | 008 | 153 | 415 | 802 | 953 | 992 | 999 | 1−  | 1−  | 1−  | 1−  | 1−  | 1−  | 2  |
|    | 3  | 0+  | 030 | 158 | 552 | 839 | 960 | 994 | 999 | 1−  | 1−  | 1−  | 1−  | 1−  | 3  |
|    | 4  | 0+  | 004 | 044 | 302 | 645 | 876 | 971 | 996 | 1−  | 1−  | 1−  | 1−  | 1−  | 4  |
|    | 5  | 0+  | 0+  | 009 | 130 | 416 | 721 | 910 | 982 | 998 | 1−  | 1−  | 1−  | 1−  | 5  |
|    | 6  | 0+  | 0+  | 001 | 044 | 219 | 514 | 788 | 942 | 992 | 1−  | 1−  | 1−  | 1−  | 6  |

$$\sum_{x=r}^{n} \binom{n}{x} p^x q^{n-x}$$

| n | r | .01 | .05 | .10 | .20 | .30 | .40 | $\frac{p}{.50}$ | .60 | .70 | .80 | .90 | .95 | .99 | r |
|---|---|-----|-----|-----|-----|-----|-----|-----|-----|-----|-----|-----|-----|-----|---|
|   | 7 | 0+ | 0+ | 0+ | 012 | 093 | 308 | 605 | 850 | 969 | 998 | 1− | 1− | 1− | 7 |
|   | 8 | 0+ | 0+ | 0+ | 002 | 031 | 150 | 395 | 692 | 907 | 988 | 1− | 1− | 1− | 8 |
|   | 9 | 0+ | 0+ | 0+ | 0+ | 008 | 058 | 212 | 486 | 781 | 956 | 999 | 1− | 1− | 9 |
|   | 10 | 0+ | 0+ | 0+ | 0+ | 002 | 018 | 090 | 279 | 584 | 870 | 991 | 1− | 1− | 10 |
|   | 11 | 0+ | 0+ | 0+ | 0+ | 0+ | 004 | 029 | 124 | 355 | 698 | 956 | 996 | 1− | 11 |
|   | 12 | 0+ | 0+ | 0+ | 0+ | 0+ | 001 | 006 | 040 | 161 | 448 | 842 | 970 | 1− | 12 |
|   | 13 | 0+ | 0+ | 0+ | 0+ | 0+ | 0+ | 001 | 008 | 047 | 198 | 585 | 847 | 992 | 13 |
|   | 14 | 0+ | 0+ | 0+ | 0+ | 0+ | 0+ | 0+ | 001 | 007 | 044 | 229 | 488 | 869 | 14 |
| 15 | 0 | 1 | 1 | 1 | 1 | 1 | 1 | 1 | 1 | 1 | 1 | 1 | 1 | 1 | 0 |
|   | 1 | 140 | 537 | 794 | 965 | 995 | 1− | 1− | 1− | 1− | 1− | 1− | 1− | 1− | 1 |
|   | 2 | 010 | 171 | 451 | 833 | 965 | 995 | 1− | 1− | 1− | 1− | 1− | 1− | 1− | 2 |
|   | 3 | 0+ | 036 | 184 | 602 | 873 | 973 | 996 | 1− | 1− | 1− | 1− | 1− | 1− | 3 |
|   | 4 | 0+ | 005 | 056 | 352 | 703 | 909 | 982 | 998 | 1− | 1− | 1− | 1− | 1− | 4 |
|   | 5 | 0+ | 001 | 013 | 164 | 485 | 783 | 941 | 991 | 999 | 1− | 1− | 1− | 1− | 5 |
|   | 6 | 0+ | 0+ | 002 | 061 | 278 | 597 | 849 | 966 | 996 | 1− | 1− | 1− | 1− | 6 |
|   | 7 | 0+ | 0+ | 0+ | 018 | 131 | 390 | 696 | 905 | 985 | 999 | 1− | 1− | 1− | 7 |
|   | 8 | 0+ | 0+ | 0+ | 004 | 050 | 213 | 500 | 787 | 950 | 996 | 1− | 1− | 1− | 8 |
|   | 9 | 0+ | 0+ | 0+ | 001 | 015 | 095 | 304 | 610 | 869 | 982 | 1− | 1− | 1− | 9 |
| 15 | 10 | 0+ | 0+ | 0+ | 0+ | 004 | 034 | 151 | 403 | 722 | 939 | 998 | 1− | 1− | 10 |
|   | 11 | 0+ | 0+ | 0+ | 0+ | 001 | 009 | 059 | 217 | 515 | 836 | 987 | 999 | 1− | 11 |
|   | 12 | 0+ | 0+ | 0+ | 0+ | 0+ | 002 | 018 | 091 | 297 | 648 | 944 | 995 | 1− | 12 |
|   | 13 | 0+ | 0+ | 0+ | 0+ | 0+ | 0+ | 004 | 027 | 127 | 398 | 816 | 964 | 1− | 13 |
|   | 14 | 0+ | 0+ | 0+ | 0+ | 0+ | 0+ | 0+ | 005 | 035 | 167 | 549 | 829 | 990 | 14 |
|   | 15 | 0+ | 0+ | 0+ | 0+ | 0+ | 0+ | 0+ | 0+ | 005 | 035 | 206 | 463 | 860 | 15 |
| 16 | 0 | 1 | 1 | 1 | 1 | 1 | 1 | 1 | 1 | 1 | 1 | 1 | 1 | 1 | 0 |
|   | 1 | 149 | 560 | 815 | 972 | 997 | 1− | 1− | 1− | 1− | 1− | 1− | 1− | 1− | 1 |
|   | 2 | 011 | 189 | 485 | 859 | 974 | 997 | 1− | 1− | 1− | 1− | 1− | 1− | 1− | 2 |
|   | 3 | 001 | 043 | 211 | 648 | 901 | 982 | 998 | 1− | 1− | 1− | 1− | 1− | 1− | 3 |
|   | 4 | 0+ | 007 | 068 | 402 | 754 | 935 | 989 | 999 | 1− | 1− | 1− | 1− | 1− | 4 |
|   | 5 | 0+ | 001 | 017 | 202 | 550 | 833 | 962 | 995 | 1− | 1− | 1− | 1− | 1− | 5 |
|   | 6 | 0+ | 0+ | 003 | 082 | 340 | 671 | 895 | 981 | 998 | 1− | 1− | 1− | 1− | 6 |
|   | 7 | 0+ | 0+ | 001 | 027 | 175 | 473 | 773 | 942 | 993 | 1− | 1− | 1− | 1 | 7 |
|   | 8 | 0+ | 0+ | 0+ | 007 | 074 | 284 | 598 | 858 | 974 | 999 | 1− | 1− | 1− | 8 |
|   | 9 | 0+ | 0+ | 0+ | 001 | 026 | 142 | 402 | 716 | 926 | 993 | 1− | 1− | 1− | 9 |
|   | 10 | 0+ | 0+ | 0+ | 0+ | 007 | 058 | 227 | 527 | 825 | 973 | 999 | 1− | 1− | 10 |
|   | 11 | 0+ | 0+ | 0+ | 0+ | 002 | 019 | 105 | 329 | 660 | 918 | 997 | 1− | 1− | 11 |
|   | 12 | 0+ | 0+ | 0+ | 0+ | 0+ | 005 | 038 | 167 | 450 | 798 | 983 | 999 | 1− | 12 |
|   | 13 | 0+ | 0+ | 0+ | 0+ | 0+ | 001 | 011 | 065 | 246 | 598 | 932 | 993 | 1− | 13 |
|   | 14 | 0+ | 0+ | 0+ | 0+ | 0+ | 0+ | 002 | 018 | 099 | 352 | 789 | 957 | 999 | 14 |

$$\sum_{x=r}^{n} \binom{n}{x} p^x q^{n-x}$$

| | | | | | | | | *p* | | | | | | | |
|---|---|---|---|---|---|---|---|---|---|---|---|---|---|---|---|
| *n* | *r* | .01 | .05 | .10 | .20 | .30 | .40 | .50 | .60 | .70 | .80 | .90 | .95 | .99 | *r* |
| | 15 | 0+ | 0+ | 0+ | 0+ | 0+ | 0+ | 0+ | 003 | 026 | 141 | 515 | 811 | 989 | 15 |
| | 16 | 0+ | 0+ | 0+ | 0+ | 0+ | 0+ | 0+ | 0+ | 003 | 028 | 185 | 440 | 851 | 16 |
| 17 | 0 | 1 | 1 | 1 | 1 | 1 | 1 | 1 | 1 | 1 | 1 | 1 | 1 | 1 | 0 |
| | 1 | 157 | 582 | 833 | 977 | 998 | 1− | 1− | 1− | 1− | 1− | 1− | 1− | 1− | 1 |
| | 2 | 012 | 208 | 518 | 882 | 981 | 998 | 1− | 1− | 1− | 1− | 1− | 1− | 1− | 2 |
| | 3 | 001 | 050 | 238 | 690 | 923 | 988 | 999 | 1− | 1− | 1− | 1− | 1− | 1− | 3 |
| | 4 | 0+ | 009 | 083 | 451 | 798 | 954 | 994 | 1− | 1− | 1− | 1− | 1− | 1− | 4 |
| | 5 | 0+ | 001 | 022 | 242 | 611 | 874 | 975 | 997 | 1− | 1− | 1− | 1− | 1− | 5 |
| | 6 | 0+ | 0+ | 005 | 106 | 403 | 736 | 928 | 989 | 999 | 1− | 1− | 1− | 1− | 6 |
| | 7 | 0+ | 0+ | 001 | 038 | 225 | 552 | 834 | 965 | 997 | 1− | 1− | 1− | 1− | 7 |
| | 8 | 0+ | 0+ | 0+ | 011 | 105 | 359 | 685 | 908 | 987 | 1− | 1− | 1− | 1− | 8 |
| | 9 | 0+ | 0+ | 0+ | 003 | 040 | 199 | 500 | 801 | 960 | 997 | 1− | 1− | 1− | 9 |
| | 10 | 0+ | 0+ | 0+ | 0+ | 013 | 092 | 315 | 611 | 895 | 989 | 1− | 1− | 1− | 10 |
| | 11 | 0+ | 0+ | 0+ | 0+ | 003 | 035 | 166 | 448 | 775 | 962 | 999 | 1− | 1− | 11 |
| | 12 | 0+ | 0+ | 0+ | 0+ | 001 | 035 | 072 | 264 | 597 | 894 | 995 | 1− | 1− | 12 |
| | 13 | 0+ | 0+ | 0+ | 0+ | 0+ | 003 | 025 | 126 | 389 | 758 | 978 | 999 | 1− | 13 |
| | 14 | 0+ | 0+ | 0+ | 0+ | 0+ | 0+ | 006 | 046 | 202 | 549 | 917 | 991 | 1− | 14 |
| | 15 | 0+ | 0+ | 0+ | 0+ | 0+ | 0+ | 001 | 012 | 077 | 310 | 762 | 950 | 999 | 15 |
| | 16 | 0+ | 0+ | 0+ | 0+ | 0+ | 0+ | 0+ | 002 | 019 | 118 | 482 | 792 | 988 | 16 |
| | 17 | 0+ | 0+ | 0+ | 0+ | 0+ | 0+ | 0+ | 0+ | 002 | 023 | 167 | 418 | 843 | 17 |
| 18 | 0 | 1 | 1 | 1 | 1 | 1 | 1 | 1 | 1 | 1 | 1 | 1 | 1 | 1 | 0 |
| | 1 | 165 | 603 | 850 | 982 | 998 | 1− | 1− | 1− | 1− | 1− | 1− | 1− | 1− | 1 |
| | 1 | 014 | 226 | 550 | 901 | 986 | 999 | 1− | 1− | 1− | 1− | 1− | 1− | 1− | 2 |
| | 3 | 001 | 058 | 266 | 729 | 940 | 992 | 999 | 1− | 1− | 1− | 1− | 1− | 1− | 3 |
| | 4 | 0+ | 011 | 098 | 499 | 835 | 967 | 996 | 1− | 1− | 1− | 1− | 1− | 1− | 4 |
| | 5 | 0+ | 002 | 028 | 284 | 667 | 906 | 985 | 999 | 1− | 1− | 1− | 1− | 1− | 5 |
| | 6 | 0+ | 0+ | 006 | 133 | 466 | 791 | 952 | 994 | 1− | 1− | 1− | 1− | 1− | 6 |
| | 7 | 0+ | 0+ | 001 | 051 | 278 | 626 | 881 | 980 | 999 | 1− | 1− | 1− | 1− | 7 |
| | 8 | 0+ | 0+ | 0+ | 016 | 141 | 437 | 760 | 942 | 994 | 1− | 1− | 1− | 1− | 8 |
| | 9 | 0+ | 0+ | 0+ | 009 | 060 | 263 | 593 | 865 | 979 | 999 | 1− | 1− | 1− | 9 |
| | 10 | 0+ | 0+ | 0+ | 001 | 021 | 135 | 407 | 737 | 940 | 996 | 1− | 1− | 1− | 10 |
| | 11 | 0+ | 0+ | 0+ | 0+ | 006 | 058 | 240 | 563 | 859 | 984 | 1− | 1− | 1− | 11 |
| | 12 | 0+ | 0+ | 0+ | 0+ | 001 | 020 | 119 | 374 | 722 | 949 | 999 | 1− | 1− | 12 |
| | 13 | 0+ | 0+ | 0+ | 0+ | 0+ | 006 | 048 | 209 | 534 | 867 | 994 | 1− | 1− | 13 |
| | 11 | 0+ | 0+ | 0+ | 0+ | 0+ | 001 | 015 | 094 | 333 | 716 | 972 | 998 | 1− | 14 |
| | 15 | 0+ | 0+ | 0+ | 0+ | 0+ | 0+ | 004 | 033 | 165 | 501 | 902 | 989 | 1− | 15 |
| | 16 | 0+ | 0+ | 0+ | 0+ | 0+ | 0+ | 001 | 008 | 060 | 271 | 734 | 942 | 999 | 16 |
| | 17 | 0+ | 0+ | 0+ | 0+ | 0+ | 0+ | 0+ | 001 | 014 | 099 | 450 | 774 | 986 | 17 |
| | 18 | 0+ | 0+ | 0+ | 0+ | 0+ | 0+ | 0+ | 0+ | 002 | 018 | 150 | 397 | 835 | 18 |

$$\sum_{x=r}^{n} \binom{n}{x} p^x q^{n-x}$$

| n | r | .01 | .05 | .10 | .20 | .30 | .40 | .50 | .60 | .70 | .80 | .90 | .95 | .99 | r |
|---|---|---|---|---|---|---|---|---|---|---|---|---|---|---|---|
| 19 | 0 | 1 | 1 | 1 | 1 | 1 | 1 | 1 | 1 | 1 | 1 | 1 | 1 | 1 | 0 |
| | 1 | 174 | 623 | 865 | 986 | 999 | 1− | 1− | 1− | 1− | 1− | 1− | 1− | 1− | 1 |
| | 2 | 015 | 245 | 580 | 917 | 990 | 999 | 1− | 1− | 1− | 1− | 1− | 1− | 1− | 2 |
| | 3 | 001 | 067 | 295 | 763 | 954 | 995 | 1− | 1− | 1− | 1− | 1− | 1− | 1− | 3 |
| | 4 | 0+ | 013 | 115 | 545 | 867 | 977 | 998 | 1− | 1− | 1− | 1− | 1− | 1− | 4 |
| | 5 | 0+ | 002 | 035 | 327 | 718 | 930 | 990 | 999 | 1− | 1− | 1− | 1− | 1− | 5 |
| | 6 | 0+ | 0+ | 009 | 163 | 526 | 837 | 968 | 997 | 1− | 1− | 1− | 1− | 1− | 6 |
| | 7 | 0+ | 0+ | 002 | 068 | 334 | 692 | 916 | 988 | 999 | 1− | 1− | 1− | 1− | 7 |
| | 8 | 0+ | 0+ | 0+ | 023 | 182 | 512 | 820 | 965 | 997 | 1− | 1− | 1− | 1− | 8 |
| | 9 | 0+ | 0+ | 0+ | 007 | 084 | 333 | 676 | 912 | 989 | 1− | 1− | 1− | 1− | 9 |
| | 10 | 0+ | 0+ | 0+ | 002 | 033 | 186 | 500 | 814 | 967 | 998 | 1− | 1− | 1− | 10 |
| | 11 | 0+ | 0+ | 0+ | 0+ | 011 | 088 | 324 | 667 | 916 | 993 | 1− | 1− | 1− | 11 |
| | 12 | 0+ | 0+ | 0+ | 0+ | 003 | 035 | 180 | 488 | 818 | 977 | 1− | 1− | 1− | 12 |
| | 13 | 0+ | 0+ | 0+ | 0+ | 001 | 012 | 084 | 308 | 666 | 932 | 998 | 1− | 1− | 13 |
| | 14 | 0+ | 0+ | 0+ | 0+ | 0+ | 003 | 032 | 163 | 474 | 837 | 991 | 1− | 1− | 14 |
| | 15 | 0+ | 0+ | 0+ | 0+ | 0+ | 001 | 010 | 070 | 282 | 673 | 965 | 998 | 1− | 15 |
| | 16 | 0+ | 0+ | 0+ | 0+ | 0+ | 0+ | 002 | 023 | 133 | 455 | 885 | 987 | 1− | 16 |
| | 17 | 0+ | 0+ | 0+ | 0+ | 0+ | 0+ | 0+ | 005 | 046 | 337 | 705 | 933 | 999 | 17 |
| | 18 | 0+ | 0+ | 0+ | 0+ | 0+ | 0+ | 0+ | 001 | 010 | 083 | 420 | 755 | 985 | 18 |
| | 19 | 0+ | 0+ | 0+ | 0+ | 0+ | 0+ | 0+ | 0+ | 001 | 014 | 135 | 377 | 826 | 19 |
| 20 | 0 | 1 | 1 | 1 | 1 | 1 | 1 | 1 | 1 | 1 | 1 | 1 | 1 | 1 | 0 |
| | 1 | 182 | 642 | 878 | 988 | 999 | 1− | 1− | 1− | 1− | 1− | 1− | 1− | 1− | 1 |
| | 2 | 017 | 264 | 608 | 931 | 992 | 999 | 1− | 1− | 1− | 1− | 1− | 1− | 1− | 2 |
| | 3 | 001 | 075 | 323 | 794 | 965 | 996 | 1− | 1− | 1− | 1− | 1− | 1− | 1− | 3 |
| | 4 | 0+ | 016 | 133 | 589 | 893 | 984 | 999 | 1− | 1− | 1− | 1− | 1− | 1− | 4 |
| | 5 | 0+ | 003 | 043 | 370 | 762 | 949 | 994 | 1− | 1− | 1− | 1− | 1− | 1− | 5 |
| | 6 | 0+ | 0+ | 011 | 196 | 584 | 874 | 979 | 998 | 1− | 1− | 1− | 1− | 1− | 6 |
| | 7 | 0+ | 0+ | 002 | 087 | 392 | 750 | 942 | 994 | 1− | 1− | 1− | 1− | 1− | 7 |
| | 8 | 0+ | 0+ | 0+ | 032 | 228 | 584 | 868 | 979 | 999 | 1− | 1− | 1− | 1− | 8 |
| | 9 | 0+ | 0+ | 0+ | 010 | 113 | 404 | 748 | 943 | 995 | 1− | 1− | 1− | 1− | 9 |
| | 10 | 0+ | 0+ | 0+ | 003 | 048 | 245 | 588 | 872 | 983 | 999 | 1− | 1− | 1− | 10 |
| | 11 | 0+ | 0+ | 0+ | 001 | 017 | 128 | 412 | 755 | 952 | 997 | 1− | 1− | 1− | 11 |
| | 12 | 0+ | 0+ | 0+ | 0+ | 005 | 057 | 252 | 596 | 887 | 990 | 1− | 1− | 1− | 12 |
| | 13 | 0+ | 0+ | 0+ | 0+ | 001 | 021 | 132 | 416 | 772 | 968 | 1− | 1− | 1− | 13 |
| | 14 | 0+ | 0+ | 0+ | 0+ | 0+ | 006 | 058 | 250 | 608 | 913 | 998 | 1− | 1− | 14 |
| | 15 | 0+ | 0+ | 0+ | 0+ | 0+ | 002 | 021 | 126 | 416 | 804 | 989 | 1− | 1− | 15 |
| | 16 | 0+ | 0+ | 0+ | 0+ | 0+ | 0+ | 006 | 051 | 238 | 630 | 957 | 997 | 1− | 16 |
| | 17 | 0+ | 0+ | 0+ | 0+ | 0+ | 0+ | 001 | 016 | 107 | 411 | 867 | 984 | 1− | 17 |
| | 18 | 0+ | 0+ | 0+ | 0+ | 0+ | 0+ | 0+ | 004 | 035 | 206 | 677 | 925 | 999 | 18 |
| | 19 | 0+ | 0+ | 0+ | 0+ | 0+ | 0+ | 0+ | 001 | 008 | 069 | 392 | 736 | 983 | 19 |
| | 20 | 0+ | 0+ | 0+ | 0+ | 0+ | 0+ | 0+ | 0+ | 001 | 012 | 122 | 358 | 818 | 20 |

An entry in the table is the proportion under the entire curve which is between $Z = 0$ and a positive value of $Z$. Areas for negative values of $Z$ are obtained by symmetry.

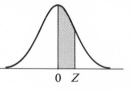

0  Z

| Z | .00 | .01 | .02 | .03 | .04 | .05 | .06 | .07 | .08 | .09 |
|---|---|---|---|---|---|---|---|---|---|---|
| 0.0 | .0000 | .0040 | .0080 | .0120 | .0160 | .0199 | .0239 | .0279 | .0319 | .0359 |
| 0.1 | .0398 | .0438 | .0478 | .0517 | .0557 | .0596 | .0636 | .0675 | .0714 | .0753 |
| 0.2 | .0793 | .0832 | .0871 | .0910 | .0948 | .0987 | .1026 | .1064 | .1103 | .1141 |
| 0.3 | .1179 | .1217 | .1255 | .1293 | .1331 | .1368 | .1406 | .1443 | .1480 | .1517 |
| 0.4 | .1554 | .1591 | .1628 | .1664 | .1700 | .1736 | .1772 | .1808 | .1844 | .1879 |
| 0.5 | .1915 | .1950 | .1985 | .2019 | .2054 | .2088 | .2123 | .2157 | .2190 | .2224 |
| 0.6 | .2257 | .2291 | .2324 | .2357 | .2389 | .2422 | .2454 | .2486 | .2517 | .2549 |
| 0.7 | .2580 | .2611 | .2642 | .2673 | .2703 | .2734 | .2764 | .2794 | .2823 | .2852 |
| 0.8 | .2881 | .2910 | .2939 | .2967 | .2995 | .3023 | .3051 | .3078 | .3106 | .3133 |
| 0.9 | .3159 | .3186 | .3212 | .3238 | .3264 | .3289 | .3315 | .3340 | .3365 | .3389 |
| 1.0 | .3413 | .3438 | .3461 | .3485 | .3508 | .3531 | .3554 | .3577 | .3599 | .3621 |
| 1.1 | .3643 | .3665 | .3686 | .3708 | .3729 | .3749 | .3770 | .3790 | .3810 | .3830 |
| 1.2 | .3849 | .3869 | .3888 | .3907 | .3925 | .3944 | .3962 | .3980 | .3997 | .4015 |
| 1.3 | .4032 | .4049 | .4066 | .4082 | .4099 | .4115 | .4131 | .4147 | .4162 | .4177 |
| 1.4 | .4192 | .4207 | .4222 | .4236 | .4251 | .4265 | .4279 | .4292 | .4306 | .4319 |
| 1.5 | .4332 | .4345 | .4357 | .4370 | .4382 | .4394 | .4406 | .4418 | .4429 | .4441 |
| 1.6 | .4452 | .4463 | .4474 | .4484 | .4495 | .4505 | .4515 | .4525 | .4535 | .4545 |
| 1.7 | .4554 | .4564 | .4573 | .4582 | .4591 | .4599 | .4608 | .4616 | .4625 | .4633 |
| 1.8 | .4641 | .4649 | .4656 | .4664 | .4671 | .4678 | .4686 | .4693 | .4699 | .4706 |
| 1.9 | .4713 | .4719 | .4726 | .4732 | .4738 | .4744 | .4750 | .4756 | .4761 | .4767 |
| 2.0 | .4772 | .4778 | .4783 | .4788 | .4793 | .4798 | .4803 | .4808 | .4812 | .4817 |
| 2.1 | .4821 | .4826 | .4830 | .4834 | .4838 | .4842 | .4846 | .4850 | .4854 | .4857 |
| 2.2 | .4861 | .4864 | .4868 | .4871 | .4875 | .4878 | .4881 | .4884 | .4887 | .4890 |
| 2.3 | .4893 | .4896 | .4898 | .4901 | .4904 | .4906 | .4909 | .4911 | .4913 | .4916 |
| 2.4 | .4918 | .4920 | .4922 | .4925 | .4927 | .4929 | .4931 | .4932 | .4934 | .4936 |
| 2.5 | .4938 | .4940 | .4941 | .4943 | .4945 | .4946 | .4948 | .4949 | .4951 | .4952 |
| 2.6 | .4953 | .4955 | .4956 | .4957 | .4959 | .4960 | .4961 | .4962 | .4963 | .4964 |
| 2.7 | .4965 | .4966 | .4967 | .4968 | .4969 | .4970 | .4971 | .4972 | .4973 | .4974 |
| 2.8 | .4974 | .4975 | .4976 | .4977 | .4977 | .4978 | .4979 | .4979 | .4980 | .4981 |
| 2.9 | .4981 | .4982 | .4982 | .4983 | .4984 | .4984 | .4985 | .4985 | .4986 | .4986 |
| 3.0 | .4987 | .4987 | .4987 | .4988 | .4988 | .4989 | .4989 | .4989 | .4990 | .4990 |

# APPENDIX VI: CRITICAL VALUES OF CHI-SQUARE

| $\nu$ | $\chi^2 0.995$ | $\chi^2 0.990$ | $\chi^2 0.975$ | $\chi^2 0.950$ | $\chi^2 0.900$ |
|---|---|---|---|---|---|
| 1 | 0.0000393 | 0.0001571 | 0.0009821 | 0.0039321 | 0.0157908 |
| 2 | 0.0100251 | 0.0201007 | 0.0506356 | 0.102587 | 0.210720 |
| 3 | 0.0717212 | 0.114832 | 0.215795 | 0.351846 | 0.584375 |
| 4 | 0.206990 | 0.297110 | 0.484419 | 0.710721 | 1.063623 |
| 5 | 0.411740 | 0.554300 | 0.831211 | 1.145476 | 1.61031 |
| 6 | 0.675727 | 0.872085 | 1.237347 | 1.63539 | 2.20413 |
| 7 | 0.989265 | 1.239043 | 1.68987 | 2.16735 | 2.83311 |
| 8 | 1.344419 | 1.646482 | 2.17973 | 2.73264 | 3.48954 |
| 9 | 1.734926 | 2.087912 | 2.70039 | 3.32511 | 4.16816 |
| 10 | 2.15585 | 2.55821 | 3.24697 | 3.94030 | 4.86518 |
| 11 | 2.60321 | 3.05347 | 3.81575 | 4.57481 | 5.57779 |
| 12 | 3.07382 | 3.57056 | 4.40379 | 5.22603 | 6.30380 |
| 13 | 3.56503 | 4.10691 | 5.00874 | 5.89186 | 7.04150 |
| 14 | 4.07468 | 4.66043 | 5.62872 | 6.57063 | 7.78953 |
| 15 | 4.60094 | 5.22935 | 6.26214 | 7.26094 | 8.54675 |
| 16 | 5.14224 | 5.81221 | 6.90766 | 7.96164 | 9.31223 |
| 17 | 5.69724 | 6.40776 | 7.56418 | 8.67176 | 10.0852 |
| 18 | 6.26481 | 7.01491 | 8.23075 | 9.39046 | 10.8649 |
| 19 | 6.84398 | 7.63273 | 8.90655 | 10.1170 | 11.6509 |
| 20 | 7.43386 | 8.26040 | 9.59083 | 10.8508 | 12.4426 |
| 21 | 8.03366 | 8.89720 | 10.28293 | 11.5913 | 13.2396 |
| 22 | 8.64272 | 9.54249 | 10.9823 | 12.3380 | 14.0415 |
| 23 | 9.26042 | 10.19567 | 11.6885 | 13.0905 | 14.8479 |
| 24 | 9.88623 | 10.8564 | 12.4011 | 13.8484 | 15.6587 |
| 25 | 10.5197 | 11.5240 | 13.1197 | 14.6114 | 16.4734 |
| 26 | 11.1603 | 12.1981 | 13.8439 | 15.3791 | 17.2919 |
| 27 | 11.8076 | 12.8786 | 14.5733 | 16.1513 | 18.1138 |
| 28 | 12.4613 | 13.5648 | 15.3079 | 16.9279 | 18.9392 |
| 29 | 13.1211 | 14.2565 | 16.0471 | 17.7083 | 19.7677 |
| 30 | 13.7867 | 14.9535 | 16.7908 | 18.4926 | 20.5992 |
| 40 | 20.7065 | 22.1643 | 24.4331 | 26.5093 | 29.0505 |
| 50 | 27.9907 | 29.7067 | 32.3574 | 34.7642 | 37.6886 |
| 60 | 35.5346 | 37.4848 | 40.4817 | 43.1879 | 46.4589 |
| 70 | 43.2752 | 45.4418 | 48.7576 | 51.7393 | 55.3290 |
| 80 | 51.1720 | 53.5400 | 57.1432 | 60.3915 | 64.2778 |
| 90 | 59.1963 | 61.7541 | 65.6466 | 69.1260 | 73.2912 |
| 100 | 67.3276 | 70.0648 | 74.2219 | 77.9295 | 82.3581 |

| $\chi^2 0.100$ | $\chi^2 0.050$ | $\chi^2 0.025$ | $\chi^2 0.010$ | $\chi^2 0.005$ | $\nu$ |
|---|---|---|---|---|---|
| 2.70554 | 3.84146 | 5.02389 | 6.63490 | 7.87944 | 1 |
| 4.60517 | 5.99147 | 7.37776 | 9.21034 | 10.5966 | 2 |
| 6.25139 | 7.81473 | 9.34840 | 11.3449 | 12.8381 | 3 |
| 7.77944 | 9.48773 | 11.1433 | 13.2767 | 14.8602 | 4 |
| 9.23635 | 11.0705 | 12.8325 | 15.0863 | 16.7496 | 5 |
| 10.6446 | 12.5916 | 14.4494 | 16.8119 | 18.5476 | 6 |
| 12.0170 | 14.0671 | 16.0128 | 18.4753 | 20.2777 | 7 |
| 13.3616 | 15.5073 | 17.5346 | 20.0902 | 21.9550 | 8 |
| 14.6837 | 16.9190 | 19.0228 | 21.6660 | 23.5893 | 9 |
| 15.9871 | 18.3070 | 20.4831 | 23.2093 | 25.1882 | 10 |
| 17.2750 | 19.6751 | 21.9200 | 24.7250 | 26.7569 | 11 |
| 18.5494 | 21.0261 | 23.3367 | 26.2170 | 28.2995 | 12 |
| 19.8119 | 22.3621 | 24.7356 | 27.6883 | 29.8194 | 13 |
| 21.0642 | 23.6848 | 26.1190 | 29.1413 | 31.3193 | 14 |
| 22.3072 | 24.9958 | 27.4884 | 30.5779 | 32.8013 | 15 |
| 23.5418 | 26.2962 | 28.8454 | 31.9999 | 34.2672 | 16 |
| 24.7690 | 27.5871 | 30.1910 | 33.4087 | 35.7185 | 17 |
| 25.9894 | 28.8693 | 31.5264 | 34.8053 | 37.1564 | 18 |
| 27.2036 | 30.1435 | 32.8523 | 36.1908 | 38.5822 | 19 |
| 28.4120 | 31.4104 | 34.1696 | 37.5662 | 39.9968 | 20 |
| 29.6151 | 32.6705 | 35.4789 | 38.9321 | 41.4010 | 21 |
| 30.8133 | 33.9244 | 36.7807 | 40.2894 | 42.7956 | 22 |
| 32.0069 | 35.1725 | 38.0757 | 41.6384 | 44.1813 | 23 |
| 33.1963 | 36.4151 | 39.3641 | 42.9798 | 45.5585 | 24 |
| 34.3816 | 37.6525 | 40.6465 | 44.3141 | 46.9278 | 25 |
| 35.5631 | 38.8852 | 41.9232 | 45.6417 | 48.2899 | 26 |
| 36.7412 | 40.1133 | 43.1944 | 46.9630 | 49.6449 | 27 |
| 37.9159 | 41.3372 | 44.4607 | 48.2782 | 50.9933 | 28 |
| 39.0875 | 42.5569 | 45.7222 | 49.5879 | 52.3356 | 29 |
| 40.2560 | 43.7729 | 46.9792 | 50.8922 | 53.6720 | 30 |
| 51.8030 | 55.7585 | 59.3417 | 63.6907 | 66.7659 | 40 |
| 63.9671 | 67.5048 | 71.4202 | 76.1539 | 79.4900 | 50 |
| 74.3970 | 79.0819 | 83.2976 | 88.3794 | 91.9517 | 60 |
| 85.5271 | 90.5312 | 95.0231 | 100.425 | 104.215 | 70 |
| 96.5782 | 101.879 | 106.629 | 112.329 | 116.321 | 80 |
| 107.565 | 113.145 | 118.136 | 124.116 | 128.299 | 90 |
| 118.498 | 124.342 | 129.561 | 135.807 | 140.169 | 100 |

# Answers

## CHAPTER 1

### Section 1-1

1. $S = \{8, 10, 12\}$.   3. $V = \{a, e, i, o, u\}$.
5. $A = \{x : x \geq 13, x \in W\}$.
7. $O = \{x : x = 2n - 1, n \in W, n \neq 0\}$.
9. $5 \in W$.   11. $^{-}1 \notin W$.   13. $17 \notin (C \cup D)$.
15. $A \subset B$.   17. $\{0, 1, 2, 4, 5, 6, 8\}$.
19. $\{0, 1, 2, 5, 6, 9, 10, 11, 12\}$.   21. $\{0, 1, 2, 3, 4, 5, 6, 7, 8, 11\}$.
23. $\emptyset$.   25. $\{0, 1, 2, 5, 6\}$.   27. $\emptyset$.
29. $\emptyset$.   31. $\{0, 1, 2, 4, 5, 6, 8\}$.
33. $\{0, 3, 5, 7, 9, 11\}$.   35. $\emptyset$.   37 $A$.
39. $\{0, 3, 5, 7, 9, 11\}$.   41. $A$.

### Section 1-2

1. True   3. True.
5. True.
7. True.
9. True.
11. No.   13. All are denumerable.

375

## Section 1-3

| | | | | | |
|---|---|---|---|---|---|
| 1. | 1.7. | 3. | 3. | 5. | 3.6. |
| 7. | $\sqrt{3}$. | 9. | No. | 11. | .25 |
| 13. | $.\overline{3}$ | 15. | $.0\overline{9}$ | 17. | $.41\overline{6}$ |
| 19. | $\frac{1}{4}$. | 21. | $\frac{5}{8}$. | 23. | $\frac{11}{100}$. |
| 25. | $\frac{3}{8}$. | 27. | 1. | 29. | $\frac{34}{333}$. |
| 31. | $\dfrac{1234}{9999}$. | 33. | $\frac{129}{198}$. | | |

## Section 1-4

1. a. $\frac{1}{4}, \frac{1}{3}, \frac{2}{5}, \frac{1}{2}, \frac{5}{8}, \frac{2}{3}$.
   b. $\frac{6}{7}, \frac{7}{8}, \frac{8}{9}, \frac{64}{71}, \frac{7}{6}, 2\frac{1}{3}$.
   c. 1.25, 2.011, 21.72, 21.721, 23.7.
   d. 2.734, 2.737, 3.0416, 3.1416, 3.14165.
3. $x < 2$.   5. $x < \frac{5}{2}$.   7. $x > \frac{28}{3}$.   9. $0 < x < 2$.   11. $x > \frac{5}{3}$.
13. $x > \frac{-1}{5}$ or $x < ^-1$.
★15. By Property 4: $a < b \Rightarrow a \cdot a < b \cdot a$ or $a^2 < ba$ since $a > 0$.
    By Property 4: $a < b \Rightarrow a \cdot b < b \cdot b$ or $ba < b^2$ since $b > 0$.
    By Property 6: $a^2 < b^2$, since $a^2 < ba$ and $ba < b^2$.
★17. $a < b \Rightarrow ac < bc$   for $c > 0$.
    $c < d \Rightarrow bc < bd$   for $b > 0$.
    ∴ $ac < bc$ and $bc < bd$, so $ac < bd$.
★19. $a < b \Rightarrow a - a < b - a \Rightarrow 0 < b - a$, and
    $0 < b - a \Rightarrow 0 - b < b - a - b \Rightarrow ^-b < ^-a$.
★21. Suppose the conclusion is false, i.e., $\frac{1}{a} \leq 0$. Then $a \cdot \frac{1}{a} \leq a \cdot 0$ for $a > 0$
    or $1 \leq 0$. This is a contradiction. ∴ $\frac{1}{a} > 0$.
★23. By Problem 22: $y < g \Rightarrow \frac{1}{g} < \frac{1}{y}$.
    By Property 4: $\frac{1}{g} \cdot a < \frac{1}{y} \cdot a$ or $\frac{a}{g} < \frac{a}{y}$ for $a > 0$.
    By Problem 21: $\frac{1}{y} > 0$, since $y > 0$.
    By Property 4: $a \cdot \frac{1}{y} < x \cdot \frac{1}{y}$ or $\frac{a}{y} < \frac{x}{y}$, since $a < x$.
    By Property 6: $\frac{a}{g} < \frac{x}{y}$, since $\frac{a}{g} < \frac{a}{y}$ and $\frac{a}{y} < \frac{x}{y}$.
    Similarly, $\frac{x}{y} < \frac{b}{c}$. ∴ $\frac{a}{g} < \frac{x}{y} < \frac{b}{c}$ by Property 6.

## Section 1-5

1. $[3, 5]$.
3. $(7, 9]$.
5. $[a, b)$.
7. $[a, a + 1]$.
9. $^-1 < x < 0$.
11. $^-5 \leq x \leq 2$.
13. $a < x \leq c$.
15. $b \leq x < b + 2$.
17. No, $c$ is not between 3, 4.
19. No, $[3, 5)$ is not an open interval.
21. No, $3 \notin (3, 4)$.
23. Yes.

## Section 1-6

1. 14.
3. 3.
5. 195.
7. 1050.
9. $\frac{67}{99}$.
11. $\frac{754}{999}$.
13. GLB = 2, LUB = 3.
15. GLB = 5, no LUB.
17. LUB = 0, no GLB.
19. No, no.

## Section 1-7

1. a. $\{(x_1, y_1)(x_2, y_2)(x_3, y_3)\}$.
   b. $\{(x_1, y_1)(x_2, y_1)(x_3, y_1)\}$.
   c. $\{(x_1, y_1)(x_2, y_3)(x_3, y_3)\}$.
   d. $\{(x_1, y_3)(x_2, y_1)(x_3, y_2)\}$.
3. a. $D(g) = \{x_1, x_2, x_3\}$.
      $R(g) = \{y_1, y_2, y_3\}$.
   b. $D(g) = \{x_1, x_2, x_3, x_4\}$.
      $R(g) = \{y_1, y_2, y_3, y_4\}$.
   c. $D(r) = \{x_1, x_2, x_3, x_4\}$.
      $R(r) = \{y_1, y_2, y_3, y_4\}$.
   d. $D(q) = \{x_2, x_3, x_4\}$.
      $R(q) = \{y_1, y_2, y_3, y_4\}$
5. a. 1–1.
   b. Collapsing.
   c. 1–1.
   d. Collapsing.
   e. 1–1.
   f. Collapsing.

## Section 1-8

1. 2.
3. 2.
5. 0.
7. $\frac{5}{2}$.
9. $\frac{5}{2}$.
11. $^-5.1$.
13. 5.1.
15. 1.
17. 1.
19. 7.

21.

23.

25.

27.

29.

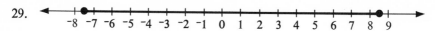

31.

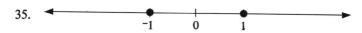

★33.           $a > 0:$
$$-c \leq ax - b \leq c$$
$$b - c \leq ax \qquad \leq b + c$$
$$\frac{b - c}{a} \leq x \qquad \leq \frac{b + c}{a}$$

Midpoint is $\dfrac{1}{2}\left(\dfrac{b - c}{a} + \dfrac{b + c}{a}\right) = \dfrac{b}{a}$

$a < 0:$
$$-c \leq ax - b \leq c$$
$$b - c \leq ax \qquad \leq b + c$$
$$\frac{b - c}{a} \geq x \qquad \geq \frac{b + c}{a}$$

Midpoint is $\dfrac{1}{2}\left(\dfrac{b - c}{a} + \dfrac{b + c}{a}\right) = \dfrac{b}{a}$

35.

37.

39.

41.

43.

45.

47.   $|a - b| = |a + (^-b)| \leq |a| + |^-b|$ by Exercise 46,
                    $\leq |a| + |b|.$

49.   Yes.                    51.    Yes.

53.   No; $|x - 4| \geq 2$ is not an interval.

## Section 1-9

1. a. (1, 1).　　　b. (2, 2).　　　c. (5, 4).
   d. (2, 4).　　　e. ($^-$2, 4).　　　f. ($^-$2, 1),
   g. ($^-$3, 5).　　　h. ($^-$6, 2).　　　i. ($^-$5, $^-$1).
   j. ($^-$3, $^-$3).　　　k. ($^-$5, $^-$4).　　　l. ($^-$3, $^-$5).
   m. (4, $^-$2).　　　n. (3, $^-$5).　　　o. (2, $^-$6).
   p. (4, 0).　　　q. (0, 2).　　　r. (0, 0).
   s. (0, $^-$3).　　　t. ($^-$4, 0).

## Section 1-10

1.

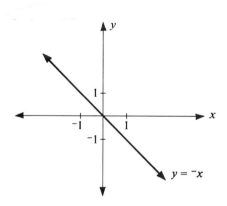

$y = {}^-x$

3.

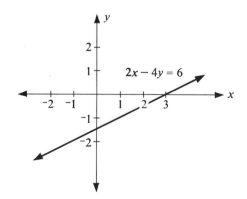

$2x - 4y = 6$

5.

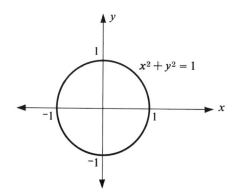

7.

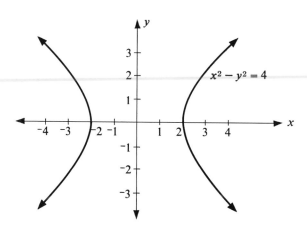

9.

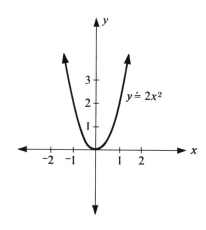

11.

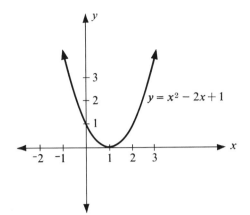

$y = x^2 - 2x + 1$

13.

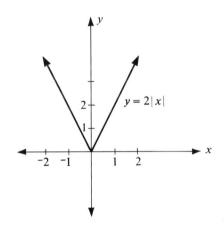

$y = 2|x|$

15.

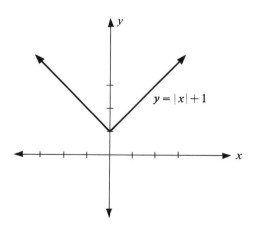

$y = |x| + 1$

## Section 1-11

|     |     | Slope | y-intercept |
|-----|-----|-------|-------------|
| 1.  | a.  | 3     | 2           |
|     | b.  | $^-3$ | 2           |
|     | c.  | 3     | $^-2$       |
|     | d.  | $^-3$ | $^-2$       |
|     | e.  | $-\frac{3}{2}$ | 2  |

|     |     | Equation | Slope | y-intercept |
|-----|-----|----------|-------|-------------|
| 3.  | a.  | $y = \frac{3}{2}x - 6$ | $\frac{3}{2}$ | $^-6$ |
|     | b.  | $y = \frac{3}{4}x + 3$ | $\frac{3}{4}$ | 3 |
|     | c.  | $y = \frac{-3}{2}x + 2$ | $-\frac{3}{2}$ | 2 |
|     | d.  | $y = \frac{6}{7}x - 6$ | $\frac{6}{7}$ | $^-6$ |

5. Least amount of inequality: army officers.
   Most amount of inequality: lawyers.
7. a. Supply.    b. Supply.    c. Demand.    d. Demand.

# CHAPTER 2

## Section 2-1

1. statement—simple.          3. statement—compound.
5. statement—compound.        7. statement—simple.
9. not a statement.          11. not a statement.
13. statement—compound.

## Section 2-2

1. a. The chief cause of pollution is not overpopulation.
   b. The world is not doomed.
   c. The chief cause of pollution is overpopulation and the world is doomed.
   d. The chief cause of pollution is overpopulation or the world is doomed.
   e. The chief cause of pollution is not overpopulation and the world is not doomed.
   f. The chief cause of pollution is not overpopulation or the world is not doomed.
3. True.

5. If it is not a dog, then it does not have four feet.
7. a. $P \rightarrow Q$.
   b. $Q \rightarrow P$, $\sim P \rightarrow \sim Q$, $\sim Q \rightarrow \sim P$.
   c. $\sim Q \rightarrow \sim P$.
   d. $\sim Q \rightarrow \sim P$.
   e. $\sim P \rightarrow \sim Q$.
   (f) $\sim P \rightarrow \sim Q$.

## Section 2-3

*15. (a) $T(\sim P) = 1 - T(P)$

| $P$ | $T(P)$ | $\sim P$ | $T(\sim P)$ | $1 - T(P)$ |
|---|---|---|---|---|
| T | 1 | F | 0 | 0 |
| F | 0 | T | 1 | 1 |

(b) $T(P \vee Q) = T(P) + T(Q) - T(P)T(Q)$.

| $P$ | $Q$ | $T(P)$ | $T(Q)$ | $T(P) + T(Q) - T(P)T(Q)$ | $T(P \vee Q)$ |
|---|---|---|---|---|---|
| T | T | 1 | 1 | $1 + 1 - 1 = 1$ | 1 |
| T | F | 1 | 0 | $1 + 0 - 0 = 1$ | 1 |
| F | T | 0 | 1 | $0 + 1 - 0 = 1$ | 1 |
| F | F | 0 | 0 | $0 + 0 - 0 = 0$ | 0 |

(c) $T(P \wedge Q) = T(P)T(Q)$.

| $P$ | $Q$ | $T(P)$ | $T(Q)$ | $T(P)T(Q)$ | $T(P \wedge Q)$ |
|---|---|---|---|---|---|
| T | T | 1 | 1 | 1 | 1 |
| T | F | 1 | 0 | 0 | 0 |
| F | T | 0 | 1 | 0 | 0 |
| F | F | 0 | 0 | 0 | 0 |

(d) $T(P \rightarrow Q) = 1 - T(P) + T(P)T(Q)$.

| $P$ | $Q$ | $T(P)$ | $T(Q)$ | $1 - T(P) + T(P)T(Q)$ | $T(P \rightarrow Q)$ |
|---|---|---|---|---|---|
| T | T | 1 | 1 | $1 - 1 + 1 = 1$ | 1 |
| T | F | 1 | 0 | $1 - 1 + 0 = 0$ | 0 |
| F | T | 0 | 1 | $1 - 0 + 0 = 1$ | 1 |
| F | F | 0 | 0 | $1 - 0 + 0 = 1$ | 1 |

(e)  $T(P \leftrightarrow Q) = 1 - T(P) - T(Q) + 2T(P)T(Q).$

| $P$ | $Q$ | $T(P)$ | $T(Q)$ | $1 - T(P) - T(Q) + 2T(P)T(Q)$ | | | | | $T(P \leftrightarrow Q)$ |
|-----|-----|--------|--------|------|------|------|------|------|------|
| T | T | 1 | 1 | $1 -$ | $1$ | $- 1$ | $+$ | $2 \cdot 1 = 1$ | 1 |
| T | F | 1 | 0 | $1 -$ | $1$ | $- 0$ | $+$ | $2 \cdot 0 = 0$ | 0 |
| F | T | 0 | 1 | $1 -$ | $0$ | $- 1$ | $+$ | $2 \cdot 0 = 0$ | 0 |
| F | F | 0 | 0 | $1 -$ | $0$ | $- 0$ | $+$ | $2 \cdot 0 = 1$ | 1 |

17a.  Let $G = \sim(P \wedge \sim Q)$ and $H = (\sim Q \vee P)$

$$T(S) = T(G) + T(H) - T(G)T(H)$$
$$= T(G) + T(H)[1 - T(G)].$$

Note.

$$T(G) = 1 - T(P \wedge \sim Q) = 1 - T(P)T(\sim Q)$$

and

$$T(H) = T(\sim Q) + T(P) - T(\sim Q)T(P).$$

So,

$$T(S) = 1 - T(P)T(\sim Q)$$
$$+ T(P)T(\sim Q)[T(\sim Q) + T(P) - T(\sim Q)T(P)]$$
$$= 1 - T(P)T(\sim Q) + T(P)T(\sim Q) + T(P)T(\sim Q) - T(\sim Q)T(P)$$
$$= 1 \qquad\qquad \text{(Note: } [T(\sim Q)]^2 = T(\sim Q)$$
$$\text{and } [T(P)]^2 = T(P)) = 1.$$

$S$ is true regardless of truth value of $P$ and $Q$. $\therefore$ $S$ is logically true.

17b.  $T[S \leftrightarrow R] = 1 - T(S) - T(R) + 2T(S)T(R)$

$$T(R) = T(\sim P)T(\sim Q) = [1 - T(P)][1 - T(Q)]$$
$$= 1 - T(P) - T(Q) + T(P)T(Q)$$
$$T(S) = 1 - T(P \vee Q) = 1 - T(P) - T(Q) + T(P)T(Q)$$

Hence $T(R) = T(S)$. Replacing $T(R)$ by $T(S)$ in expression for $T[S \leftrightarrow R]$,

$$T[S \leftrightarrow R] = 1 - T(S) - T(S) + 2[T(S)]^2$$
$$= 1 - T(S) - T(S) + 2T(S)$$
$$= 1.$$

$S \leftrightarrow R$ is true regardless of truth value of $S$ and $R$. $\therefore$ $S$ and $R$ are logically equivalent.

17c. $(P \rightarrow Q) \wedge (Q \rightarrow P) \Leftrightarrow Q \leftrightarrow P$

| | |
|---|---|
| $P \rightarrow Q$ | $\Leftrightarrow (P \wedge \sim Q) \rightarrow \sim P$ |
| $P \rightarrow Q$ | $\Leftrightarrow \sim Q \rightarrow \sim P$ |
| $P \rightarrow Q$ | $\Leftrightarrow (P \wedge \sim Q) \rightarrow Q$ |

## Section 2-4

1. There is at least one number that is not even.
3. At least one plane figure does not have points.
5. No rabbits hop.
7. Some bunnies are rabbits.
9. $(\exists x)|x| < x$
11. $(\exists x)x \neq x$
13. There exists a student who is a radical.
15. Every student is a radical.
17. No students are radicals.
19. There exists a student who is not a radical.

## Section 2-5

7. valid. 9. valid.

## CHAPTER 3

## Section 3-1

1. $(3 \quad ^-8 \quad 0)$. 
3. $\begin{pmatrix} 7 \\ 3 \end{pmatrix}$. 
5. $\begin{pmatrix} ^-5 \\ 3 \\ 0 \end{pmatrix}$. 
7. $\begin{pmatrix} ^-4 \\ ^-7 \\ 6 \end{pmatrix}$.

9. $(13 \quad ^-14 \quad ^-6)$. 
11. $(^-9 \quad 15 \quad 21)$. 
13. Not possible.

15. $(23 \quad ^-16 \quad 12)$. 
17. $(21 \quad ^-20 \quad ^-4)$. 
19. $(16 \quad ^-12 \quad 4)$.

21. Yes. 
23. $v_1 = 3, v_2 = 2, v_3 = 1, v_4 = 0$.

25. $y_1 = {}^-9, y_2 = {}^-4, y_3 = {}^-2.$

27. $\begin{pmatrix} 393.8 \\ 507.9 \\ 973.7 \\ 1422.3 \end{pmatrix}.$

29. a. $\begin{pmatrix} 138\frac{3}{4} \\ 85 \\ 365\frac{3}{4} \\ 47 \end{pmatrix}$    b. $\begin{pmatrix} 104\frac{1}{2} \\ 47 \\ 310 \\ 37\frac{1}{2} \end{pmatrix}$    c. $\begin{pmatrix} 34\frac{1}{4} \\ 38 \\ 55\frac{3}{4} \\ 9\frac{1}{2} \end{pmatrix}$

31. a. $\begin{pmatrix} 7.00 \\ 7.00 \\ 7.00 \\ 7.25 \\ 8.70 \\ 8.50 \\ 8.30 \\ 8.00 \end{pmatrix}.$    b. $\begin{pmatrix} 490 \\ 485 \\ 500 \\ 500 \\ 500 \\ 505 \\ 515 \\ 520 \end{pmatrix}.$    c. $\begin{pmatrix} 483.00 \\ 478.00 \\ 493.00 \\ 492.75 \\ 491.30 \\ 496.50 \\ 506.70 \\ 512.00 \end{pmatrix}.$

These answers are approximate.

## Section 3-2

1. $^-1.$          3. $^-1.$          5. $^-3.$          7. $^-1.$
9. 1.

11. a. $(2 \quad 3 \quad 1 \quad \frac{1}{2}).$    b. $\begin{pmatrix} 0.79 \\ 0.39 \\ 0.20 \\ 0.44 \end{pmatrix}.$    c. \$3.17.

13. a. $(6 \quad 1 \quad \frac{1}{2} \quad 3 \quad 2 \quad 1 \quad 1 \quad 2).$

    b. $\begin{pmatrix} 110 \\ 100 \\ 68 \\ 115 \\ 55 \\ 100 \\ 330 \\ 80 \end{pmatrix}.$    c. 1839 calories.

## Section 3-3

1.  *D.*                3.  *B, G.*                5.  *H.*                7.  Yes.
9.  No.                          11.  $x_{11} = 3, x_{12} = 2, x_{21} = 5, x_{22} = 0.$

13.  $\begin{pmatrix} 13 & 1 \\ 4 & {}^-1 \end{pmatrix}.$        15.  $\begin{pmatrix} {}^-8 & 4 \\ {}^-6 & 1 \end{pmatrix}.$        17.  Not possible.

19.  $\begin{pmatrix} 3 & 8 & 15 \\ 4 & 11 & 15 \\ 7 & 17 & 18 \end{pmatrix}.$        21.  $\begin{pmatrix} 13 & 2 \\ 5 & {}^-1 \end{pmatrix}.$

23.  $z_{11} = 1, z_{12} = 10, z_{21} = 9, z_{22} = {}^-2.$
25.  $x_{11} = 9, x_{22} = 12, y_{21} = 6, z_{12} = 10.$

27.  a.  $\begin{pmatrix} 514{,}875 & 1{,}699 & 3{,}514 & 3{,}813 \\ 1{,}417{,}511 & 16{,}491 & 8{,}702 & 37{,}573 \\ 825{,}750 & 2{,}122 & 2{,}348 & 3{,}741 \end{pmatrix}.$

  b.  $\begin{pmatrix} 318{,}565 & 621 & 1{,}784 & 1{,}818 \\ 918{,}191 & 10{,}640 & 3{,}893 & 20{,}171 \\ 638{,}485 & 1{,}141 & 1{,}029 & 2{,}258 \end{pmatrix}.$

  c.  $\begin{pmatrix} 196{,}310 & 1{,}078 & 1{,}730 & 1{,}995 \\ 499{,}320 & 5{,}851 & 4{,}809 & 17{,}402 \\ 187{,}265 & 981 & 1{,}319 & 1{,}483 \end{pmatrix}.$

## Section 3-4

1.  $\begin{pmatrix} 6 \\ {}^-3 \\ 9 \end{pmatrix}.$        3.  $\begin{pmatrix} 10 & 8 & 6 \\ 0 & 2 & 4 \\ 2 & {}^-4 & 2 \end{pmatrix}.$        5.  $(13 \quad 12).$

7.  $\begin{pmatrix} 34 & 5 \\ 15 & 5 \end{pmatrix}.$        9.  $\begin{pmatrix} 19 & {}^-3 & 14 \\ {}^-2 & {}^-1 & {}^-2 \end{pmatrix}.$        11.  Yes, $3 \times 5.$

13.  $(7810 \quad .48 \quad .425 \quad 163).$
15.  a.  $\begin{array}{c} \\ A \\ B \\ C \end{array} \begin{array}{ccc} A & B & C \\ \begin{pmatrix} 0 & 1 & 0 \\ 0 & 0 & 1 \\ 1 & 0 & 0 \end{pmatrix} \end{array}$        b.  $\begin{array}{c} \\ A \\ B \\ C \end{array} \begin{array}{ccc} A & B & C \\ \begin{pmatrix} 0 & 1 & 1 \\ 0 & 0 & 1 \\ 0 & 0 & 0 \end{pmatrix} \end{array}$

19.  a.                 UC   Stan   USC   UCLA

$$\begin{array}{c} \text{UC} \\ \text{Stan} \\ \text{USC} \\ \text{UCLA} \end{array} \begin{pmatrix} 0 & 1 & 0 & 0 \\ 0 & 0 & 0 & 0 \\ 1 & 1 & 0 & 1 \\ 1 & 1 & 0 & 0 \end{pmatrix}.$$

   b.  Powers: UC is 1; Stan is 0; USC is 6; UCLA is 3.
       Ranking: 1. USC; 2. UCLA; 3. UC; 4. Stan.

## Section 3-5

7.  $\begin{pmatrix} 7 & 6 & 5 \\ ^-1 & 0 & 2 \\ 3 & 1 & 2 \end{pmatrix}.$     9.  $\begin{pmatrix} 21 & 18 & 15 \\ ^-3 & 0 & 6 \\ 9 & 3 & 6 \end{pmatrix}.$     11.  $\begin{pmatrix} 3 & 0 & 0 \\ 0 & 3 & 0 \\ 0 & 0 & 3 \end{pmatrix}.$

13.  Class of square matrices with all elements zero except on the diagonal
     (from left to right) where they are all equal. (All the diagonal elements
     may be zero.)

## Section 3-6

1.  $^-14.$          3.  0.              5.  8.              7.  0.
9.  $-288.$         11.  a.  0.         13.  a.  2.         15.  a.  $^-90.$
                         b.  0.              b.  2.              b.  $^-90.$
17.  1.             19.  0.             21.  $x = \frac{24}{5}; y = \frac{11}{5}.$
23.  $x = 1; y = ^-1; z = 0.$
25.  $r = \frac{3}{5}; s = ^-\frac{2}{5}; t = \frac{3}{5}; u = ^-\frac{2}{5}.$

## Section 3-7

1.  a.  $\begin{pmatrix} 2 & ^-3 \\ ^-2 & 1 \end{pmatrix}.$     b.  $\begin{pmatrix} ^-12 & 9 \\ ^-4 & 3 \end{pmatrix}.$     c.  $\begin{pmatrix} 14 & ^-16 & ^-6 \\ 16 & ^-17 & ^-12 \\ ^-8 & 13 & 6 \end{pmatrix}.$

3.  a.  $\begin{pmatrix} ^-\frac{1}{2} & \frac{1}{2} \\ \frac{3}{4} & ^-\frac{1}{4} \end{pmatrix}.$     b.  Not possible.     c.  $\begin{pmatrix} \frac{7}{9} & \frac{8}{9} & ^-\frac{4}{9} \\ ^-\frac{8}{9} & ^-\frac{17}{18} & \frac{13}{18} \\ ^-\frac{1}{3} & ^-\frac{2}{3} & \frac{1}{3} \end{pmatrix}.$

5.  a.  $\begin{pmatrix} -2 & 1 \\ \frac{3}{2} & -\frac{1}{2} \end{pmatrix}.$  b.  $\begin{pmatrix} 7 & 10 \\ 15 & 22 \end{pmatrix}.$  c.  $\begin{pmatrix} \frac{11}{2} & -\frac{5}{2} \\ -\frac{15}{4} & \frac{7}{4} \end{pmatrix}.$

   d.  $\begin{pmatrix} \frac{11}{2} & -\frac{5}{2} \\ -\frac{15}{4} & \frac{7}{4} \end{pmatrix}.$  e.  $\begin{pmatrix} 37 & 54 \\ 81 & 118 \end{pmatrix}.$  f.  $\begin{pmatrix} -\frac{59}{4} & \frac{27}{4} \\ \frac{81}{8} & -\frac{37}{8} \end{pmatrix}.$

   g.  $\begin{pmatrix} -\frac{59}{4} & \frac{27}{4} \\ \frac{81}{8} & -\frac{37}{8} \end{pmatrix}.$  h.  $(A^{-1})^n = A^{-n}.$

## Section 3-8

1.  $a = \frac{17}{5}; b = -\frac{8}{5}.$  3.  $x = \frac{94}{17}; y = -\frac{27}{17}; z = -\frac{16}{17}.$
5.  $x = -17; y = 24; z = 33; w = 14.$

# CHAPTER 4

## Section 4-1

1.  $\frac{1}{2}.$  3.  a.  $\frac{1}{4}.$  b.  $\frac{1}{4}.$  c.  $\frac{1}{4}.$  d.  $\frac{1}{4}.$
5.  {RB, RW, RR, BW, BR, BB, WR, WB, WW}.
7.  {0, 1, 2, 3, 4, 5}.
9.  {(1, 1), (1, 2), (1, 3), (1, 4), (1, 5), (1, 6), (2, 1), (2, 2), (2, 3), (2, 4), (2, 5), (2, 6), (3, 1), (3, 2), (3, 3), (3, 4), (3, 5), (3, 6), (4, 1), (4, 2), (4, 3), (4, 4), (4, 5), (4, 6), (5, 1), (5, 2), (5, 3), (5, 4), (5, 5), (5, 6), (6, 1), (6, 2), (6, 3), (6, 4), (6, 5), (6, 6)}.
11.  a.  $\frac{1}{36}.$  b.  $\frac{5}{36}.$  13.  $\frac{3}{8}.$  15.  $\frac{9}{10}.$
17.  $\approx 0.74.$  19.  $\frac{2}{9}.$

## Section 4-2

1.  $\frac{1}{6}.$  3.  $\frac{1}{2}.$  5.  $\frac{31}{36}.$
7.  $\frac{2}{3}.$  9.  $\frac{3}{7}.$  11.  $\frac{11}{36}.$

## Section 4-3

1. $\frac{2}{11}$.

3. $\frac{1}{6}$.

5. a. $\frac{1}{4}$.
   b. $\frac{4}{19}$.
   c. $\frac{21}{38}$.

7. a. $\frac{1}{49}$.
   b. $\frac{36}{49}$.
   c. $\frac{13}{49}$.
   d. $\frac{2}{49}$.

9. a. $\frac{13}{16}$.
   b. $\frac{1}{32}$.
   c. $\frac{5}{16}$.

11. a. $\frac{1}{100,000}$.
    b. $\frac{1}{25,000,000}$

## Section 4-4

1. 120.

3. 6.

5. $\frac{n!}{3!}$

7. 5.

9. 210.

11. 34,650.

13. 12.

15. a. 35.
    b. 20.
    c. 15.

17. $\frac{500!}{250!\,250!}$.

19. 676,000.

21. $\frac{8}{15}$.

## Section 4-5

1. $\frac{40}{243}$.

3. $\frac{232}{243}$.

5. 0.20.

7. $\frac{23}{648}$.

9. $\frac{125}{729}$.

11. $\frac{425}{729}$.

13. $\frac{15}{16}$.

15. 0.001.

17. 0.988.

19. .352

## Section 4-6

1. $\approx 6.46\%$.

3. $\approx 16$.

5. $2.10.

7. $1700.

9a. $^-$$1.20;

b. $^-$$2.40.

11. $1750.

## Section 4-7

1. $-$$12, $20, $40, $36, $20.

3. $74.67, $42.67, $22.67, $26.67, $42.67.

5. 66 boxes.
7. −$38, $27, $71, $62.50, $40.

9.

| Boxes sold | Boxes stocked | | | | |
|---|---|---|---|---|---|
| | 100 | 80 | 60 | 40 | 20 |
| 100 | 0 | 40 | 80 | 120 | 160 |
| 80 | 80 | 0 | 40 | 80 | 120 |
| 60 | 160 | 80 | 0 | 40 | 80 |
| 40 | 240 | 160 | 80 | 0 | 40 |
| 20 | 320 | 240 | 160 | 80 | 0 |

11a.

| Number of boxes stocked | Expected profit | Expected loss |
|---|---|---|
| 100 | $−4 | $136 |
| 80 | 46 | 86 |
| 60 | 78 | 54 |
| 40 | 65 | 67 |
| 20 | 40 | 92 |

b. 60 boxes.

13.

| Papers sold | Papers stocked | | | |
|---|---|---|---|---|
| | 200 | 150 | 100 | 50 |
| 200 | 400¢ | 300¢ | 200¢ | 100¢ |
| 150 | ⁻100 | 300 | 200 | 100 |
| 100 | ⁻600 | ⁻200 | 200 | 100 |
| 50 | ⁻1100 | ⁻700 | ⁻300 | 100 |

15.

| Papers sold | Papers stocked | | | |
|---|---|---|---|---|
| | 200 | 150 | 100 | 50 |
| 200 | 0¢ | 100¢ | 200¢ | 300¢ |
| 150 | 400 | 0 | 100 | 200 |
| 100 | 800 | 400 | 0 | 100 |
| 50 | 1200 | 800 | 400 | 0 |

17a.

| Number of Papers stocked | Expected profit | Expected loss |
|---|---|---|
| 200 | −625 | 820¢ |
| 150 | −275 | 470 |
| 100 | − 25 | 220 |
| 50 | 100 | 95 |

b.  50.        c.  50.        d.  50.

19.    about 27 boxes.

21.

| Boxes sold | Boxes stocked | | | | | | | |
|---|---|---|---|---|---|---|---|---|
| | 30 | 29 | 28 | 27 | 26 | 25 | 24 | 23 |
| 30 | 30 | 29 | 28 | 27 | 26 | 25 | 24 | 23 |
| 29 | 28 | 29 | 28 | 27 | 26 | 25 | 24 | 23 |
| 28 | 26 | 27 | 28 | 27 | 26 | 25 | 24 | 23 |
| 27 | 24 | 25 | 26 | 27 | 26 | 25 | 24 | 23 |
| 26 | 22 | 23 | 24 | 25 | 26 | 25 | 24 | 23 |
| 25 | 20 | 21 | 22 | 23 | 24 | 25 | 24 | 23 |
| 24 | 18 | 19 | 20 | 21 | 22 | 23 | 24 | 23 |
| 23 | 16 | 17 | 18 | 19 | 20 | 21 | 22 | 23 |

23a.    $24.20, $24.87, $25.27, $25.33, $25.13, $24.53, $23.77, $23.00.

b.    $2.90, $2.23, $1.83, $1.77, $1.97, $2.57, $3.33, $4.10.

## Section 4-8

1.

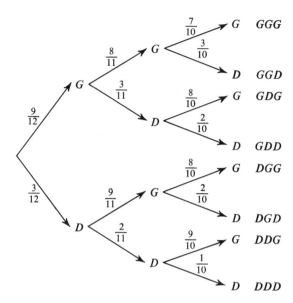

3. $\dfrac{21}{55}$.

5. $\dfrac{7}{55}$.

7. $\dfrac{11}{25}$.

9a. $\dfrac{1}{7}$.

b. $\dfrac{1}{2}$.

c. $\dfrac{5}{14}$.

11a. $\dfrac{1}{45}$.

b. $\dfrac{1}{15}$.

13. $\dfrac{1}{4}$.

15. $\dfrac{207}{2500}$.

17. $\dfrac{9136536}{244140625}$.

## Section 4-9

1. $\{S_1, S_2\}$.

3a. $\begin{pmatrix} \dfrac{11}{20} & \dfrac{9}{20} \\[2mm] \dfrac{3}{10} & \dfrac{7}{10} \end{pmatrix}$

b. $\dfrac{9}{20}$

c. $\dfrac{3}{10}$

d. $\dfrac{11}{20}$

e. $\dfrac{7}{10}$.

5. $\left(\dfrac{2}{5} \quad \dfrac{3}{5}\right)$.

7a. $\left(\dfrac{17}{40} \quad \dfrac{23}{40}\right)$.     b. $\left(\dfrac{33}{80} \quad \dfrac{47}{80}\right)$.     c. $\left(\dfrac{129}{320} \quad \dfrac{191}{320}\right)$.

9a. $\left(\dfrac{3}{5} \quad \dfrac{2}{5}\right)$.     b. $\left(\dfrac{3}{5} \quad \dfrac{2}{5}\right)$.

11a. $\left(\dfrac{1}{2} \quad \dfrac{2}{7} \quad \dfrac{3}{14}\right)$.     b. $\dfrac{1}{2}$.

13a. $\left(\dfrac{1}{3} \quad \dfrac{2}{3}\right)$.

  b.  300,000 customers.
  c.  600,000 customers.
  d.  Foods from the Sea ($F_2$).

15.  0.716.          17.  0.44.

19a. $\left(\dfrac{20}{500} \quad \dfrac{86}{500} \quad \dfrac{33}{500} \quad \dfrac{361}{500}\right)$.     b. $\left(\dfrac{40}{5000} \quad \dfrac{735}{5000} \quad \dfrac{390}{5000} \quad \dfrac{3835}{5000}\right)$.

21a.

$$
\begin{array}{c}
 & \text{Sea} \ \text{Tac} \ \text{Spo} \\
\begin{array}{c} \text{Sea} \\ \text{Tac} \\ \text{Spo} \end{array}
\left(\begin{array}{ccc}
0 & \dfrac{1}{2} & \dfrac{1}{2} \\
1 & 0 & 0 \\
\dfrac{1}{3} & \dfrac{1}{3} & \dfrac{1}{3}
\end{array}\right)
\end{array}
$$

  b.  Yes.

23.  $\dfrac{7}{18}$.

# CHAPTER 5

## Section 5-1

7.  a.  5.          b.  4.          c.  3.

## Section 5-2

1.  a.  Unordered.                    b.  Ordered, scaled, discrete.
    c.  Ordered, scaled, continuous.  d.  Ordered, scaled, continuous.

e.  Ordered, scaled, continuous.      f.  Unordered.
g.  Ordered, scaled, discrete.       h.  Unordered.

## Section 5-3

1.  a.  Mode.      b.  mean.      c.  Median.
3.  Mean: 17.32; mode: 18; median: 18.
5.  San Francisco: mean is $\approx 1.59$; mode is .005–.505, median is 1.005.
    Honolulu: mean is $\approx 1.71$; mode is .505–1.005; median is 1.505.
7.  *Radio:* mean is $\approx 198.8$; mode is multimodal (each value of data occurs once); median is 194.5.
    *Television:* mean is $\approx 70.6$; mode is 55.55–65.55; median is 68.05.
9.  b.  117.5–121.5.                     c.  130.1.
    d.  First quartile, 121.5; third quartile, 137.5.
    e.  145.5.                           f.  149.5.

## Section 5-4

The answers in 1-7 were found using ungrouped data.
1.  Means: 8 and 8.
    Standard deviations: 1.414 and 2.828.
3.  June: range is 2.4″; variance $\approx 0.41$; $\sigma \approx 0.64$.
    November: range is 2.6″; variance $\approx 0.40$; $\sigma \approx 0.63$.
    Tides vary more in June.
5.  San Francisco: range $= 4.05″$; variance $\approx 2.33$; $\sigma \approx 1.53$.
    Honolulu: range $= 3.5″$; variance $\approx 1.30$; $\sigma \approx 1.14$.
7.  *Radios:* range, 106; variance $\approx 1129$; $\sigma \approx 33.6$.
    *Television:* range, 32.5; variance $\approx 123.44$; $\sigma \approx 11.11$.
9.  Ranges not affected. 10 points added to each mean. Standard deviations unchanged.

## Section 5-5

1.  $\sigma = 1$; $\overline{X} = 6\frac{1}{2}$.
3.  a.  0.0668.      b.  0.1587.      c.  0.2417.      d.  0.3830.
5.  a.  0.3413.      b.  0.1587.      c.  0.4706.      d.  0.1587.
7.  a.  .38%.        b.  14.01%.      c.  58.99%.

## Section 5-6

1.  1.              3.  1.          5.  1.              7.  1.
9.  1.              11.  0.         13.  $\approx {}^{-}0.95$.

## Section 5-7

1. $y = 0.77x + 1.57$.

3. $y = \dfrac{59}{14}x - \dfrac{965}{7}$.

5. $y = \dfrac{1887}{14}x + \dfrac{5585}{14}$.

7. $y \approx 4.55x + 122.11$.

## Section 5-8

1a. 10.       b. 2.8.       c. 5.       d. not significant.
3a. 0.854.    b. satisfactory.
5a.

| Highest level of education | Very High | High | Average | Low | Very low | Totals |
|---|---|---|---|---|---|---|
| Postdoctorate study | 15 | 24 | 40 | 10 | 11 | 100 |
| Ph.D. | 15 | 24 | 40 | 10 | 11 | 100 |
| M.A. | 15 | 24 | 40 | 10 | 11 | 100 |
| B.A. | 15 | 24 | 40 | 10 | 11 | 100 |
| Totals | 60 | 96 | 160 | 40 | 44 | 400 |

5b. 25.58.       c. Yes.

# CHAPTER 6

## Section 6-1

1. Yes.       3. No.       5. Yes.       7. 8.       9. $^-2$.
11. Find $X \geq 0$, $Y \geq 0$ so that
    $0.2X + 0.3Y \leq 240$
    $0.04X + 0.02Y \leq 96$
    and
    profit $= 0.55X + 0.4Y$ is maximum.

13. Find $C \geq 0$ and $Y \geq 0$ so that
$2C + 3Y \leq 1600,$
$4C + 5Y \leq 3000,$
$C + 2Y \leq 1000,$
and
profit $= 0.60C + 0.50Y$ is maximum.

## Section 6-2

1.

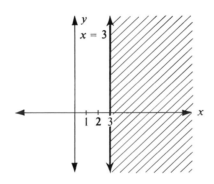

3.

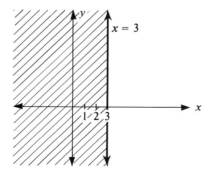

5.

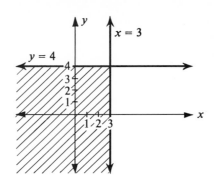

7.

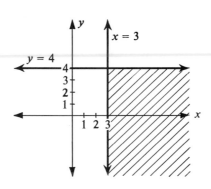

9.

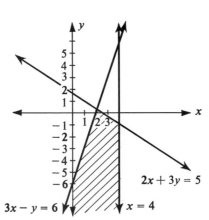

11a.  yes.        b.  yes.
13a.  no.         b.  no.
15a.  no.         b.  no.
17a.  no.         b.  no.

19.

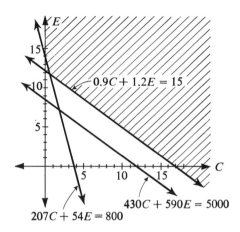

$0.9C + 1.2E = 15$

$430C + 590E = 5000$

$207C + 54E = 800$

## Section 6-3

1a.

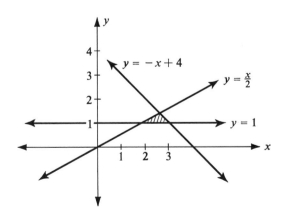

$y = -x + 4$

$y = \frac{x}{2}$

$y = 1$

b.  $(2, 1)$, $(\frac{8}{3}, \frac{4}{3})$, $(3, 1)$.
d.  Maximum of 3 at $(3, 1)$.
e.  Minimum of 1 at $(2, 1)$.

3a.

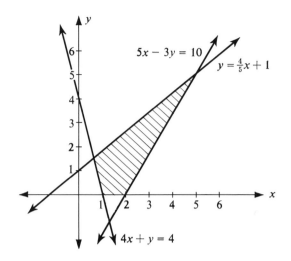

$5x - 3y = 10$

$y = \frac{4}{5}x + 1$

$4x + y = 4$

b.  $(5, 5), (1, 0), (2, 0), (\frac{5}{8}, \frac{3}{2})$.
d.  Maximum of 25 at $(5, 5)$.
e.  Minimum of $\frac{1}{2}$ at $(\frac{5}{8}, \frac{3}{2})$.

## Section 6-4

1.  $x = \dfrac{79}{25}, \qquad y = \dfrac{45}{25}, \qquad z = \dfrac{91}{25}$

3.  $x = {}^{-}20, \qquad y = 6, \qquad z = 11$.

## Section 6-5

1.  $x = 30, \qquad y = 60, \qquad P = 3900$; 2 iterations needed.
3.  $x = 0, \qquad y = 0, \qquad C = 0$; 0 iterations needed,
5.  $x = 1200, \qquad y = 0, \qquad P = \$660$; 1 iteration needed.
7.  $P = 560, \qquad M = 160, \qquad$ Profit $= \$592$; 2 iterations needed.

## Section 6-6

1.  $x = 0, \qquad y = 5, \qquad P = 25$; 1 iteration needed.

## Section 6-7

1. $x = 2.43,$     $y = 1.29,$     $N = 6.15$; 2 iterations needed.
3. $x = 25,$     $y = 0,$     $z = 0,$     $C = 150$; 1 iteration needed.
5. $A = 2\frac{6}{13}, B = 1\frac{5}{13}, C = 0,$ Cost $= \$.89$; 2 iterations needed.
7. $A = 0,$     $B = 80,$     $C = \$24{,}000$; 3 iterations needed.
9. $A = 6,$     $B = 0,$     $C = 18,$     Votes $= 108{,}000$; 3 iterations needed.

# CHAPTER 7

## Section 7-2

1. 0.          3. 6.
5. 2.          7. None.

## Section 7-3

1. $(p_1\, p_2) = (0,\, 1),$ $\begin{pmatrix} q_1 \\ q_2 \end{pmatrix} = \begin{pmatrix} 1 \\ 0 \end{pmatrix}$; $V = 2.$

3. $(p_1\, p_2) = (1,\, 0),$ $\begin{pmatrix} q_1 \\ q_2 \end{pmatrix} = \begin{pmatrix} 1 \\ 0 \end{pmatrix}$; $V = 1.$

5. $(p_1\, p_2) = (0,\, 1),$ $\begin{pmatrix} q_1 \\ q_2 \end{pmatrix} = \begin{pmatrix} 1 \\ 0 \end{pmatrix}$; $V = 1.$

## Section 7-4

1. Optimum strategy:
   $(p_1\, p_2) = (\frac{2}{5},\, \frac{3}{5})$
   $\begin{pmatrix} q_1 \\ q_2 \end{pmatrix} = \begin{pmatrix} \frac{4}{5} \\ \frac{1}{5} \end{pmatrix}$
   $V = \frac{12}{5}$

3. $(p_1\, p_2) = (\frac{1}{2},\, \frac{1}{2})$
   $\begin{pmatrix} q_1 \\ q_2 \end{pmatrix} = \begin{pmatrix} \frac{3}{4} \\ \frac{1}{4} \end{pmatrix}$
   $V = 2\frac{1}{2}$

5. $(p_1\, p_2) = (0\ 1)$
   $\begin{pmatrix} q_1 \\ q_2 \end{pmatrix} = \begin{pmatrix} 1 \\ 0 \end{pmatrix}$
   $V = 9$

7. $(p_1 \ p_2) = (\frac{1}{2}, \frac{1}{2})$

$$\begin{pmatrix} q_1 \\ q_2 \end{pmatrix} = \begin{pmatrix} \frac{1}{4} \\ \frac{3}{4} \end{pmatrix}$$

$V = 1\frac{1}{2}$

9. $(p_1 \ p_2) = (\frac{2}{5}, \frac{3}{5})$

$$\begin{pmatrix} q_1 \\ q_2 \end{pmatrix} = \begin{pmatrix} \frac{1}{5} \\ \frac{4}{5} \end{pmatrix}$$

$V = 2\frac{3}{5}$

11. $(p_1 \ p_2) = (\frac{1}{5}, \frac{4}{5})$

$$\begin{pmatrix} q_1 \\ q_2 \\ q_3 \end{pmatrix} = \begin{pmatrix} 0 \\ \frac{1}{5} \\ \frac{4}{5} \end{pmatrix}$$

$V = \frac{4}{5}$

13. $(p_1 \ p_2 \ p_3) = (\frac{1}{3}, \frac{2}{3}, 0)$

$$\begin{pmatrix} q_1 \\ q_2 \\ q_3 \end{pmatrix} = \begin{pmatrix} \frac{1}{2} \\ 0 \\ \frac{1}{2} \end{pmatrix}$$

$V = 2$

## Sections 7-5

1. $(p_1 \ p_2) = (\frac{3}{8}, \frac{5}{8})$

$$\begin{pmatrix} q_1 \\ q_2 \\ q_3 \\ q_4 \end{pmatrix} = \begin{pmatrix} \frac{1}{2} \\ 0 \\ 0 \\ \frac{1}{2} \end{pmatrix}$$

$V = \frac{7}{2}$

3. $(p_1 \ p_2 \ p_3 \ p_4 \ p_5) = (\frac{1}{5}, 0, 0, 0, \frac{4}{5})$

$$\begin{pmatrix} q_1 \\ q_2 \end{pmatrix} = \begin{pmatrix} \frac{3}{5} \\ \frac{2}{5} \end{pmatrix}$$

$V = \frac{17}{5}$

## Section*7-7

1. $(p_1 \ p_2 \ p_3) = (1, 0, 0)$

$$\begin{pmatrix} q_1 \\ q_2 \end{pmatrix} = \begin{pmatrix} 1 \\ 0 \end{pmatrix}$$

$V = 1$

# Index